ELECTRON AND ION BEAM
SCIENCE AND TECHNOLOGY

A NOTE TO THE READER

"The material herein was prepared for the June, 1966 conference. However, during the various stages of preparation of this volume, complex production problems and disputes have arisen which have made it economically impractical for Gordon and Breach Science Publishers, Incorporated to meet their usual high standards of publication. The publisher and the Society request the reader's indulgence for the typographical errors and format irregularities herein. These deficiencies should not be construed as a reflection on the authors and editors hereof.

Of course, as is their usual practice, The Metallurgical Society of AIME does not vouch for the scientific accuracy of the data or statements in these materials."

METALLURGICAL SOCIETY CONFERENCES   VOLUME

51

ELECTRON AND ION BEAM SCIENCE AND TECHNOLOGY

VOLUME 2

Proceedings of the
Second International Conference on
Electron and Ion Beam
Science and Technology,
sponsored by the
Institute of Metals Division
The Metallurgical Society of AIME
and
Electrothermics and Metallurgy Division
The Electrochemical Society, Inc.

NEW YORK, NEW YORK APRIL 1966

Edited by: ROBERT BAKISH
Bakish Materials Corporation
Englewood, New Jersey
and
Fairleigh Dickinson University
Teaneck, New Jersey

AMERICAN INSTITUTE OF MINING, METALLURGICAL,
AND PETROLEUM ENGINEERS
NEW YORK

Preface

This volume is the record of the Second International Conference on Electron and Ion Beams in Science and Technology. It is the result of the combined effort and cooperation of the conference committee, the contributors to this event, their employers, and the ECS and the AIME which co-sponsored the event.

As the person who was responsible for much of the activities which led to this conference, I wish to take the opportunity to express my sincere thanks to all those who made the event a reality. Let me also say that it was both a privilege and a pleasure to work with all of you. I believe that I speak for all responsible for the conference organization by saying that we aimed to establish the state of this technology as revealed by events in the spring of 1966. It is my opinion that this record offers a very comprehensive insight into this technology. It is a fitting sequence to the proceedings of the First International Conference on Electron and Ion Beams in Science and Technology published by John Wiley & Sons, N. Y.

Inasmuch as many who would be reading this volume were not at the conference. I regret to say that not all that transpired there is on record. Two particularly exciting round table discussions devoted to electron beam welding defects and electron and ion beams in micro electronics respectively are the most serious omission from the record. Several of the papers presented at the meeting are also missing; their authors having failed to meet the publication deadline. Further, I have assumed my prerogative as the editor, and rearranged the presentations with the hope to produce a more coherent volume. With this in mind I have also preceded several of the sections dealing with specific aspects of the technology with short introductory remarks and limited bibliographic references. I feel that in this manner a newcomer to the field can effect an easier transition from his role as outsider to that of a competent insider.

Tremendous strides have been made to date and I am confident that this progress will continue. Future conferences as those in the past will continue to help the dissemination of this valuable information. This will enable all those who suspect possibilities related to their own work to establish this for certain either personally, or through encounters with individuals who can definitely assist them to do so. As to all who participated in this event, let me say that our next "get together" is scheduled for May 6–9, 1968, at the Statler Hotel in Boston. I hope to have the opportunity to greet you again on the occasion of the Third International Conference on Electron and Ion Beams in Science and Technology for another exciting event devoted to this dynamic area of scientific endeavor.

I have just looked over the preface and it occurs to me that I almost forgot to thank the person who really helps me most, my dear wife, Ellen.

R. Bakish,

Englewood, New Jersey.

TABLE OF CONTENTS

VOLUME I

I. PHYSICS OF ELECTRON AND ION BEAMS

II. ELECTRON BEAMS IN MELTING AND REFINING-BASIC

CONTENTS

III. ELECTRON BEAMS IN MELTING AND REFINING-INDUSTRIAL

IV. ELECTRON BEAM WELDING

V. ELECTRON BEAM WELDING

CONTENTS

VOLUME 2

VI. ION PROPULSION

VII. ELECTRON BEAMS IN RECORDING
AND INFORMATION STORAGE

VII. ELECTRON BEAMS IN MICRO ELECTRONICS

IX. ION BEAMS IN MICRO ELECTRONICS

CONTRIBUTORS

Conference Chairman:

R. Bakish, Bakish Materials Corporation, Englewood, New
Jersey, and Fairleigh Dickinson University, Teaneck,
New Jersey, U.S.A.

Conference Committee and Sessions Chairmen:

M. von Ardenne, Institute M. von Ardenne, Dresden,
East Germany
E. Bas, Swiss Federal Polytech. Inst., Zurich, Switzerland
F. Benesowski, Metalwerk Plansee, Reutte/Tyrol, Austria
M. Boston, Esq., Torvac Ltd., Histon, Cambridge, England
J. Cabelka, International Institute of Welding, Bratislava,
Czechoslovakia
R. Castaing, University of Paris, Orsay (S.-et-O),
France
W. Dietrich, W. C. Heraeus, Hanau/Main, West Germany
G. W. A. Dummer, Esq., Royal Radar Establishment,
Great Malvern, England
T. Everhart, University of California, Berkeley, California,
U. S. A.
T. Forrester, University of California, Irvine, California,
U. S. A.
L. Habraken, CNRM, Liege, Belgium
C. Hayashi, Japan Vacuum Engineering Co. Ltd.,
Yokohama, Japan
A. E. Jenkins, University of New South Wales, N. S. W.,
Australia
A. Lawley, Drexel Institute, Philadelphia, Pennsylvania,
U. S. A.
G. Molenstedt, University of Tubingen, Tubingen,
West Germany

E. C. Muly, Jr. N. R. C., Newton Highlands, Massachusetts,
  U. S. A.

S. Namba, The Institute of Physical & Chemical Research,
  Tokyo, Japan

N. A. Olshanski, Moscow Power Institute, Moscow,
  U. S. S. R.

B. Paton, Institute for Electro-Welding, Kiev, U. S. S. R.

E. Rexer, Institute for Applied Physics of Pure Metals,
  Dresden, East Germany

B. W. Schumacher, Ontario Research Foundation,
  Toronto 5, Canada

J. G. Siekman, Philips Research Laboratories,
  Eindhoven, Holland

C. Spitzer, Ampex Corp., Redwood City, California,
  U. S. A.

J. A. Stohr, Centre d'Etudes Nucleaires, Saclay, France

F. Lincoln Vogel, University of Pennsylvania, Philadelphia,
  Pennsylvania, U. S. A.

O. Winkler, Balzers AG, Balzers, Lichtenstein

CONTRIBUTORS OF PRESENTATIONS

Anderson, J. R., Hughes Research Laboratories, Malibu,
California
von Ardenne, M., Research Institute M. von Ardenne,
Dresden, East Germany
Barrekette, IBM, Watson Research Center, Yorktown
Heights, New York
Bas, E. B., Department of Industrial Research, Swiss
Federal Institute of Technology, Zurich, Switzerland
Beer, A. F., Mullard Research Laboratories, Redhill,
Surrey, England
Bernheim, M., Faculty of Science, Orsay, France
Brody, M. D., M.I.T., Cambridge, Massachusetts
Castaing, R., Faculty of Science, Orsay, France
Crawford, C. K., M.I.T., Cambridge, Massachusetts
Cremosnik, G., Dept. of Industrial Research, Swiss
Federal Institute of Technology, Zurich, Switzerland
Cullum, D. G., IBM, Research Center, Yorktown Heights,
New York
Davies, I. G. A., Dept. of Materials Science, U. C. N. W.,
Bangor, Caerns, United Kingdom
Davis, J. M., United Aircraft Research Lab., East
Hartford, Connecticut
Dove, J. F., Rome Air Development Center, Rome, N. Y.
Dubbe, R. F., Minnesota Mining and Manufacturing Co.,
St. Paul, Minnesota
Duffy, J. A., IBM, Watson Research Center, Yorktown
Heights, New York
Eckhardt, W. O., Hughes Research Laboratories,
Malibu, California
Einstein, P. A., Vickers Research Establishment, Ascot,
England

Everhart, T. E., University of California, Berkeley,
California

Foti, E., Centrel Research Institute for Physics,
Budapest, Hungary

Friedler, V. E. B., Edelstahl Werk, Freital, East
Germany

Garasi, L. A., Electro Optical Systems Inc., Pasadena,
California

Gerken, J. M., TRW Equipment Laboratories, Cleveland,
Ohio

Glotin, P., Centre of Nuclear Studies, Grenoble, France

Gibbons, J. F., Stanford Electronics Lab., Stanford
University, Stanford, California

Gonzales, A. J., University of California, Berkeley,
California

Grapa, J., National Institute for Scientific Investigation,
France

Groves, M. T., TRW Equipment Laboratories, Cleveland,
Ohio

Heil, H., Hughes Research Laboratories, Malibu,
California

Hessig, U., Research Institute M. von Ardenne, Dresden,
East Germany

Hill, G. W., Semi Conductor and Thin Film Dept., British
Scientific Assoc., South Hill, Chislehurst, Kent,
England

Hughes, K. A., Dept. of Materials Science, U. C. N. W.,
Bangor, Caerns, United Kingdom

d' A. Hunt, C., Temescal Metallurgical Corp., Berkeley,
California

Husmann, O. K., formerly Hughes Research Laboratories,
Malibu, California

James, J. A., Sciaky Bros., Chicago, Illinois

Jensen, A. S., Aerospace Div., Westinghouse Defense and
Aerospace Center, Baltimore, Maryland

Kaye, S., Electro Optical Systems, Inc., Pasadena,
California

Kelley, J., Mullard Research Laboratories, Redhill,
Surrey, England

King, H., Hughes Research Laboratories, Malibu,
California

King, H. N. G., Mullard Research Laboratories, Redhill,
    Surrey, England
Kretizer, N. H., IBM Research Center, Yorktown Heights,
    New York
Kothe, A., Institute for Metal Physics and Pure Metals,
    Dresden, East Germany
Large, L. N., Services Electronics Research Laboratory,
    Baldock, England
Lawley, A., Drexel Institute, Philadelphia, Pennsylvania
Koch, F., Central Welding Institute, Halle, East Germany
Lenk, P., Research Institute M. von Ardenne, Dresden,
    East Germany
Liberman, I., Westinghouse Research Lab., Pittsburgh,
    Pennsylvania
Limansky, I. S., Westinghouse Defense and Aerospace
    Center, Baltimore, Maryland
Manchester, K. E., Sprague Electric Co., North Adams,
    Massachusetts
Masek, T. D., J. P. L., California Institute of Technology,
    Pasadena, California
Medved, B., Electro Optical Systems, Inc., Pasadena,
    California
Mesharekov, V. M., Moscow Power Engineering Institute,
    Moscow, U. S. S. R.
Meier, J. M., Hamilton Standard, Windsor Locks,
    Connecticut
Miller, K., Metals Joining Corp., Redondo Beach,
    California
Muelemans, M., Centre for Nuclear Studies, Mol, Belgium
Neve, N. F. B., Dept. of Materials Science, U. C. N. W.,
    Bangor, Caerns, United Kingdom
Norris, Jr. C. B., Stanford Electric Lab., Stanford Uni-
    versity, Stanford, California
Olshansky, N. A., Moscow Power Engineering Institute,
    Moscow, U. S. S. R.
Oman, R. M., ASD Litton Industries, Inc., Minneapolis,
    Minnesota
Panzer, J., Research Institute M. von Ardenne, Dresden,
    East Germany
Paton, B. E., E. O. Paton Institute for Welding, Kiev,
    U. S. S. R.

Pease, R. F. W., Dept. of Electrical Engineering,
   University of Calif., Berkeley, California
Peisach, M., Southern Universities Nuclear Institute
   Faure, C. P., South Africa
Pinsley, E. A., United Aircraft Research Lab., East
   Hartford, Connecticut
Poole, Darrell O., Southern Universities Nuclear
   Institute Faure, C. P., South Africa
Prekel, H. L., Franklin Institute, Philadelphia,
   Pennsylvania
Reed, E. W., Minnesota Mining and Manufacturing Co.,
   St. Paul, Minnesota
Reed, R. E., Oak Ridge National Laboratory, Oak Ridge,
   Tennessee
Reininger, W. G., Aerospace Div., Westinghouse Electric Co.
Rexer, E., Institute for Metal Physics and Pure Metals,
   Dresden, East Germany
Roberts Jr. A. S., School for Engineering, Old Dominion
   College, Norfolk, Virginia
Roberts, E. D., Mullard Research Laboratories, Redhill,
   Surrey, England
Rose, R. M., M.I.T., Cambridge, Massachusetts
Rolick, G. P., Electro Optical Systems, Inc., Pasadena,
   California
Ruth, R. P., Autonetics Div., North American Aviation,
   Inc., Anaheim, California
Schiller, S., Research Institute M. von Ardenne, Dresden,
   East Germany
Schlat, F., Institute for Metal Physics and Pure Metals,
   Dresden, East Germany
Schofield, J. M. S., Mullard Research Laboratories,
   Redhill, Surrey, England
Schonberg, H. V. E. B. L. E. W. Henningsdorf, East
   Germany
Schwartz, M., Advanced Manufacturing Technology,
   Martin-Baltimore, Maryland
Scott, B. W., Hughes Research Laboratories, Malibu,
   California
Shaw, A., Dept. of Materials Science, U. C. N. W.,
   Bangor, Caerns, United Kingdom

Siekman, J. G., Philips Research Laboratories, N. V.
  Philips Gloelampenfabrieken, Eindhoven, Netherlands
Smith, H. R., Temescal Metallurgical Corp., Berkeley,
  California
Skinner, L. G., M.I.T., Cambridge, Massachusetts
Stevens, H., Dept. of Ind. Research, Swiss Federal
  Institute of Technology, Zurich, Switzerland
Soloman, J., Sciaky Bros., Chicago, Illinois
Stohr, J. A., French Atomic Energy Commission,
  Saclay, France
Sulway, D. V., Department of Materials Science,
  U. C. N. W., Bangor, Caerns, United Kingdom
Thieme, O., Research Institute M. von Ardenne, Dresden,
  East Germany
Thomas, R. N., Department of Industrial Research,
  Swiss Federal Institute of Technology, Zurich,
  Switzerland
Thornton, P. R., Dept. of Materials Science, U. C. N. W.,
  Bangor, Caerns, United Kingdom
Varek, C. J., Westinghouse Molecular Electronics Div.,
  Elk Ridge, Maryland
Walsh, A. P., United Aircraft Research Lab., East
  Hartford, Connecticut
Wayte, R. C., Dept. of Materials Science, U. C. N. W.,
  Bangor, Caerns, United Kingdom
Wehe, H. G., Bell Telephone Lab., Murray Hill,
  New Jersey
Wiedmer, H. B., Institute of Technology, Zurich,
  Switzerland
Wolf, P. A., Bell Telephone Laboratories, Inc.,
  Murray Hill, New Jersey
Zeheb, D., IBM Research Center, Yorktown Heights,
  New York

Introductory Remarks

Ladies and Gentlemen:

It gives me great pleasure to welcome you on behalf of the AIME and ECS here in New York on the occasion of the Second International Conference on Electron and Ion Beams in Science and Technology. I hope that all of you who are here today, and those who will be coming for specific sessions of the conference in the days to follow, will find this event in accordance with your expectation and that you will have a profitable and pleasant conference.

At this time I must take the opportunity to express my most sincere thanks to the conference committee members and session chairmen for their effort in organizing the conference program. Thanks and deep appreciation are also due to all the speakers who have traveled extensive distances to be with us for the event and to share with you the findings of their work in this dynamic technology. Thanks also are due to both the AIME and the ECS, the sponsoring societies, for the effort which they invested so that this event might become a reality.

Electron and Ion Beams in their many ramifications are exerting a powerful influence in our modern technology. We are seeing here, as in other areas of scientific endeavor, an increasing pace in the move of findings from the research laboratory to the production line. Science itself advances more rapidly than ever before and yet it is in the engineering accomplishment and the reduction of advanced scientific thought to practice that ultimately advances the welfare of our society. The subject matter of the conference covers the spectrum from fundamental studies through industrial applications. The two years which expired since the first conference have seen much excitement take place. I look with great confidence to the future and the even greater influence that electron and ion beams will play in shaping of industrial progress.

The conference sessions will essentially follow the outlined program and your sessions chairman will advise you of minor program changes which might take place. In view of all the material that we intend to cover here, I wish to request that the speakers do not forget that others will speak after them. I would be deeply grateful if they will adhere to the speech duration time allotted to them by the session chairman. Every morning at the author's breakfast each speaker will be notified of the time allotted for his presentation.

But you did not come to listen to me talk. Have a pleasant stay in our city and do try to take in at least some of its many exciting sites and activities to complement the scientific exposure provided by the conference.

Thank You.

R. Bakish,

New York, April 17, 1966.

ION PROPULSION

Development and Long Life Performance of Single Strip Ion Engines *

J. R. Anderson

Hughes Research Laboratories

INTRODUCTION

The use of ion propulsion for satellite applications is receiving increased attention for two principal reasons. First, low-thrust ion engines are inherently capable of operation for mission lifetimes on the order of five to ten years, such as those contemplated for near future satellites. Furthermore, since the rate of propellant usage in ion engines is small, an ion propulsion system for control of a given long-life satellite weighs considerably less than any other reaction control system.

For the north-south station keeping of a 1000 lb synchronous satellite, a thrust level on the order of 0.30 mlbf is necessary. Three ion engines of this class could maintain such a satellite on station to an accuracy of better than 0.1 deg in both longitude and latitude with a total propellant requirement of less than 2 lb/yr. [1] Alternatively, with the incorporation of electrostatic beam deflection, [2, 3] six lightweight single-strip thrustors could be positioned to provide both station keeping and three-axis attitude control of a 5000 lb synchronous satellite for five years with a total control system weight of less than 150 lb and an average power of about 300 W.

Under the sponsorship of the Lewis Research Center of the National Aeronautics and Space Administration, the

*This work was supported by the NASA-Lewis Research Center under Contract NAS 3-4117, and is continuing under Contract NAS 3-7927. D. M. Shellhammer is the NASA Project Manager for this program.

Hughes Research Laboratories is conducting a research and development program on linear-strip ion thrustors covering the thrust range from 0.1 mlbf to 1.0 mlbf.

An optimized ion propulsion system for control of a synchronous satellite would require each of the north-south thrustors to operate 10 hours per day. This is equivalent to 3650 hours of thrusting time per year. Because of this long life requirement, steady-state life tests on ion thrustors have been a necessary part of the present development program.

The attitude control portion of the system must hold a satellite to a given attitude accuracy about each of three axes in the presence of disturbance torques resulting from both external effects (e.g. solar radiation pressure, micrometeorite impact) and internal effects (e.g. gas leakage, moving parts). The largest internal torques will be caused by the thrust misalignment of the station keeping engines and by the uncertainty in the position of gravity. In order to keep these disturbance torques to less than 10% of those from the unbalanced solar pressure, in certain cases the station keeping thrust vector must be aligned to an accuracy greater than 0.02 deg. For a combined attitude control and station keeping system, therefore, the alignment of the thrust vector to the precise center of gravity of the satellite is of utmost importance. This can be accomplished quite effectively through the use of electrostatic deflection of the ion beam.

For a mass expulsion system the thrust duty cycle is generally the critical performance parameter. However, in the high specific impulse ion propulsion system, the most important performance parameter is the average power consumption. Because of the unique nature of the cesium surface-contact ion engine, power must be supplied to heat the ionizer for some period before each firing of the attitude control thrustor. In general, since the duty cycle associated with attitude control is low, it is more economic (powerwise) to warm the ionizer for each firing than to heat it continuously at the operating temperature. For this reason, cyclic operation of thrustors for many tens of thousands of cycles is necessary to demonstrate the capability of ion engines to perform the attitude control function. Typically, for a 1000 lb synchronous satellite subjected to a disturbance torque of 100 dyn-cm, each attitude control thrustor will be cycled approximately 45,000 times/year. Cesium cyclic tests of two thrustors are being conducted to demonstrate the capability of the linear ion engine for application to an attitude control system. The objective of these life tests is 50,000 thrust cycles on each engine.

THRUSTOR DESIGN

The design philosophy employed is one of simplicity and ruggedness combined with conservative operating parameters so as to maximize reliability and lifetime without serious derating of the over-all engine performance.

Schematic drawings of the thrustor design are shown in Fig. 1. Several features of this ion engine are novel. The ionizer assembly has been designed specifically for very low mass and low heat capacity so as to permit rapid warm-up of the ionizer to its operating temperature. In this low-mass ionizer the heaters are encased within a tubular tungsten sheath, positioned in intimate contact with the porous tungsten ionizer on both sides of the emitter. The ionizer assembly is entirely tungsten, with the various elements electron beam welded to each other. The use of electron beam welding eliminates any contaminating braze materials. The ionizer heater itself consists of a tightly wound tungsten helix which is coated with alimunum oxide and placed within a protective ceramic sleeve. The ceramic sleeve is slotted to permit direct radiative heat transfer from the heater coil to the porous tungsten emitter. The heater subassembly simply slides through the tungsten sheath and is easily replaceable. The over-all weight of the ionizer assembly, less mounting brackets and heat shields, is only 1.5 gm/cm of linear length.

The accelerator electrode is designed as a bimetallic element of the engine. Sheet stock of stainless steel and copper are brazed together and then machined to provide the correct boundary shapes for the ion optical structure. Those surfaces of the accel electrode which are susceptible to ion bombardment are made of copper. The remaining surface of the accel electrode which radiates to free space consists of oxidized stainless steel so as to maximize the emittance and maintain a low temperature during operation of the engine. Since the accel temperature can be held to less than 200°C this results in a minimum amount of

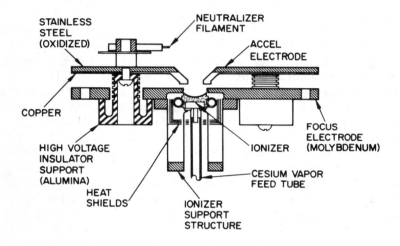

Figure 1. Isometric and orthographic drawings of the Hughes Linear Ion Engine.

thermionic back emission of electrons from the cesiated copper surface to the positive high voltage electrodes.

A third feature of the engine design is the use of a carburized, thoriated-tungsten filament for generation of the neutralizing electrons. This neutralizer design has proved to be quite rugged and reliable and has operated with no deterioration in electron emission characteristics for a period of 2000 hours in the presence of a cesium ion beam. Filament lifetimes of over 10, 000 hours are predicted at a temperature of 1950° K and a specific emission of 35 mA/W.

Major thrustor design parameters are listed in Table I.

Table I. Thrustor Electrical Parameters (Nominal Design Values)

Thrustor Model	LB	LD
Ionizer Length	8 cm	4. 6 cm
Thrust	0. 5 mlbf	0. 3 mlbf
Specific Impulse	5000 sec	4600 sec
Beam Current	32 mA	21 mA
Beam Voltage	1. 67 kV	1. 42 kV
Ionizer Current Density	7 mA/cm^2	8 mA/cm^2
Power-Thrust Ratio	225 W/mlbf	200 W/mlbf
Weight	0. 5 lb	0. 5 lb

STEADY-STATE LIFE TESTS

A major milestone in development of cesium-contact ion engines was the successful completion of a 2000 hr. endurance test of a single-strip thrustor (Model LB) on 30 July 1965. The test was conducted in two 1000 hr. segments because it was necessary to reload the cesium feed system. In addition, a scaled down thrustor (Model LD) was life tested for 610 hr. Major performance results from these and other tests are summarized in Table II.

Post-test analyses of the components from both the 2000 hour and 610 hour tests show that the lifetime of the engine is far greater than these test periods. There appears to be no fundamental barrier to attaining very long operating life, particularly if improved ionizer materials are used which have work functions higher than that of tungsten. Evaluation of numerous tests has revealed the

Table II.   Linear Ion Engine Performance Summary

Steady-State:	Duration (hr)	Thrust (mlbf)	Power/Thrust (W/mlbf)
8 cm Thrustors	226 2000	0.60 0.56	220 at 5500 sec
4.6 cm Thrustors	610	0.36	196 at 5000 sec
Cesium-Cyclic: 4.6 cm Thrustors (2)	25,000~ 20,000~ both con- tinuing	0.30 0.30	- - -
Thermal-Cyclic:	Duration (cycles)	Heatup Energy (W-hr)	Time to 1100°C (sec)
8 cm Thrustors (4)	40,492 to 85,035	0.77 to 0.65	20
5 cm Thrustor	1,636	0.44	11

similarity of thrustor performance.   Although specific illustrations will be taken from a particular test, the performance
of one thrustor is usually characteristic of all and can be
generalized to cover single-strip thrustors as a class.

Power-to-thrust values for both the 2000 hour and
610 hour test thrustors meet the design requirements and
are plotted versus specific impulse in Fig. 2.   The minimum P/T of 196 W/mlbf occurred between 4500 and 5000
sec specific impulse.   The dashed curve in this figure
shows the performance expected in the near future after
certain thermal improvements are incorporated.

An encouraging aspect of the 2000 hour test was the fact
that the neutralizer, which is a simple carburized, thoriated
tungsten filament, remained intact and suffered no errosion.
The specific electron emission measured after completion of
2000 hours of beam on time was 50 mA/W at 1900°K.   This
is an excellent value for this type of electron emitter.

Post-Test Analyses

Some of the highlights of metallurgical and spectrographic analyses conducted on the thrustors are presented

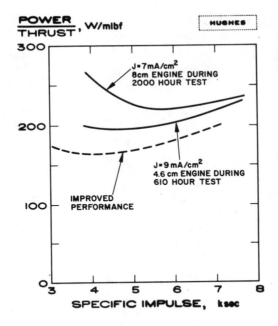

Figure 2. Power-to-thrust versus specific impulse for single-strip ion thrustors.

below.   The distinguishing feature of all post-test examinations was the integrity of thrustor components.   No area could be pinpointed where failure was imminent.   Findings during post-test analysis of thrustor LD-2 (610 hour test) were predictable from the previous analysis of LB-7 (2000 hour test).   All data confirm the conclusions that useful life of the thrustors is many times longer than the test periods and performance is consistent from one thrustor to another.

Accel Electrodes

Part of the beam aperture of the LB-7 accel electrode after 2000 hours is shown in Fig. 3.   Note the good definition of the ion optical edges and surfaces in the slit region.   Of immediate interest are the pit-type erosion regions located at the ends of the accel slit on the downstream side.   This type of erosion was present in LD-2 to a much lesser degree.

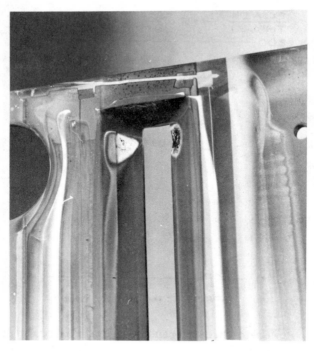

Figure 3.　Closeup photograph of portion of LB-7 accel aperture showing areas pitted by ion bombardment after 200 hour life test.

　　　Photomicrographs of the accel electrode at the central slit area and pitted area are shown in Fig. 4.　In the central slit area, charge exchange erosion was so slight that deposition of copper from the collector completely masked it.　Even in the pitted area, no erosion was observed on the upstream side (facing the ionizer) or in the slit region of the accel electrode.

　　　The ion optical design with end effect correction was successful in preventing primary ions from impinging on the accel electrode.　However, quantitative measurements made on a beam from this optical design show that the current density near the ends of the strip beam 0. 1 inch downstream from the accel electrode attains a peak value approximately five times greater than in the central regions of the beam.　Since the charge exchange collision probability varies approximately as the ion current density times the neutral particle density, it is evident that the charge exchange collision frequency near the ends of the strip is higher than in the center. If the distribution of these charge exchange ions is identical with that in the central region, then the ion bombardment rate and hence the erosion of the accel at the ends are also higher than in the central regions.

Because material sputtered from the downstream side of the accel has a very low probability of returning to the ionizer, a simple method can be employed to reduce the erosion in this region: vis., all downstream surfaces can be fabricated from a low sputter yield material rather than copper.

Ionizer

Microscopic examination of discolored areas on the ionizer and focus electrode of LB-7 revealed surface erosion in these regions. Roughening of the surface produces a darker appearance. Spectrographic analysis of deposits on the ionizer side of the accel showed significant percentages of tungsten, supporting the ionizer erosion observation.

The erosion pattern consisted typically of two grooves along each side of the ionizer strip, terminating in a rounded area near the end of the strip. The rounded area has been identified as a shallow crater. A photomicrograph section of the edge grooves is shown in Fig. 5.

Ionizer erosion requires high energy particles and these are assumed to be negative ions. The negative ions are created within the gun; otherwise they could not penetrate the negative potential barrier formed by the accel electrode. Ionization of residual gas within the gun by some interaction with the positive ion beam is considered insignificant because the ionizer erosion pattern produced by a "steady rain" of gas ions would be much more uniform and might tend to be more pronounced along the center of the strip. The erosion pattern on the ionizer strongly suggests that the accel electrode is the ion source, especially at the ends where the pattern curves inward, as does the accel electrode. Erosion may be heavier at the ends because ions from a relatively large area of accel

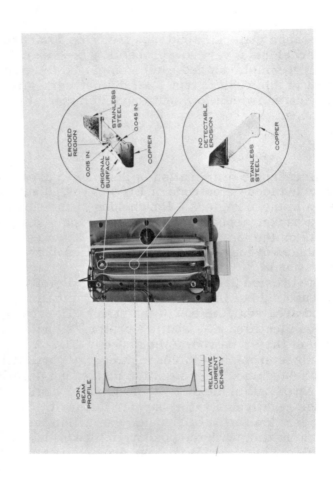

Figure 4.   Accel electrode after 2000 hour test of LB-7 comparing a sputtered region to a section through the central area of the accel where erosion was negligible.

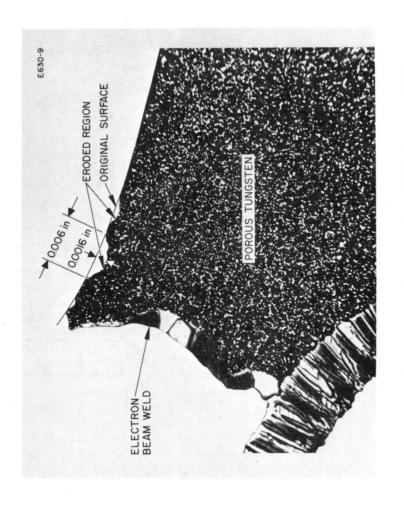

Figure 5.   Photomicrograph of groove in ionizer after 2000 hour life test.

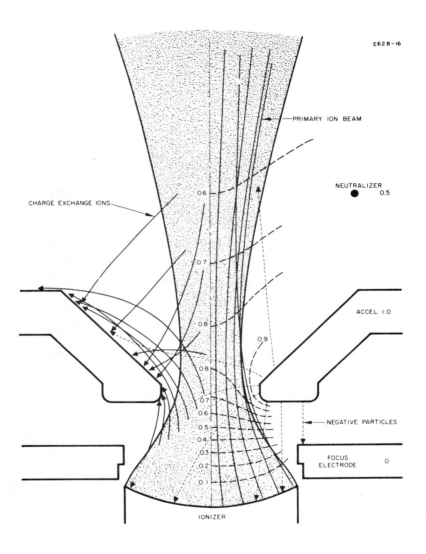

Figure 6. Charged particle trajectories in the linear, single-strip ion engine (Model 70 optics) used for the 2000 hour steady-state life test. Solution is for 3/4 of full space charge.

are focused into a relatively small area of ionizer; in addition, as mentioned above, charge exchange erosion is higher at the ends of the accel than at the center. Trajectory studies of the ion optics show that if negative ions were created, they would follow approximately the paths shown in Fig. 6.

The effect of this phenomenon depends on the accel sputtering yield, the percentage of negative ions emitted, thruster ion optics, and neutral fraction. The sputtering yield and negative ion yield may be altered by changing the accel material. The single-strip ion optics has the advantage of being able to focus some of the negative ions downstream. As with many thrustor phenomena, reducing the neutral fraction would reduce adverse effects. The grooving of the ionizer did not pose any problem in beam generation and focusing during the 2000 hour test of LB-7.

THRUSTOR LIFETIME

Calculations have been performed to determine lifetime of a cesium-contact ion engine. The life limiting process is assumed to be sputter erosion of thirty percent of the accel electrode by bombardment of ions due to charge exchange collisions. The calculations are based on a theory [4] which examines in detail the effects of charge exchange ions on the accelerator system incorporated in all the linear ion engine designs discussed herein.

The results of the lifetime calculations are shown in Fig. 7 where life for both copper and nickel accel electrodes is plotted versus ionizer current density with neutral fraction as the independent variable. [5] It is seen that the lifetime of thrustors using porous tungsten ionizers operating at 7 mA/cm^2 should be approximately 14,000 hours or 1.6 years for copper accel electrodes. If the lower sputter yield nickel is used in place of copper, the lifetime figure becomes approximately 37,000 hours or 4.2 years.

Improved ionizer materials with work functions higher than that of tungsten extends this lifetime capability considerably as indicated by the curve for iridium-coated tungsten. [6] Furthermore, the use of high work function ionizers permits safe operation at higher current densities.

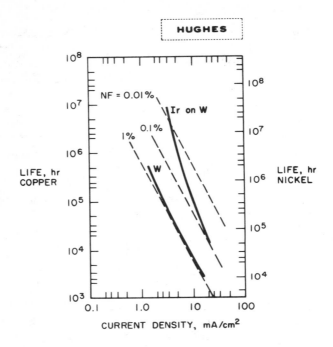

Figure 7.   Engine life limited by erosion of the accel electrode due to charge exchange ion bombardment.

This results in significant improvement of the thrustor power efficiency. For example, Fig. 7 indicates that a linear ion engine using an iridium and operating at 15 mA/cm^2 could have a potential lifetime of 92,000 hours or 10.5 years if the accel electrode is fabricated from nickel.

     With such long times before the accel electrode is sputtered away, charge exchange erosion may no longer be the fundamental limit to ion engine life. Other processes, such as closure of the ionizer pores, may become of more concern. Consequently, the sintering kinetics of porous refractory ionizers is being studied in detail by Roger Turk at the Hughes Research Laboratories.

     The principal point is that cesium-contact ion engines of the linear-strip class inherently have very long life - on the order of 5 to 10 years - and are therefore excellent candidates for use as the thrustors in a control system for long-life satellites.

THRUSTOR CYCLIC TESTS

Attitude control of a 1000 lb synchronous satellite subjected to disturbance torques on the order of 100 dyn-cm will require approximately 45,000 corrective thrust cycles per year for each attitude axis. Operation of an ion engine in a pulse mode is significantly different from steady-state operation. In steady-state operation, the lifetime of an ion engine is of prime importance. On the other hand, pulse or cyclic operation requires greater reliability with regard to the predictability and repeatability of thrustor characteristics. Therefore, extensive laboratory testing is necessary to determine thrustor cyclic characteristics.

Among the most severe requirements is that of heating the ionizer from ambient to its operating temperature in a time on the order of 20 sec in order to minimize the warmup energy. The new technology applied to the linear strip ionizer to achieve this capability is described in detail elsewhere. [7] Thermal cyclic tests on four thrustors have been completed successfully, thus demonstrating the thermomechanical integrity of the linear ion engine with regard to this mode of operation. The thermal cyclic performance is summarized in Table II. The test sequence was as follows: 20 sec warmup, 5 sec period during which both ionizer and neutralizer temperature were regulated, all power off for 3 min.

Limited cyclic testing with cesium up to several thousand cycles per thrustor in 1965 demonstrated that the linear ion engine is capable of operating in pulse mode with predictable performance. In order to verify the long-duration cyclic capabilities of these thrustors, two identical thrust stations, housing 4.6 cm thrustors, are presently undergoing cesium life tests. The principal goal is 50,000 cycles per station at a thrust level of 0.3 mlbf. This cyclic operation is commensurate with requirements for attitude control of a 1000 lb synchronous satellite over a period of one year. One station, complete with neutral atom detector, is pictured in Fig. 8. A schematic representation of this station is shown in Fig. 9.

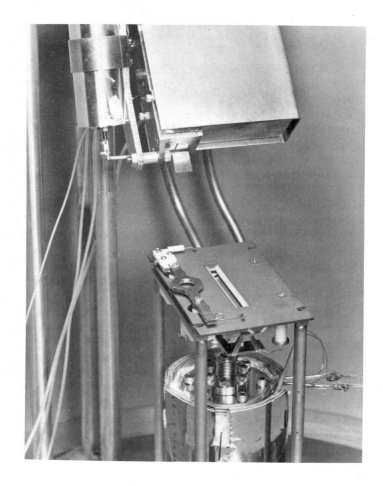

Figure 8.   Photograph of thrust station and accompanying neutral detector.

The experiment is being conducted in a vacuum chamber 2 ft in diameter by 6 ft long, pictured in Fig. 10 and shown schematically in Fig. 11. The chamber is evacuated by a 10 in. oil diffusion pump with a liquid-nitrogen-cooled zeolite trap inserted between the pump and the chamber. The chamber is lined with a liquid-nitrogen cryowall. An ion-pumped vacuum lock can be evacuated independently of the main chamber and vice

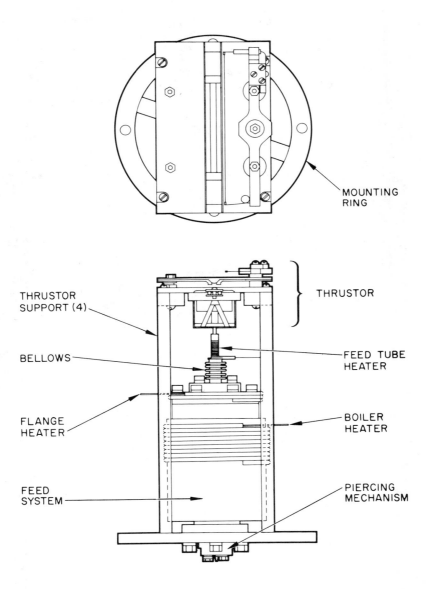

Figure 9.   Schematic drawing of thrustor station for cyclic cesium testing.

Figure 10.   Photograph of vacuum chamber system being used for
cyclic cesium life tests.

versa, allowing separate startup or servicing of either
station.   The vacuum lock is separated from the main
chamber by a 10 in. gate valve.   One thrustor station is
located in the vacuum lock and the beam fires through the
open valve.   The neutral detector for this station is positioned on the chamber side of the valve.   The second station
is inserted in the other end of the chamber, and the two
sections are separated by a dual collector in the center of
the tank.
        Both stations are powered by an Automatic Life Test
Console which switches from one to the other as required,
regulates the ionizer temperature during the thrust period,
and controls the thrust level by sensing the beam current
during a portion of the thrusting period and adjusting the
cesium reservoir power to correct for deviations from the
set point.   The sequence of operation is illustrated in Fig.
12, and is as follows:

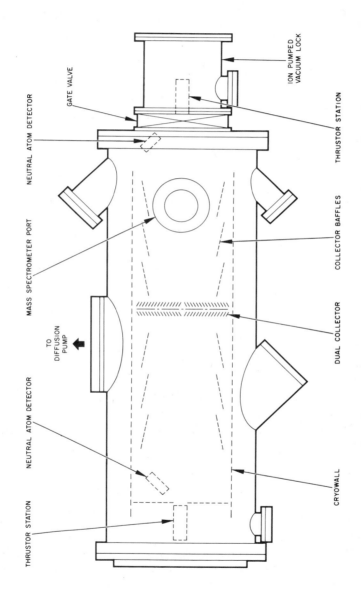

Figure 11. Schematic of vacuum chamber used for cesium cyclic testing.

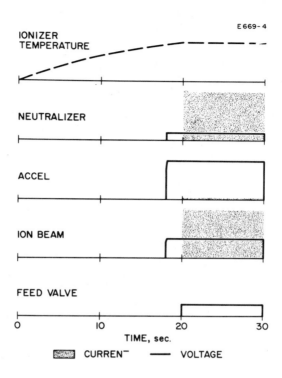

Figure 12.   Representation of thrustor waveforms showing sequence during cesium cyclic tests.

    1.   Ionizer heater power is applied to the station at time t_o.
    2.   At t_o + 18 sec the ionizer heater supply is switched to the "regulate" mode, and the ionizer temperature is controlled about a preset point.   Simultaneously, the main drive and accel high voltages are applied with a soft turn on, and the neutralizer filament power is turned on.
    3.   At t_o + 20 sec the feed valve is opened.
    4.   At t_o + 30 sec the feed valve, ionizer heater, main drive, accel, and neutralizer filament powers are shut off and the console switches to the alternate station.
    The alternate station receives ionizer heater power 75 sec later and goes through the same cycle.   Each station is cycled once every 3. 5 min.   Reservoir heater power

remains on at all times.   To date, the thrustors have been
cycled 25, 000 and 20, 000 times.   Thrustor parameters
during a typical cycle are

Warmup energy	0. 56 W-hr
Ionizer temperature	1100° C
Ionizer high voltage	+ 1. 7 kV
Accel high voltage	- 4. 8 kV
Beam current	19. 4 mA
Ionizer current density	7. 3 mA/cm^2
Specific impulse	5000 sec
Thrust	0. 3 mlbf

APPLICATIONS

To indicate the potential usefulness of ion propulsion
systems for satellite control, two applications will be discussed briefly.   The first relates to east-west station
keeping of a satellite which has gravity-gradient stabiliza-
tion.   The second system would use several linear ion engines to provide both station keeping and three-axis attitude
control of a large (5000 lb to 10, 000 lb) synchronous communications satellite.

Ten Micropound Ion Propulsion System

During early 1965 a ten-micropound thrust ion propulsion system was designed, fabricated, and tested with
Hughes Aircraft Company funds.   An important feature of
the thrustor is the inclusion of electrostatic beam deflection
for providing thrust vector control.

An isometric drawing of the propulsion system is shown
in Fig. 13.   The purpose of this design arrangement is to
minimize thermal radiation losses in the radial and rear
directions so that there will be no serious thermal integration problems with the spacecraft.

To simplify the design of the power conditioning high
voltage power supplies, the operating point of the thrustor
was chosen at an accel-decel ratio of two.   The power conditioning was designed to operate at a frequency of 20 kc
square wave.

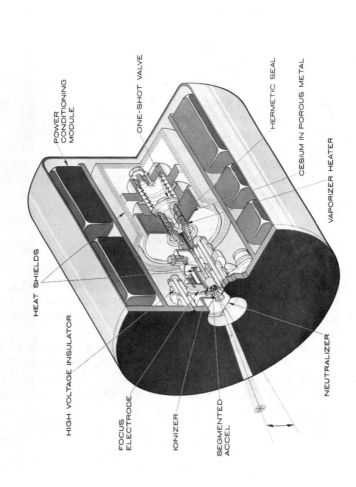

Figure 13.   Isometric drawing of the ten-micropound thrust ion propulsion system.

The principal design parameters and objectives were

Thrust	10 μ lbf
Specific impulse	5200 sec
Beam voltage	1800 V
Beam current	620 μ A
Current density	4. 6 mA/cm^2
Thrustor and feed system power	9 W
Input to power conditioning	15 W at -24 V dc
Lifetime	5 years
System weight	3 lb

The over-all package is 4 in. in diameter and 4. 5 in. long. The propulsion unit, without the power conditioning modules, weighs 1 lb, 6 oz.

In September and October, 1965 several units were tested with bread-board 20 kc power conditioning. The major performance results are summarized below:

1. 50 hours continuous operation with 20 kc power conditioning in a closed-loop control mode.

2. Operation at a thrust level of 16. 7 μ lbf at 6700 sec with a beam current of 800 μ A. Accel current was less than 2 μ A.

3. Ion beam deflection of ± 9 deg at a bias voltage of ± 150 V applied to two accel quadrants. This is a deflection sensitivity of 0. 03 deg/V. No increase in accel current during deflection was observed.

4. Combined thrustor and feed system power requirement of 8. 5 W at 5500 sec. Thrust level at this specific impulse was 10. 5 μ lbf for J = 4. 6 mA/cm^2. The power-to-thrust characteristic is shown in Fig. 14.

Station Keeping and Attitude Control System

Trajectory tracer results indicate that ion beams from available thrustor designs can be electrostatically deflected by as much as 30 deg from the normal axial direction. With this degree of deflection fully half of the thrust can be directed perpendicular to the normal thrust vector. In the case of a satellite control system using

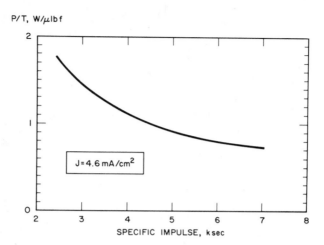

Figure 14. Power-to-thrust ration versus specific impulse for the 10 μ lbf ion engine.

linear-strip thrustors, this means that a single ion engine can be used for both station keeping and attitude control about one axis.   If two such thrustors are mounted with the electrode structures in the same plane but orthogonal to each other, two-axis control from a single station is possible.   Figure 15 shows the general outline of such a station mounted to a common feed system.   The two-thrustor station with electrostatic beam deflection performs the functions of five static thrustors.

There are additional advantages to using two-thrustor station for satellite control.   These may be summarized as follows:

1.   Redundant Thrustor Operations: Since the thrust from each engine is normally directed the same way, the engines can be operated alternately without changing the forces on the spacecraft.   Three stations could provide station keeping, three-axis attitude control, plus 100% redundancy.

2.   Vernier Control of Translation Force: In a flight test it may be highly desirable to correct for minor

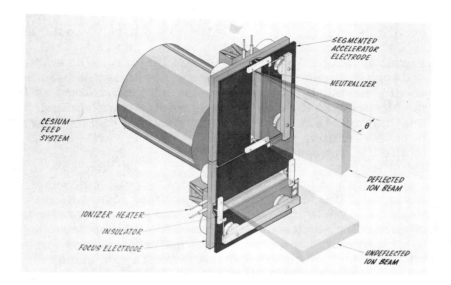

Figure 15. Double-beam thruster station.

misalignment of the thrust vector from an engine operated continuously. The direction of the thrust vector can be varied by ground command to a precision of 0. 01 deg or better.

3. Control System Simplification. Electrostatic beam control allows for a much faster and more flexible satellite control system than original designs based on static thrustors. Since disturbance torques as high as 5000 dyn-cm can be accommodated, the control system can be applied to a wide variety of satellites.

4. Parallel operation of thrustors will permit a thrust level of several millipounds. Station keeping of synchronous satellites in the 5000 lb class can be provided with a control system weight of less than 150 lb for 5 to 10 years.

CONCLUDING REMARKS

The Hughes Linear Ion Engine, with some 3000 hours of test history on several thrustors, is believed to have a potential lifetime on the order of five to ten years. However, this lifetime figure is extremely difficult to establish with any degree of precision for two principal reasons. First, the proper criteria for end of life are not known. Although contemporary knowledge points to erosion of the accel electrode by charge exchange ion bombardment as the fundamental life limiting mechanism, translation of this limitation into a practical criterion for engine failure is purely intuitive at the present state of the art. Second, no life test yet conducted on any ion engine has yielded definitive data on the time dependence of erosion.

Interpretation of the Linear Ion Engine performance during long life tests with regard to power losses (particularly accel drain) was clouded because of the presence of an artifical sputtering environment within the vacuum test chamber. Some of the target material sputtered by the impinging ion beam re-deposited on the ion engine itself, with consequent alteration of the thermal balance between the accelerator electrode and ionizer. In particular, it was observed that the emittance of the downstream surface of the accel electrode decreased with time, so that the accelerator temperature gradually rose during the early portion of the life tests. This resulted in an increase of thermionic electron emission from the cesiated surfaces of the accelerator to the positive high voltage electrodes. Since such an environment of back-sputtered target material does not simulate in any way the real space environment, it is believed that the ion engines were forced to operate under conditions which were less favorable than would be experienced in space.

Because cesiated surfaces can exhibit very low work functions, an increase of electrode temperature due to backsputtered target material has significantly greater influence on the performance of ion engines using cesium instead of other propellants. It is well known that if the arrival flux of sputtered target material on a tungsten ionizer is sufficiently high, the ionizer work function can be altered so that the surface ionization characteristics and overall engine performance are changed to the point where they do not correspond to free-space performance. Consequently, either a readily evaporated material, such as copper, is generally used for ion beam collectors, or the collector is removed to a location remote from the ionizer to decrease the flux of returning particles. However, these measures are insufficient when one is attempting to maintain a given isothermal surface over a very long period of time, particularly if the electrode is designed for cooling principally by thermal radiation.

REFERENCES

1. J. H. Molitor, "Ion Propulsion System for Stationary-Satellite Control, " J. Spacecraft and Rockets 1, 170-175 (1964).
2. J. R. Anderson and G. A. Work, "The Capabilities of Microthrust Electric Propulsion, " post-deadline paper presented at Microthrust Engine Technology Session, AIAA Propulsion Joint Specialist Conference, Colorado Springs, 14-18 June 1965.
3. J. R. Anderson and G. A. Work, "Ion Beam Deflection for Thrust Vector Control, " AIAA Paper No. 66-204, Fifth Electric Propulsion Conference, San Diego, March 1966.
4. G. R. Brewer, "On the Nature of Leakage Currents in Cesium-Contact Ion Engines, " Research Report No. 281, Highes Research Laboratories, Malibu, California, August 1963.
5. R. L. Zimmerman and H. L. Garvin, "Development of Multistrip Cesium-Contact Thrustors, " AIAA Paper No. 66-235, Fifth Electric Propulsion Conference, San Diego, March 1966.
6. D. E. Zuccaro and H. L. Garvin, "Evaluation of Iridium-and Rhenium-Coated Porous Tungsten Ionizer Materials Demonstrating Very Low Cesium Neutral Fraction Characteristics, " AIAA Paper No. 66-217, Fifth Electric Propulsion Conference, San Diego, March 1966.

7. J. R. Anderson, R. Kuberek, and S. A. Thompson, "Development of Linear-Strip Ion Thrustors for Attitude Control," NASA CR 54673, Summary Report, Contract NAS 3-4117, Hughes Research Laboratories, Malibu, California, 13 January 1966.

High - Current Ion Source*

H. J. King and W. O. Eckhardt

Hughes Research Laboratories
Malibu, California

1. INTRODUCTION

The ion source described herein was designed for use as a thrustor for space vehicles. Therefore, high power efficiency, high mass utilization, and long term reliability and stability have been emphasized in the design. The general configuration is that of a low-voltage Penning discharge, first used by Kaufman [1] as an ion thrustor.

In the original design, the useful thrustor lifetime was limited by two components. The most critical of these was initially thought to be the ion-optical structure, which unavoidably suffers some direct bombardment by high-energy (~ 5 kV) ions from the plasma and by charge-exchange ions in the acceleration region. A deeper understanding of the mechanism by which ions are extracted from the plasma, coupled with computer-aided design techniques, [2] has reduced this problem to the point where electrode lifetimes greater than 10^4 hours can be achieved. The second problem involved the lifetime of the prime electron source in the discharge. All conventional thermionic emitters suffer from erosion caused by ions from the plasma which fall through the cathode sheath and strike the cathode with energies above the sputtering threshold (> 20 V). Although considerable progress has been made in the design of long-lived thermionic emitters for this use, [3, 4] only the

*The effort reported herein was partially supported by NASA-Lewis Research Center under Contract NAS 3-6262.

liquid-mercury (LM) cathode [5, 6] has exhibited no ob-
servable change in either structure or performance after
life tests of 3000 hours or more.   Because mercury has
inherent advantages as a propellant, the LM cathode has
been extensively investigated in our laboratory.   The LM
cathode concept is not limited to mercury but can also be
used with other liquid metals.   This report outlines the
basic cathode concept, its incorporation into the discharge,
and the characteristics of the ion source which make it
useful as part of an ion thrustor system, as well as for
other applications which require broad (5 to 50 cm diameter), high current (up to an exceeding 1 A) beams of
metal ions with energies of approximately 1 kV or greater.
Other characteristics of this source are that the beam is
composed almost entirely of singly ionized ions, the
source may be repeatedly exposed to air without damage
to the cathode or other components, and it may be stopped
and restarted rapidly and repeatedly without adverse effects.

2.   LM CATHODE

The gravity-independent, force-fed liquid-metal
cathode provides practically unlimited cathode life in gas
discharge devices and is particularly applicable to mercury electron-bombardment thrustors.   Since the concept
and the first experimental results were presented, [5] a
device has been evolved which has confirmed the anticipated performance improvement. [6, 7]
With all liquid-metal cathodes, the discharge is operated in the liquid-metal pool arc mode to cause electrons
to be emitted from the surface. In addition to emitting electrons at the arc spot, the liquid-metal surface also emits
atoms of the liquid metal, as a result of local heating (and
possibly sputtering) by ion bombardment and by radiation
from the dense spot plasma. An additional efflux of atoms
from the liquid results from evaporation from the inactive
part of the cathode surface. Our gravity-independent,
force-fed version of the liquid-metal cathode maintains the
position of the liquid-metal surface in stable equilibrium
by using a pool-keeping structure which permits dynamic
balancing of the feed pressure against the sum of arc forces,
surface-tension, and viscous drag in the pool-keeping

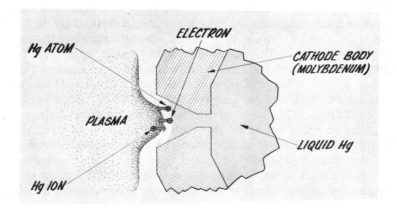

Figure 1. Particle flow at surface of liquid-mercury cathode.

structure. The most favorable results to date were obtained
with pool-keeping structures of divergent-nozzle geometry
(see Fig. 1). The majority of the experiments were performed with mercury as the liquid metal. Figure 2 is a
photograph of an LM cathode in operation. In the ion source
application of this cathode, the removal of metal atoms
from the cathode surface is used to feed the expellant into
the discharge chamber.

In order to optimize the usefulness of the LM cathode
for electron bombardment thrustors, it was necessary
first to identify and then to eliminate the possible per-
formance-limiting mechanisms. The following problems
were found to require attention: (a) thermal instability
at high current and low heat rejection rates, (b) feed rate
fluctuations, and (c) possible interaction of the arc spot
with the magnetic field in the discharge chamber.

The cathode designs resulting after elimination of
these detrimental effects have yielded electron-to-atom
emission ratios of > 100, which is an order of magnitude
above those of conventional pool cathodes and far exceeds
those required for optimum thrustor operation. This has
made possible high-temperature operation of LM cathodes
and has led to a reduction of heat rejection requirements,
thus making presently available LM cathodes attractive for
actual space missions. Advanced designs which will soon
be tested should lead to the practical removal of all thermal

constraints in thrustor applications. [7] Life tests have shown that cathodes of this type would definitely not be the life-limiting element of electron-bombardment thrustors.

A liquid-metal cathode will be stable against small perturbations of feed rate or discharge current if the total evaporation rate decreases when the exposed liquid-metal surface decreases (and vice versa). However, this correlation (decrease of the total evaporation rate resulting from a decrease of the exposed area) will prevail only if the effect of a decrease of the exposed surface area is not overcompensated by a large increase in evaporation rate per unit area. Therefore, the stability requirement means that any change in surface temperature which accompanies a change in surface area must be either in the favorable direction or sufficiently small.

The arc spot changes its position very rapidly along the circumference of the exposed liquid-metal surface, spending approximately equal times at any portion of this circumference. Therefore, the density of thermal power flow into the exposed liquid-metal surface (and, consequently, its temperature and evaporation rate per unit area) will increase when the exposed liquid-metal surface area decreases. This means that the temperature-area dependence is in the unfavorable direction and, if not kept sufficiently small by a suitable thermal design, will render the cathode unstable.

This property of liquid-metal cathodes has been observed under operating conditions representing a thermal overload (current too high or heat rejection too low), and the above explanation was fully verified by temperature measurements with an annular thermocouple junction surrounding the pool-keeping structure.

The crucial design objective is to maximize the thermal conductance between the minimum-cross-section region of the pool-keeping structure and the heat sink. In addition, the temperature-area dependence is adjusted to a suitable level by reducing the thermal conductance between the downstream end of the pool-keeping structure and the heat sink as required.

Even when the thermal design of a liquid-metal cathode permits stable operation in the presence of small perturbations of feed rate or discharge current, the permissible

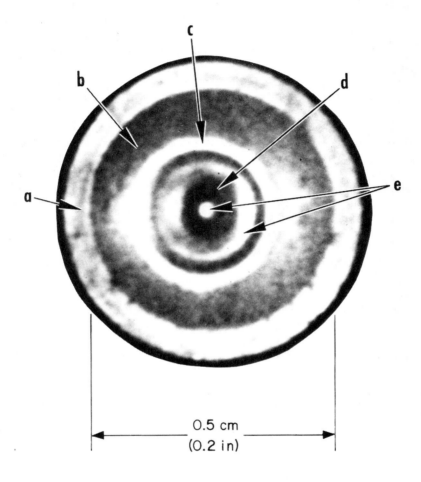

Figure 2. Liquid-mercury cathode in operation, viewed along the axis of symmetry.

a = rim of divergent nozzle
b = exposed nozzle surface
c = annular arc-spot pattern at edge of exposed mercury surface
d = exposed mercury surface
e = reflections of external light source in concave mercury surface

amplitude of these perturbations is limited by the range
of exposed liquid-metal surface area which the particular
cathode geometry can accommodate.

Visual observation of an LM cathode with an early
nozzle geometry (operated within its range of thermal
stability) showed that, under various operating conditions,
rather regular short-term fluctuations of the LM surface
position did indeed exist whose amplitude was not contained by the nozzle cone. It was decided that this problem should be attacked both by increasing the amplitude
which can be contained by the nozzle geometry and by
trying to locate and reduce the effects causing the fluctuation.

A possible cause of short-term fluctuations was seen
in the existence of a large plenum chamber between flow
impedance and orifice. Especially in conjunction with a
cathode operating close to the limit of thermal stability,
the liquid metal contained in the plenum volume will change
its temperature (and hence its density) as a function of
the surface position in the cone, as discussed above.
Because of the direction of the correlation between surface position, temperature, and liquid metal density, this
situation can give rise to a nonlinear oscillation of the
surface position. Such an oscillation is equivalent to a
feed rate fluctuation and can exist even when the actual
feed rate through the flow impedance remains constant.

To suppress these short-term fluctuations, we minimize the effect of thermal expansion of the liquid-metal
volume bounded on the upstream side by the flow impedance
and on the downstream side by the free surface in the
orifice. To this effect, the plenum chamber created by
a separation between flow impedance and nozzle throat is
made as small as possible. The lower limit for this
minimization is given by the requirement for utilizing the
entire cross section of the flow impedance.

The arc spot behavior of a liquid-metal cathode can be
influenced considerably by the presence of an axial magnetic field, as was revealed by visual observation of an
LM cathode operating in a Penning discharge chamber.
A magnetic field of sufficient intensity causes the arc
spot pattern to rotate around the circumference of the exposed mercury surface. When the mercury surface is

located in a divergent nozzle, the force acting on a rotating arc spot causes the arc spot to move to a location of larger radial position, i. e. , downstream in the nozzle cone. In moving, the arc spot pulls the circumference of the exposed mercury surface along, and the surface continuity will be disrupted if the force exerted by the interaction of the arc spot with the applied magnetic field exceeds the surface tension force. This will result in extinction of the arc, and therefore determines an upper limit for the magnetic field which can be tolerated on the cathode axis.

The maximum permissible magnetic field, as determined by this mechanism, may (especially for thrustors of relatively small diameter) be well below the field required for optimum thrustor performance. Therefore, if this effect were permitted to occur, it would result in a performance limitation.

Two basically different possibilities exist for making the magnetic field in the cathode nozzle region independent of the field inside the discharge chamber: magnetic shielding by a high-permeability field shunt, or creation of a cusp-shaped field configuration and placement of the cathode orifice in the vicinity of the saddle point. Both of these approaches have relative advantages, and the choice depends strongly on the discharge-chamber field geometry. We have used both approaches successfully in electron-bombardment thrustors employing either solenoids or permanent magnets.

To date, LM cathodes have been used only in mercury ion sources because they are most desirable for ion propulsion purposes. With suitable thermal design of the pool-keeping structure, cathodes of the geometry described above could be made to operate with a variety of other metals, including the alkalis and some of the heavier metals such as lead, bismuth, and thallium. Thus the concept is applicable to many areas other than ion propulsion.

3. THRUSTOR

The basic thrustor geometry is shown in Fig. 3. Note that both the neutral atoms and the primary electrons come from concentrated source — the arc spot at the cathode surface. The baffle serves to radially deflect both electrons

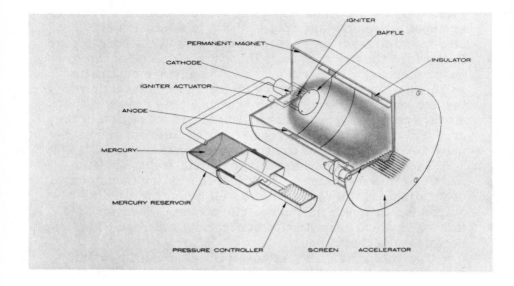

Figure 3.   Light-weight LM cathode thrustor and feed system.

and atoms in order to produce a more uniform plasma and hence a more uniform ion beam.   The electrons are confined axially by the screen and cathode end plate, both of which are at cathode potential, and radially by the magnetic field which makes the electron cyclotron radius less than one fourth of the anode diameter.   Typical performance of a mercury ion thrustor with a 20-cm diameter anode is:

I_{Beam}	0. 5 to 1. 0 A
$I_{Accelerator}$ (interception)	$5 \times 10^{-3} \, I_{Beam}$
V_{Beam}	2 kV (minimum)
$I_{Discharge}$	10 to 20 A ($\sim 20 \, I_{Beam}$)
$V_{Discharge}$	25 to 30 V
Axial Magnetic Field	10 to 30 G
Mass Utilization	85%

The initial thrustor geometry was identical to that used with the conventional Kaufman thrustor. [4]   The most important modification in improving performance with an LM cathode was the insertion of a baffle, as described above. It was subsequently found advantageous to use this baffle to magnetically shield the plasma region immediately downstream from the cathode. This provided a cyclotron radius larger than the baffle for the electrons in the low field region between the cathode and baffle, which allowed them to diffuse around it more readily; this decreased the arc resistance and the source energy per ion* expended in the discharge chamber. It was also found that the relative positions of baffle, cathode, and thrustor end plate could be optimized to improve performance.

Figure 4. shows beam profiles taken with a divergent magnetic field with and without a baffle. The baffle flattens the distribution while raising the beam current by nearly

*Source energy per ion $= \dfrac{\text{discharge power}}{\text{beam current}} = \left[\dfrac{eV}{ion}\right]$

Note that a low source energy per ion is associated with a high power efficiency.

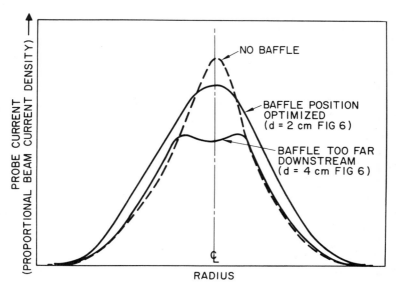

Figure 4. Effect of baffle on beam profiles measured 3 cm downstream of accel electrode. The total width of the graph represents 25 cm diameter.

a factor of two in this case. When the baffle is moved downstream (with a divergent magnetic field), the distribution becomes double peaked. This results because the plasma does not have time to "spill over" into the center, as it does when the baffle is closer to the cathode.

Because of the nonuniformity of the plasma density as a function of radius (see Fig. 4), it has been necessary to develop ion-optical systems with nonuniform perveance density to properly focus the ions extracted from the source. Methods for exact perveance matched designs have been discussed in Ref. 2. Such sophisticated designs have not been employed to date in high-current thrustors because the final configuration of the discharge chamber, and hence the plasma density profile, have not yet been determined. Meanwhile simpler designs with variable, but lower, perveance have been successfully used. As shown in Fig. 3, the ion optics consist of two thin (~ 1 mm) molybdenum plates perforated with a hexagonal close-packed array of circular holes. First-order perveance matching is achieved by "dishing" the accelerator (downstream) electrode, so that the distance between the screen electrode (which serves to confine the plasma) and the accelerator is two to three times as great at the anode radius as at the center. The plasma side of each aperture in the screen electrode is countersunk, thus permitting the plasma surface to assume the exact position for a space-charge limited current to be focused through each aperture. This procedure has been studied with an electrolytic tank and analog computer. [8] Using these relatively simple techniques, it is possible to draw ion currents exceeding 1 A with accelerator currents less than 5×10^{-3} of the total beam current.

As a result of these studies of discharge chamber and ion optics, the thrustor performance has shown steady improvement. The current performance is shown in Fig. 5 in the form of a plot of the source energy per ion expended in the discharge chamber for various mass utilization. The two upper curves indicate recent improvements resulting from the use of closed-loop mercury flow control and better baffle shapes.

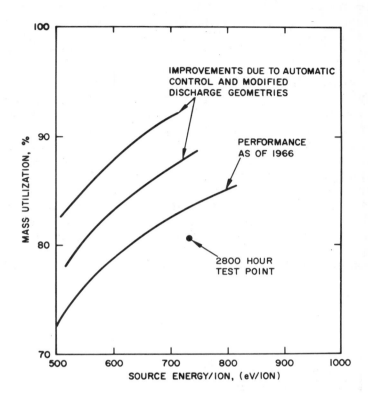

Figure 5. Source energy per ion versus mass utilization.

4. PROPELLANT FEED AND CONTROL SYSTEM

Because liquid mercury is fed directly to the cathode from the storage reservoir, the propellant feed system can be very simple. The system consists basically of a pressurized feed tank and the constant flow impedance presented by the cathode, and can operate in zero gravity as well as on the ground. By adjusting the driving pressure, the feed rate can be controlled over a wide range. The problem lies more in measuring the flow than in regulating it, since the flow rate is very small (< 1 cm^3/ hour). Another design requirement was a pressurizing

system which would continuously regulate the pressure
without requiring a large high-pressure gas storage vessel,
as would be necessary with a conventional relief-valve
type of system which can reduce pressure only by venting
gas.

A propellant feed system which satisfies both design
requirements is shown in Fig. 6. The piston is sealed to
the cylinder wall with a rolling diaphragm, thus providing
a low friction seal which requires no lubricant. The force
on the piston is provided by a pressurizer unit which consists of a bellows sealed inside a housing. The space between bellows and housing is filled with a liquid — in this
case distilled water. When the water is heated, some of
it is changed to vapor. Thus the pressure in the system
is a function of temperature, accurately following the
saturated vapor pressure curve. The double piston arrangement is necessary to provide thermal isolation between pressurizer and reservoir, thus minimizing the

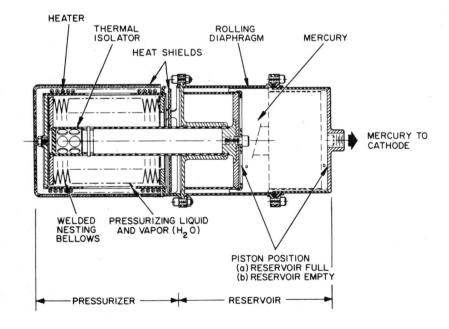

Figure 6. Liquid mercury feed system.

response time constant of the system. If the water were simply placed on the opposite side of the rolling diaphragm from the mercury, so that the two were in intimate thermal contact, it would be necessary to temperature control the entire volume of mercury (which could be greater than 100 lb.) and the response would be very sluggish.

The invariance of the mass utilization during the 2750 hour life test is demonstrated in Section 5. For a given magnetic field and cathode current, the ratio of beam current to propellant flow rate is a constant, independent of time. Thus the mass flow rate may be accurately determined by monitoring the beam current. Closed-loop operation was achieved by using a signal proportional to the beam current to regulate the feed system pressure. The only other regulation required for the LM cathode thrustor is a discharge power supply which maintains the discharge current at a pre-set value.

5. THRUSTOR LIFE TESTS

The goal of the life test is to establish the cathode lifetime in a working thrustor by testing the complete unit for time increments of approximately 1000 hours duration. To date, 2800 hours have been accumulated. At intervals of 500 to 1000 hours it has been necessary to withdraw the thrustor from the test facility and remove the material sputtered back from the collector onto the thrustor electrodes. The cathode was not cleaned at these times.

The 20-cm thrustor used for the test was supplied by NASA-LeRC. It was modified to accept the LM cathode assembly and to permit operation at magnetic fields up to 200 G if required. Normal operation with the LM cathode requires much lower fields. The NASA ion-optical system was replaced by a unit fabricated at HRL in which the screen was countersunk on the plasma side, as described above. The center spacing between screen and accel was 0.13 cm, and the perimeter spacing was 0.37 cm. The closer spacing in the center provided a quasi-matching of perveance and current density. The optics had a hexagonal close-packed array of 1027 holes with a nominal diameter of 0.43 cm on 0.58 cm centers drilled in 0.14 cm thick molybdenum plates. The total hole area is 177 cm^2, corresponding to an open area of 56%.

Table I.   Thrustor Performance Summary

	Objectives of Test	Performance (50 hour averages)	
		at 150 hour	at 2708 hour
Beam Current	600 mA ± 10%	589 mA	588 mA
Beam Power	≥ 3 kW	3.66 kW	3.65 kW
Effective Specific Impulse	6000 sec ± 15%	6370 sec	6380 sec
Propellant Mass Utilization	≥ 80%	80.8%	81.0%
Source Energy Per Ion	≤ 1000 eV/ion	729 eV/ion	724 eV/ion
Accel Current		2.9 mA	2.8 mA
Magnetic Field at Screen		26 G	26 G

Table I shows the operating parameter ranges for this test compared with operating points taken near the beginning and end of the test. There is no degradation of performance over the test period. The time invariance of the thrustor characteristics is also illustrated in Figs. 7 and 8. These data show the reproducibility of the mass utilization and discharge voltage (at constant discharge current) at various times during the test. The spread in the measured points is less than ± 1% over 2800 hours. Figure 7 is a condensed time history of the test results. Each point is an average of 50 data points taken at 1 hour intervals. The test was conducted with an open-loop control system. This was possible because of the inherent stability of the cathode and thrustor characteristics.

Throughout the test the accel interception current remained stable at 0.5% (~ 2.9 mA). The maximum accel erosion occurred near the center on the downstream side of the accel electrode in triangular-shaped pits between aperatures. Adjacent pits were interconnected by shallower troughs of erosion. The edges of the apertures were notably free from erosion. A photograph of the downstream side of the accel electrode after 2780 hours is shown in Fig. 9. The pits were formed by slow charge-exchange ions created in the beam plasma and focused by the concave part of the plasma miniscus which separates the downstream plasma from the nonplasma region. [2, 9] Projecting the erosion rate of the deepest pits gives an accelerator electrode life of >10, 000 hours, assuming that the deepest pits reach a depth equal to the thickness of the molybdenum.

The radial dependence of both the erosion on the downstream face of the accel electrode and the enlargement of the accel apertures is plotted in Fig. 10. The enlargement of the accel holes is caused by the small percentage of ions which are extracted from the plasma but are not focused through the accel aperture. The peak at approximately $r = 2.5$ cm results from the combined effects of the reduction in perveance with increasing r (due to the electrode spacing which increases with r) and of an annular peak in the plasma density due to the effects of the baffle. The increased plasma density in this annular region has been observed visually. It is caused by electrons

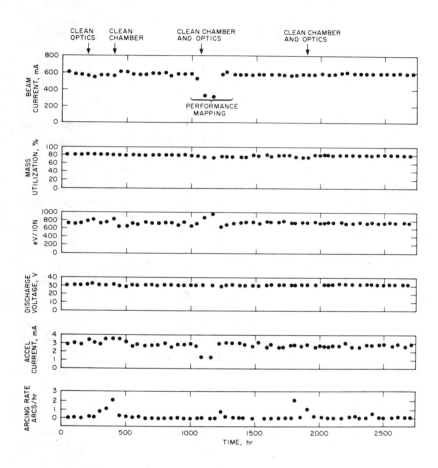

Figure 7.   Life test parameters as function of time.

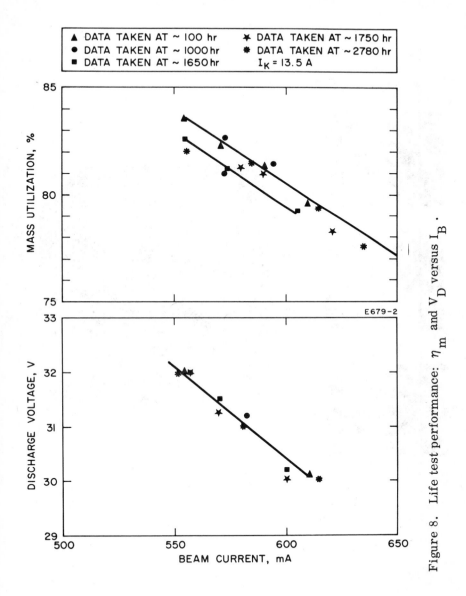

Figure 8. Life test performance: η_m and V_D versus I_B.

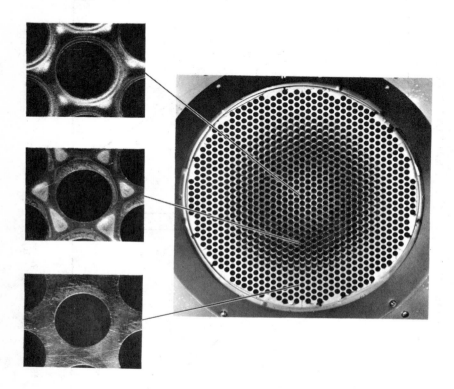

Figure 9. Photograph of accelerator electrode after 2750 hours of testing.

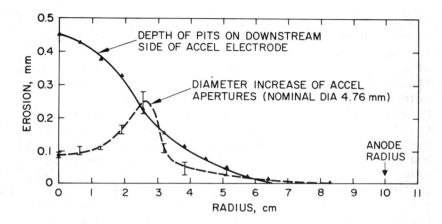

Figure 10. Charge–exchange and direct interception erosion of accelerator.

streaming out around the baffle and following magnetic field lines which intersect the screen electrode at approximately r = 2.5 cm.

The charge–exchange erosion on the face of the accel electrode is peaked at the center. Since the local charge–exchange ion production rate is directly proportional to the product of beam current density and neutral efflux density, one can conclude from the results that the neutral efflux must be peaked in the center by a sufficient amount to compensate for the central dip in beam current density. This dip has been inferred from the accel aperture erosion measurements and from the visual observation of the annular plasma density peak.

The significant results of the life test are summarized below:

    1.   No cathode erosion or degradation observed.

    2.   Cathode and thrustor characteristics completely stable (time invariant) during test.

    3.   Extrapolated accelerator lifetime $> 10^4$ hours.

    4.   No performance variations associated with stop-start operation or exposure to air.

6. IMPROVED THRUSTOR DESIGNS

A continuing program is under way to improve the over-all thrustor performance in the areas of mass utilization and power efficiency, thrust to weight ratio, accelerator electrode lifetime, and compatibility with the spacecraft environment.   The discharge configuration and magnetic field shapes discussed above have been implemented using a light-weight permanent magnet structure (Fig. 11), thus eliminating the magnet power and the associated system weight.   First-order perveance matching between the ion optical system and the plasma has been achieved by using a dished accelerator electrode.   Considerable further improvement can be achieved by adjusting the aperture sizes in the electrodes to conform to the plasma density profiles as well.   This adjustment has been postphoned

Figure 11.   Light-weight permanent magnet thrustor.

until the optimization of the discharge chamber is completed because each change in discharge configuration produces a change in plasma density profile, therefore the two studies cannot proceed in parallel.

7. SYSTEMS

Thrustors of the type discussed here are compatible in all respects with the system requirements defined recently [10] in an extensive analytical study of solar powered, electrically propelled space vehicles. The power would be generated by large arrays of solar cells which produce approximately 100 W/m^2 of surface. A power of 150 kW is required to produce 1 lb of thrust. One example from the above analysis indicated that a space vehicle incorporating a 23 kW solar array could be launched by a Saturn 1B-Centaur, and that such a system could deliver a 2300 lb lander vehicle plus a 3600 lb orbiter vehicle to Mars in approximately one year. The scientific payload placed in orbit exceeds the capability of chemical rockets by a factor of four.

8. CONCLUSION

Both the LM cathode and the particular discharge geometry described above have been developed to satisfy the requirements for space propulsion. The reliability and efficiency required by this application make the device useful for any other application requiring ion beams of large size and high total current.

REFERENCES

1. H. R. Kaufman, "An Ion Rocket with an Electron-Bombardment Ion Source, " NASA TN D-585, January 1961.
2. J. Hyman, Jr. , W. O. Eckhardt, R. C. Knechtli, and C. R. Buckey, "Formation of Ion Beams from Plasma Sources: Part I, " AIAA J. 2, 1739 (1964). W. O. Eckhardt, J. Hyman, Jr. , G. Hagen, C. R. Buckey, and R. C. Knechtli, "Research Investigation of Ion Beam Formation from Electron-Bombardment

Ion Sources, " Technical Summary Report, Contracts NAS 3-2511 and NAS 3-3546 (March 1964). (Copies available from NASA Office of Scientific and Technical Information, Washington 25, D. C. , Attention: AFSS-A.)

3. W. Knauer, G. Hagen, H. Gallagher, and E. Stack, "Investigation of the Discharge in Electron Bombardment Thrustors, " AIAA Paper No. 66-244 (March 1966).

4. P. D. Reader, "Durability Tests of Mercury Electron-Bombardment Ion Thrustors, " AIAA Paper No. 66-231 (March 1966).

5. W. O. Eckhardt, J. A. Snyder, H. J. King, and R. C. Knechtli, "A New Cathode for Mercury Electron-Bombardment Thrustors, " AIAA Paper No. 64-690 (August 1964).

6. H. J. King, W. O. Eckhardt, J. Ward, R. C. Knechtli, "Electron-Bombardment Thrustors using Liquid Mercury Cathodes, " AIAA Paper No. 66-232 (March 1966).

7. W. O. Eckhardt, H. J. King, J. A. Snyder, and R. C. Knechtli, "Liquid-Metal Cathode Research, " AIAA Paper No. 66-245 (March 1966).

8. N. B. Kramer, "Ion Optics for the Electron Bombardment Engine, " Hughes Research Laboratories internal report No. 324 (February 1965).

9. S. L. Eilenberg, W. Seitz, and E. Caplinger, "Evaluation of Electrode Shapes for Ion Engines, " AIAA J. 3, 866 (1965).

10. J. H. Molitor, D. Berman, R. Seliger, and R. Olson, "Design of a Solar Electric Propulsion System for Interplanetary Spacecraft, " AIAA Paper No. 66-214 (March 1966).

Plasma Characteristics of the Electron Bombardment Ion Engine

Tommy D. Masek

Jet Propulsion Laboratory
California Institute of Technology
Pasadena, California

I. INTRODUCTION

Continuing interest in the application of the electron bombardment ion engine to future spacecraft has prompted studies of the overall operation of such engines. [1-3] These studies have concentrated primarily on ion extraction, ion focusing, and on general performance characteristics; they have been, in general, quite successful. Engines of this type have operated for many thousands of hours with both mercury and cesium as propellants. However, the plasma which is the source of ions for the engine has not been examined extensively. Previous investigations [4-6] have presented experimental data on the plasma properties and have analyzed these properties; thus far, however, a general analytical model predicting the plasma characteristics is not available.

The need for an analytical model is clear considering that most improvements and optimizations of the electron bombardment engine have been based on experimental trial and error methods. Since the formation of the plasma

*This work presents the results of one phase of research carried out in the Propulsion Research and Advanced Concepts Section of the Jet Propulsion Laboratory, California Institute of Technology, under Contract NAS 7-100, sponsored by the National Aeronautics and Space Administration.

represents the major source of engine inefficiency, information on the formation mechanisms and the factors affecting plasma properties would be useful in the design of new engines and improvement of existing ones. Specifically, factors such as propellant distribution, cathode position, and engine geometry, which are presently studied only experimentally, could be analytically assessed more generally. In addition, it would be useful to determine scaling relationships to simplify future engine development. Basic solutions for the plasma properties and scaling factors can only be determined after a model is developed. The purpose of this paper is to develop an analytical model for the plasma and to indicate the steps and assumptions involved in obtaining solutions.

The equations describing the plasma are nonlinear partial differential equations requiring numerical solutions in general. However, by making certain reasonable assumptions, the equations of motion for ions and electrons can be simplified to allow a solution for the radial and axial plasma potential in terms of the ion density. The ion density cannot be solved for analytically because the flux continuity equations include a nonlinear ion production term; however, the plasma potential solutions can be applied and compared to measure potentials by using measured ion densities in the solutions. In addition, by using the plasma potential solutions, the axial ion flux density can be obtained and compared with measured ion flux in the beam to provide an additional correlation of theory and measurement. This procedure provides a method for justifying the assumptions and determining the validity of the analytical model. The results of this study provide a starting point for the complete solution of the plasma equations.

II.   PLASMA THEORY

A typical electron bombardment ion engine is shown schematically in Fig. 1. The engine is composed of the following elements: cathode, anode, housing, magnetic field coil, screen grid, and accelerating grid. The cathode provides, thermionically, electrons which are attracted toward the anode. The axial magnetic field produced by the

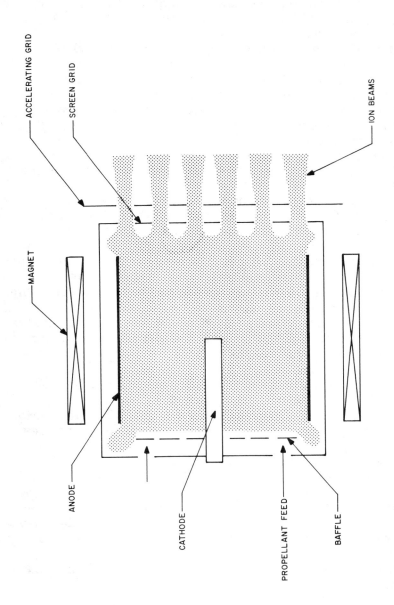

Figure 1. Conventional electron bombardment ion engine schematic diagram.

field coil causes electrons to have spiral paths and increases their effective mean free path. Propellant gas injected into the chamber is ionized by the electrons to form a plasma of ions, electrons, and neutral atoms. In the ensuing discussion, two groups of electrons will be identified. These are referred to as primary and Maxwellian electrons. Primary electrons, those initially emitted from the cathode, have energies approximately equal to the cathode-anode potential difference [7] and form an essentially monoenergetic group. Collisions of primary electrons with neutral atoms produce ions and secondary electrons. The primary electrons lose energy through inelastic collisions with atoms, ions and secondary electrons. A portion of the primary group thus joins the lower energy secondary group which is found to have a Maxwellian energy distribution. One could reasonably expect a radially decreasing average Maxwellian energy due to the decreasing energy contribution of the primary group.

The plasma thus formed is a source of ions. A sheath formed at the screen grid provides a boundary for the plasma. Ions crossing this sheath and passing through the holes in the grid are accelerated by the electric field applied between the grids. In addition to the plasma ion loss by extraction in the beam, ions are lost through recombination in the plasma, at the cathode, and on other engine chamber surfaces.

Engine operation and efficiency are thus strong functions of the efficiency of ion production, ion loss, and the axial motion of the ions at the screen grid. Ion production, loss, and axial motion are dependent upon the properties of the plasma. That is, they depend on the ion density, electron energy, and plasma potential distributions. Therefore, the analysis must deal with these properties.

An analytical model of the plasma as it relates to the electron bombardment ion engine will be developed here. It is important to realize that the results of this study relate directly to the bombardment engine through the assumptions and the application of experimental data. The assumptions should be reviewed before application is made to other situations.

As noted, the plasma can be completely described by a series of nonlinear, partial differential equations. To obtain useful information from these equations requires a number of simplifying assumptions. A large body of literature exists in which the effects of various assumptions on the solutions are investigated. However, the choice of assumptions for any given application must be based on the properties of the particular plasma being studied. First, therefore, the general characteristics of the plasma will be presented in terms of collision times, collision and ionization cross sections, and ion production coefficients. These will be used to justify the assumptions made in the analysis that follows. Second, the general equations describing the plasma are presented, and the assumptions to be made in the solution are discussed. An analytical solution for the plasma potential is obtained, and compared with experimental data to check the validity of the analysis. The solution will be used in later work to find numerical solutions to the flux continuity equations for the ion density. Finally, the equation for the axial ion flux is derived and put in terms of the ion density gradient. This flux is computed and compared to measured beam current densities. An energy equation for the primary and Maxwellian electrons has not yet been established but does not limit the analysis presented here.

A. General Characteristics

As indicated previously, the primary electrons enter the plasma with energies approximately equal to the arc (cathode-anode) voltage. Collisions of primary electrons with secondary electrons and neutrals reduce a portion of the primary electrons to a Maxwellian distribution. The time required for primary electron energy to be lost can be estimated by considering collision and relaxation times.

In steady state, the time required for a monoenergetic distribution of primary electrons of energy ϵ_p to relax to a Maxwellian distribution with energy $(3/2)kT_e$ when interacting with a Maxwellian group of this same energy is given approximately by [8]

$$\tau_e = \frac{3.20 \times 10^4 \epsilon_p^{3/2}}{n_e G(\xi) \ln \Lambda} \tag{1}$$

where

ϵ_p = primary electron energy, ev

T_e = electron temperature, $^\circ$K

n_e = electron number density, m^{-3}

$\ln \Lambda$ = $\ln \left[12\pi (\epsilon_0 kT_e)^{3/2} / e^3 n_e^{1/2} \right]$

k = Boltzmann constant, Joule $^\circ$K^{-1}

ϵ_0 = permittivity of vacuum, coul$^2 \cdot$ n$^{-1} \cdot$ m^{-2}

e = electron charge, coul

and

$$G(\xi) = \frac{\phi(\xi) - \xi \frac{d\phi}{d\xi}}{2\xi^2} \tag{2}$$

with

$$\xi = \left(\frac{\epsilon_p}{kT_e} \right)^{1/2}$$

and

$$\phi(\xi) = \frac{2}{\pi^{1/2}} \int_0^\xi e^{-y^2} dy \tag{3}$$

$G(\xi)$ has been tabulated by Spitzer. [8] Equation (1) is plotted in Fig. 2 for a range of electron energies for $n_e = 10^{11}$ cm^{-3}. This time can be easily estimated for other densities since $\ln \Lambda$ varies slowly with n_e.

The time between primary electron-ion collisions can be determined from the equation [8]

$$\tau_{ei} = \frac{3.2 \times 10^4 \epsilon_p^{3/2}}{n_e [\phi(\xi) - G(\xi)] \ln \Lambda} \tag{4}$$

where the terms are defined as before. The $\ln \Lambda$ factor is found from the Maxwellian electron group as before, since it involves the Debye length determined by the Maxwellian electron temperature. This time is plotted in Fig. 3 for $n_e = 10^{11}$ cm^{-3}.

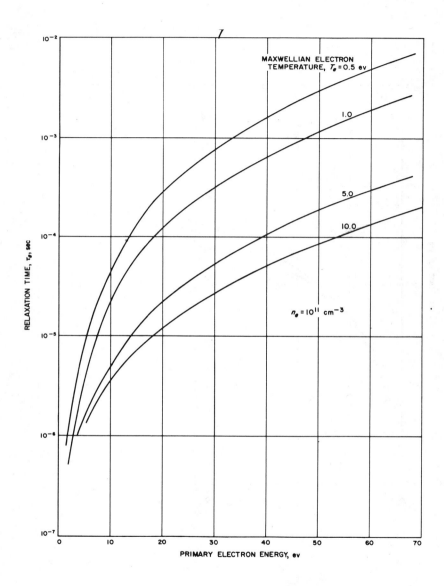

Figure 2.   Primary electron relaxation time.

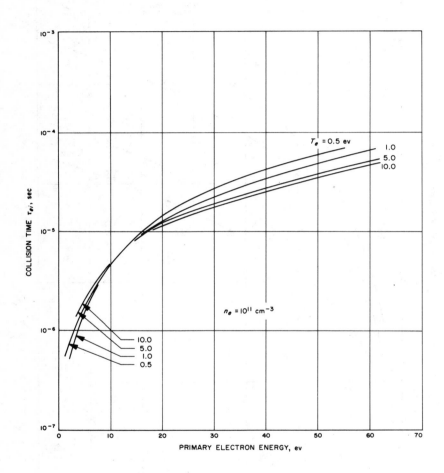

Figure 3.   Primary electron-ion collision times.

The time between electron-electron collisions within the Maxwellian group can be computed from the "self collision" time equation [8]

$$\tau_m = 1.8 \times 10^5 \frac{\epsilon_m^{3/2}}{n_e \ln \Lambda} \qquad (5)$$

where ϵ_m is the average Maxwellian electron energy in electron volts. This collision time is plotted in Fig. 4 for a range of electron densities and average energies. Maxwellian electron-ion elastic collision times are essentially those for electron-electron collisions. [9] The electron-ion energy exchange times, however, should be long compared to electron-electron energy exchange times, since energy is transferred more effectively between electrons. Electron-ion relaxation is therefore neglected. The electrons are assumed to have much higher temperatures than the ions; thus the plasma is not in thermal equilibrium.

A note is needed here to point out the convention used in describing electron temperature. When temperature is discussed it is understood that either °K is to be used or the electron volt equivalent $e/k = 11,600°K \cdot volt^{-1}$ is to be used in conversion when T_e is given in ev. When electron energy is discussed in ev, the conversion $(3/2)kT_e$ must be used to find T_e. This distinction is made because the Langmuir probe measurements described later give T_e in electron volts and should not be confused with the average energy of the Maxwellian distribution.

The inelastic electron-atom collision times can be computed from [9]

$$\tau_{ea} = \frac{1}{n_o Q_{ea} V_e} \qquad (6)$$

where

n_o = neutral atom density, cm^{-3}

Q_{ea} = inelastic collision cross section, cm^2

V_e = electron velocity, $cm \cdot sec^{-1}$

The cross section Q_{ea} includes ionization and excitation. Sovie and Dugan [10] have calculated τ_{ea} for cesium using Gryziński's classical theory [11] and their curve is shown in Fig. 5. The mercury calculation, also plotted in Fig. 5,

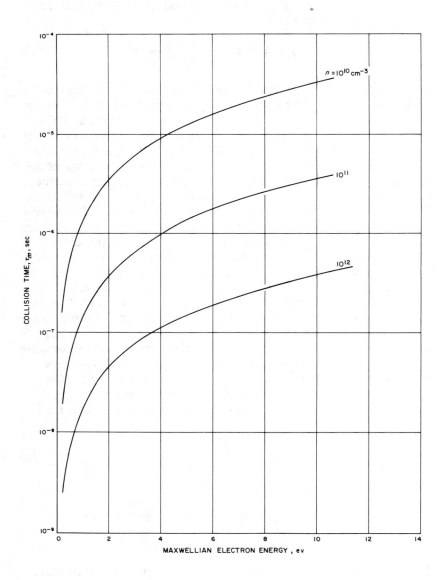

Figure 4. Maxwellian electron-self collision times.

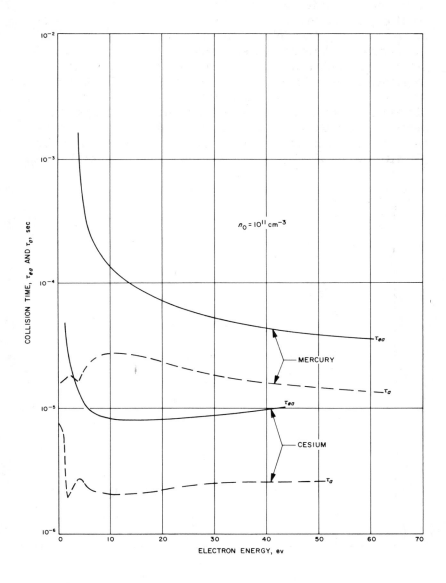

Figure 5. Elastic and inelastic electron-atom collision times.

was made using the experimental data of Refs. 12 and 13 to form the inelastic cross section. The inelastic cross sections are shown in Fig. 6. The cesium curve was obtained by using Eq. (6) and the collision times of Ref. 10.

The time between elastic electron-atom collisions is pertinent in determining the time required for electrons to be scattered without energy exchange. Since the electron-ion collisions are also essentially elastic, the faster of electron-atom or electron-ion collision times should determine scattering. The electron-atom collision time, τ_a, can be estimated by using an equation similar to Eq. (6) with the total collision cross section. The total cross

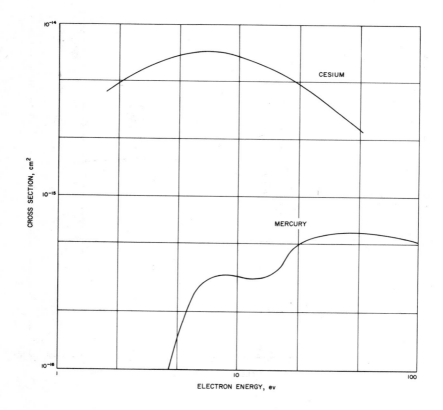

Figure 6. Inelastic electron-atom collision cross sections for mercury [12, 13] and cesium [10].

sections [14, 15] are shown in Figs. 7 and 8 and the times are shown in Fig. 5 for $n_0 = 10^{11}$ cm^{-3}. The upper right curve in Fig. 8 was used in calculating the cesium collision times. The various curves and data points in this figure are referenced in Ref. 15 and serve to show the wide variation in reported cross sections.

The arc voltages in the cesium and mercury engine are typically 10 and 50 v, respectively. [16, 17] The primary electrons are found to have energies about equal to the arc voltage and the Maxwellian electrons' energies about one-tenth the arc voltage. [18] Near the cathode, the plasma should be highly ionized. Assuming 90% ionization, and an electron density of 10^{12} cm^{-3}, the various collision times for cesium and mercury are

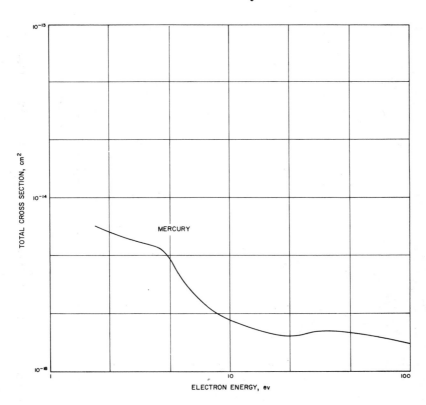

Figure 7. Total electron-atom collision cross section for mercury [14].

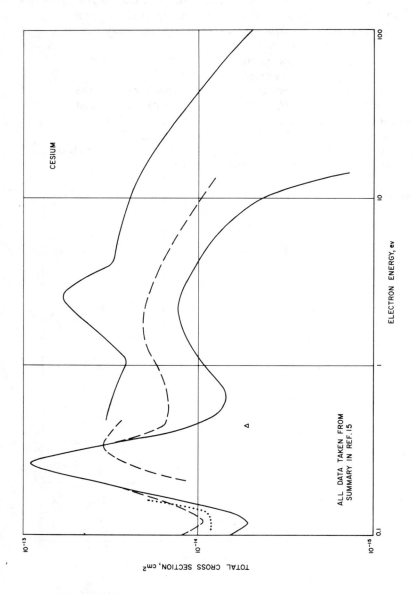

Figure 8. Total electron-atom collision cross section for cesium [15].

Cs	Hg	
$\tau_e = 2 \times 10^{-6}$ sec	$\tau_e = 2 \times 10^{-5}$	
$\tau_{ei} = 4 \times 10^{-7}$	$\tau_{ei} = 4 \times 10^{-6}$	(7)
$\tau_{ea} = 8 \times 10^{-6}$	$\tau_{ea} = 4 \times 10^{-5}$	
$\tau_a = 2 \times 10^{-6}$	$\tau_a = 2 \times 10^{-5}$	

An important characteristic of these plasmas is the relative concentration of primary and Maxwellian electrons. The population of primary electrons can be expressed as

$$n_p(r) = n_p(0)\, e^{-t/\tau} \tag{8}$$

where τ is the time required for energy exchange and $n_p(0)$ is the initial density. In order to compare the primary ratio $n_p(r)/n_p(0)$ for mercury and cesium, a discussion of t and τ of Eq. (8) is needed. For our purposes, t will be taken as the time required for electrons to traverse the radius of the chamber and τ will be taken as the time required for primaries to join the Maxwellian distribution or $\tau = \tau_e$. The traverse time will depend on a combination of the electron-atom or electron-ion times. Since the atom and ion densities vary radially, the relative importance of τ_{ei} and τ_a cannot be distinguished. Also, since the cross sections are relatively inaccurate for electron-atom collisions as indicated in Fig. 8, it is assumed that t is the same in both plasmas. The solid line in Fig. 9 shows a plot of Eq. (8) including only τ_e and including an estimate for electron energy loss because of collisions with atoms and ions shown by the dashed curve. The time t is interpreted as a distance divided by a velocity. The velocity is that determined by an electron moving one cyclotron radius per collision. Experimentally, the primary ratio at the anode, designated as point R, is approximately 10^{-3}. The dashed mercury curve is fairly representative of the measured primary distributions. The dashed cesium curve was estimated from the mercury curve. Considering the dashed curve for cesium, it is apparent that an extremely low fraction of primaries would be expected in cesium relative to mercury. It will be shown that in fact no primaries are detected in cesium plasma measurements.

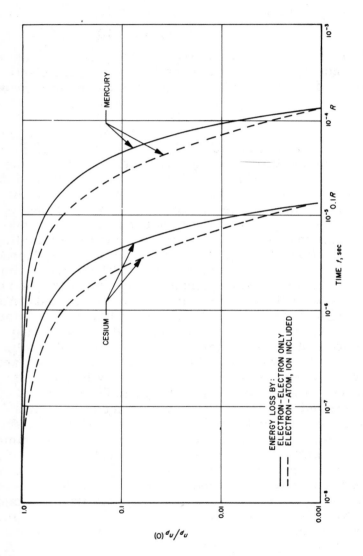

Figure 9. Relative primary electron decay rate for mercury and cesium plasmas.

The effectiveness of primary and Maxwellian electrons in producing ionization can be calculated following the method of Refs. 6 and 19. The production rate per unit volume is

$$\nu\,(r,\ \epsilon) = \frac{dn_i\,(r,\ \epsilon)}{dr} \tag{9}$$

where ν is the production rate at position r by electrons of energy ϵ. Assuming that the electron energy distribution function can be represented by

$$f(r,\ \epsilon) = f_p(\epsilon)n_p(r) + f_m(\epsilon)n_m(r) \tag{10}$$

where

$f_p(\epsilon)$ = primary electron distribution function

$\quad = \delta(\epsilon_p)$ = delta function

$f_m(\epsilon)$ = Maxwellian distribution function

$n_p(r)$ = primary electron density at position r

the production rate is

$$\nu(r,\ \epsilon) = \left(\frac{2\,\epsilon}{m_e}\right)^{1/2} n_o(r)Q_i(\epsilon)f(r,\ \epsilon) \tag{11}$$

where Q_i is the ionization cross section for single ionization and $n_0(r)$ is the neutral particle density at position r.

Experimental measurements of Q_i for mercury and cesium are shown in Figs. 10 and 11 along with Gryziński's theory. [13, 20, 21] The theoretical curves were computed using

$$Q_i = \Sigma N_k Q_k \tag{12}$$

with

$$Q_k = \frac{6.56 \times 10^{-14}}{U_i^2}\ g(\zeta) \tag{13}$$

where U_i is the energy required to remove a single electron from the kth atomic state, N_k is the number of electrons in the kth state, $\zeta = \epsilon/U_i$

$$g(\zeta) = \frac{1}{\zeta}\left(\frac{\zeta - 1}{\zeta + 1}\right)\left[1 + \frac{2}{3}\ \left(1 - \frac{1}{2\zeta}\right)\ \ln\,(2.7 + \sqrt{\zeta - 1})\right] \tag{14}$$

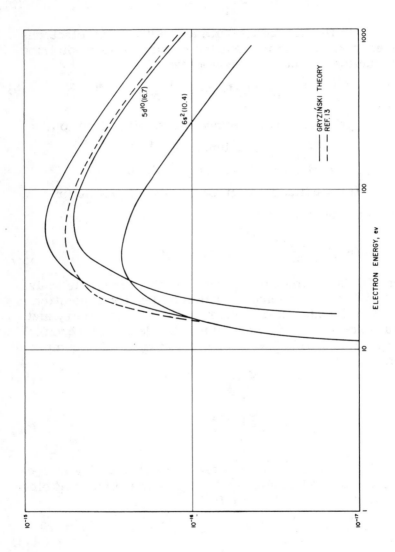

Figure 10.   Ionization cross section for producing singly charged mercury ions.

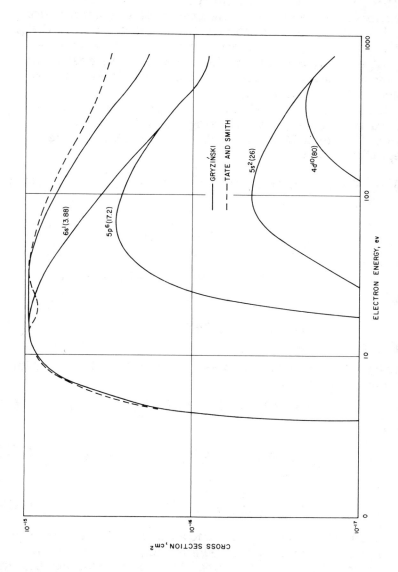

Figure 11. Ionization cross section for producing singly charged cesium ions.

and ϵ is the energy of the colliding electron. The ionization energies for each state are needed for this calculation and were obtained from Ref. 22 on atomic spectra. The notation on the theoretical curves designates the state, the number of electrons in the ground state configuration and the energy required to remove an electron from that state. In the case of mercury, it is interesting to note the large contribution from the 5d state. The cesium experimental data was adjusted to match the theory as suggested by McFarland. [23]

Integration of Eq. (11) has been previously accomplished for mercury [6, 19] using Eq. (10) and for cesium [4] for a Maxwellian distribution alone. The integration yields

$$\nu(r) = \left(\frac{2}{m_e}\right)^{1/2} Q_i(\epsilon_p) n_o(r) n_p(r) \epsilon_p^{1/2} + \tag{15}$$

$$\left(\frac{2}{m_e}\right)^{1/2} n_o(r) n_m(r) R_m$$

where

$$n_m(r) = \text{Maxwellian electron density}$$

and

$$R_m = \int_0^\infty f_m Q_i(\epsilon) \epsilon^{1/2} \, d\epsilon$$

Slightly different functions were used in Ref. 19. Equation (15) can be written as

$$\nu(r) = n_o(r)\left[n_p(r)\Sigma_p + n_m(r)\Sigma_m\right] \tag{16}$$

where

$$\Sigma_p = \left(\frac{2}{m_e}\right)^{1/2} Q_i(\epsilon_p) \epsilon_p^{1/2} \tag{17}$$

$$\Sigma_m = \left(\frac{2}{m_e}\right)^{1/2} R_m \tag{18}$$

the functions Σ_p and Σ_m are shown in Fig. 12 for mercury and in Fig. 13 for cesium. The ionization cross section used in calculating Σ_m^{Cs} in Ref. 4 was not stated but should be accurate enough for our purpose here. Using the

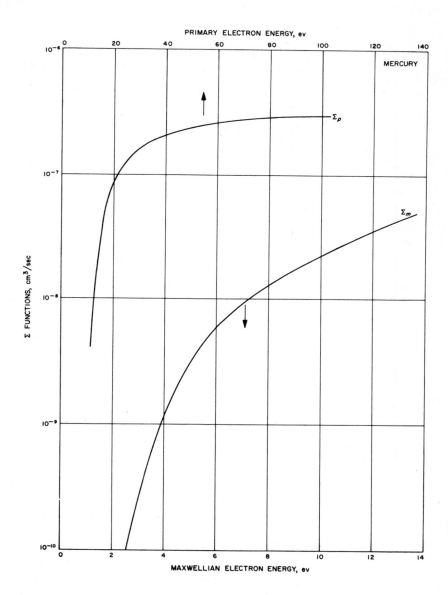

Figure 12. Ion production coefficients for primary and Maxwellian electrons in mercury.

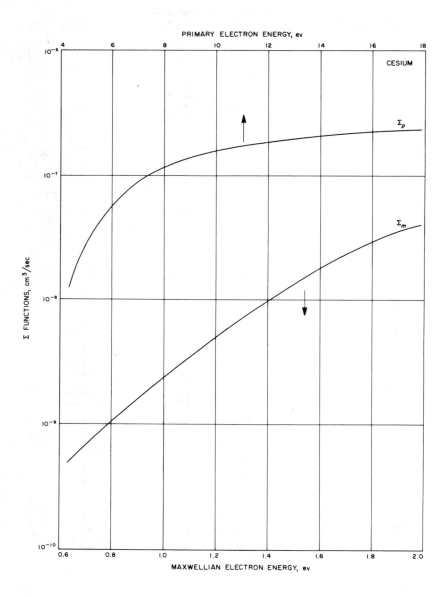

Figure 13. Ion production coefficients for primary and Maxwellian electrons in cesium.

Maxwell and primary energies assumed before, the ion production coefficients, Σ_p and Σ_m are about the same for mercury and cesium. However, there is quite a large difference between the effectiveness of Maxwellian and primary electrons. These production coefficients will be required for solving the ion and electron flux equations.

B. Diffusion Theory

The study of charged particle diffusion processes has been the subject of a great many investigations. Two comprehensive summary papers are available which list numerous references [24, 25], so a general treatment of diffusion is not attempted in this paper. This section presents the equations required to describe the plasma in the electron bombardment engine, indicates the necessary assumptions, and outlined the solution. The equations presented have previously been solved with various simplifying assumptions [24, 25], but these solutions in most cases do not apply to the problem of interest here. The following formulation assumes that the neutral particles are stationary and are included only as target particles for the charged species. The equations of motion for the charged particles can be written as [24]

$$m_\alpha \left[\frac{\delta \vec{u}_\alpha}{\delta t} + \vec{u}_\alpha \cdot \nabla \vec{u}_\alpha \right] = Z_\alpha e(\vec{E} + \vec{u}_\alpha \times \vec{B}) -$$

$$\frac{\nabla P_\alpha}{n_\alpha} + m_\alpha \frac{\delta \vec{u}_\alpha}{\delta t} \tag{19}$$

where α denotes the specie and

m_α = mass

$\vec{u}_\alpha$ = directed velocity

$Z_\alpha e$ = charge

$\vec{E}$ = electric field

$\vec{B}$ = magnetic field

P_α = hydrostatic pressure

n_α = number density

$\delta \vec{u}_\alpha / \delta t$ = momentum exchange term

The pressure can be written as

$$P_\alpha = \frac{2}{3} n_\alpha \epsilon_\alpha \tag{20}$$

which for a Maxwellian energy distribution is

$$P_\alpha = n_\alpha T_\alpha \tag{21}$$

where T_α = temperature in energy units. The momentum exchange term $\delta \vec{u}_\alpha / \delta t$ accounts for momentum transfer between species and can be written

$$m_\alpha \frac{\delta \vec{u}_\alpha}{\delta t} = - m_\alpha \sum_\beta \nu_{\alpha\beta} (\vec{u}_\alpha - \vec{u}_\beta) \tag{22}$$

where $\nu_{\alpha\beta}$ = collision frequency. An additional relationship accounting for the conservation of momentum in collisions is given by

$$n_\alpha m_\alpha \nu_{\alpha\beta} = n_\beta m_\beta \nu_{\beta\alpha} \tag{23}$$

In addition to the equations of motion, the species continuity equation, must be satisfied

$$\nabla \cdot \vec{\Gamma}_\alpha = \nu_i^\alpha - \nu_r^\alpha \tag{24}$$

in which

$$\vec{\Gamma}_\alpha = n_\alpha \vec{u}_\alpha$$

ν_i^α = species production rate

ν_r^α = species recombination rate.

The production function ν_i^α is that previously calculated and the Σ functions could be conveniently used in the numerical solutions. Recombination in the plasma, represented by ν_r^α, should be small compared to production, [19, 26] and can be neglected. The recombination at surfaces, however, will have to be included in boundary conditions. Finally, it is necessary to examine the Maxwell equations. These can be written as

$$\nabla \cdot \vec{E} = \left[n_i - (n_m + n_p) \right] \frac{e}{\epsilon_0} \tag{25}$$

$$\nabla \times \vec{E} = 0 \tag{26}$$

$$\nabla \cdot \vec{B} = 0 \tag{27}$$

$$\nabla \times \vec{B} = e \mu_0 \left[\vec{\Gamma}_i - \left(\vec{\Gamma}_m + \vec{\Gamma}_p \right) \right] \tag{28}$$

where $\mu_0 = 12.57 \times 10^{-7}$ webers $\cdot$ amp$^{-1} \cdot$ m^{-1}.

The momentum transfer equations can be simplified by eliminating the terms on the left-hand side of Eq. (19), and this is the usual procedure. The elimination of $\delta \vec{u}_\alpha / \delta t$ is certainly justified, since the plasma is known to be in a steady-state condition. In the case of the electrons, the term in $(\vec{u} \cdot \nabla) \vec{u}$ can also be eliminated, on the experimental fact that thermal electron velocities far exceed the directed velocity. The directed velocity is in turn determined by the elastic electron-atom and electron-ion collision rates. These rates can be assumed to remain relative constant across the plasma, leading to a constant drift velocity; hence, $(\vec{u}_e \cdot \nabla) \vec{u}_e = 0$ is a reasonable assumption.

In the case of the ions, however, a different situation exists. Ionic cyclotron radii are very large compared with the dimensions of the device, so the magnetic field has no effect on them. Further, for the plasmas under consideration, the mean free path of ions for momentum transfer is also large in comparison to the dimensions of the device, and the ionic thermal velocity is quite low. Thus, the existence of any appreciable potential gradients in the plasma would result in ion acceleration, and an equilibrium drift velocity could not be reached. Experimentally, such gradients are known to exist, so the term $(\vec{u}_i \cdot \nabla) \vec{u}_i$ should be retained in the ion equation of motion. This term is nonlinear and makes an analytic solution impossible. The term $\delta \vec{u}_\alpha / \delta t$ will produce a term,

μ_i, defined as the mobility, due to ion-atom collisions.
In the case of long ion mean free paths, the entire concept of mobility is questionable. Because the ionic drift
velocity is expected to be small compared to electron
velocities, it is not unreasonable to lump the effects of
$(\vec{u_i} \cdot \nabla)\vec{u_i}$ into the ion mobility and treat this mobility as
a parameter. The solutions can then be adjusted by means
of μ_i to fit experimental data. Such solutions would only
be valid if the mobility so determined is consistent in both
the radial and axial solutions.

The primary electron, Maxwellian electron and ion
equations of motion will now be presented. These will
then be simplified with the use of the following additional
assumptions: (1) The primary electrons only affect the
plasma near the cathode and can be neglected in the bulk
of the plasma. The neglect of primary electrons in
cesium is experimentally justified; but this assumption
must be verified for mercury. (2) The ion and electron
densities are equal locally and Eq. (25) is neglected. [27]
(3) The magnetic field is constant and has only an axial
(z) components. (4) There is no azimuthal electric field
or density gradient although these terms are included for
generality. (5) The temperatures are constant but are
not equal. Both the electron and ion temperatures are
carried within the differential as far as possible.
(6) Plasma currents are small enough not to affect the
applied magnetic field; thus, Eqs. (27) and (28) can be
eliminated. (7) The ion density is a separable function of
coordinates so that (26) can be neglected as indicated in
Ref. 27.

The individual species equations of motion for ions,
Maxwellian electrons and primary electrons can be
written in the following manner:

ions
$$eE + e\vec{u_i} \times \vec{B} = \frac{\nabla P_i}{n_i} + m_i\nu_{im}\left(\vec{u_i} - \vec{u_m}\right)$$
$$+ m_i\nu_{in}\vec{u_i} + m_i\nu_{ip}\left(\vec{u_i} - \vec{u_p}\right) \tag{29}$$

Maxwellian electrons

$$-e\vec{E} - e\vec{u}_m \times \vec{B} = \frac{\nabla P_m}{n_m} + m_e \nu_{mi}\left(\vec{u}_m - \vec{u}_i\right)$$

$$+ m_e \nu_{mp}\left(\vec{u}_m - \vec{u}_p\right) + m_e \nu_{mn}\vec{u}_m \qquad (30)$$

Primary electrons

$$-e\vec{E} - e\vec{u}_p \times \vec{B} = \frac{\nabla P_p}{n_p} + m_e \nu_{pi}\left(\vec{u}_p - \vec{u}_i\right)$$

$$+ m_e \nu_{pm}\left(\vec{u}_p - \vec{u}_m\right) + m_e \nu_{pn}\vec{u}_p \qquad (31)$$

We now make use of the definitions

$$\eta_m = \frac{m_e \nu_{mi}}{n_m e^2} \qquad\qquad \eta_{pm} = \frac{m_e \nu_{pm}}{n_p e^2}$$

$$\eta_p = \frac{m_e \nu_{pi}}{n_p e^2} \qquad\qquad \mu_m = \frac{e}{m_e \nu_{mn}} \qquad (32)$$

$$\mu_i = \frac{e}{m_i \nu_{in}} \qquad\qquad \mu_p = \frac{e}{m_e \nu_{pn}}$$

where
$$\eta = \text{resistivity}$$
$$\mu = \text{mobility}$$

and (23) to find

$$n_i \vec{E} + \vec{\Gamma}_i \times \vec{B} = \nabla(n_i T_i) + \eta_m n_m e\left(\frac{n_m}{n_i}\vec{\Gamma}_i - \vec{\Gamma}_m\right)$$

$$+ \eta_p n_p e\left(\frac{n_p}{n_i}\vec{\Gamma}_i - \vec{\Gamma}_p\right) + \frac{\vec{\Gamma}_i}{\mu_i} \qquad (33)$$

$$-n_m \vec{E} - \vec{\Gamma}_m \times \vec{B} = \nabla(n_m T_m) + \eta_m n_m e\left(\vec{\Gamma}_m - \vec{\Gamma}_i \frac{n_m}{n_i}\right)$$

$$+ \eta_{pm} n_p e\left(\frac{n_p}{n_m}\vec{\Gamma}_m - \vec{\Gamma}_p\right) + \frac{\vec{\Gamma}_m}{\mu_m} \qquad (34)$$

T. D. MASEK

$$-n_p \vec{E} - \vec{\Gamma}_p \times \vec{B} = \frac{2}{3} \nabla (n_p \epsilon_p) + \eta_p n_p e \left(\vec{\Gamma}_p - \frac{n_p}{n_i} \vec{\Gamma}_i \right)$$

$$+ \eta_{pm} n_p e \left(\vec{\Gamma}_p - \frac{n_p}{n_m} \vec{\Gamma}_m \right) + \frac{\vec{\Gamma}_p}{\mu_p} \quad (35)$$

Note that μ_i is now the "effective" mobility and cannot be computed using ion-atom collision times of Section A. The primary electrons are now neglected as indicated previously. The ion and Maxwellian electron equations are reduced with the definitions, $\eta_m = \eta$ and $n_i = n_m = n$.

$$-\vec{\Gamma}_i \times \vec{B} - n\vec{E} + \nabla (n_i T_i) = -\frac{\vec{\Gamma}_i}{\mu_i} + \eta e n \left(\vec{\Gamma}_e - \vec{\Gamma}_i \right) \quad (36)$$

$$\vec{\Gamma}_e \times \vec{B} + n\vec{E} + \nabla (n T_e) = -\frac{\vec{\Gamma}_e}{\mu_e} - \eta\, e n \left(\vec{\Gamma}_e - \vec{\Gamma}_i \right) \quad (37)$$

The components of (36) and (37) for the r-, θ-, and z- directions are:

r-direction

$$- \Gamma_\theta^i B - nE_r + \frac{\delta}{\delta r} (n T_i) = -\frac{\Gamma_r^i}{\mu_i} + \eta e n \left(\Gamma_r^e - \Gamma_r^i \right) \quad (38)$$

$$\Gamma_\theta^e B + nE_r + \frac{\delta}{\delta r} (n T_e) = -\frac{\Gamma_r^e}{\mu_e} - \eta e n \left(\Gamma_r^e - \Gamma_r^i \right) \quad (39)$$

θ-direction

$$\Gamma_r^i B - nE_\theta + \frac{1}{r} \frac{\delta}{\delta \theta} (n T_i) = -\frac{\Gamma_\theta^i}{\mu_i} + \eta e n \left(\Gamma_\theta^e - \Gamma_\theta^i \right) \quad (40)$$

$$-\Gamma_r^e B + nE_\theta + \frac{1}{r} \frac{\delta}{\delta \theta} (n T_e) = -\frac{\Gamma_\theta^e}{\mu_e} - \eta e n \left(\Gamma_\theta^e - \Gamma_\theta^i \right) \quad (41)$$

z-direction

$$-nE_z + \frac{\delta}{\delta z}(nT_i) = -\frac{\Gamma_z^i}{\mu_i} + \eta en\left(\Gamma_z^e - \Gamma_z^i\right) \qquad (42)$$

$$nE_z + \frac{\delta}{\delta z}(nT_e) = -\frac{\Gamma_z^i}{\mu_e} - \eta en\left(\Gamma_z^e - \Gamma_z^i\right) \qquad (43)$$

These are the same equations as derived in Ref. 27 using the Boltzmann transport equation. An interesting feature of the equations is that the z-direction equations are un-coupled from the r and θ equations.

The r and θ equations (38-41) can now be solved for the radial plasma potential distribution. This is accomplished by making the assumptions that the mobilities are constant and that $\Gamma_\theta^i \ll \Gamma_\theta^e$. Ecker [28] has also solved these equations assuming that $\Gamma_\theta^e = \lambda\Gamma_r^i$, where λ is a constant, and the ratio of Γ_θ^i to Γ_θ^e is found to be

$$\frac{\Gamma_\theta^i}{\Gamma_\theta^e} = \left[\frac{1 + \sigma_e(1-\lambda)}{-\lambda + \sigma_i(1-\lambda)}\right]\frac{\mu_i}{\mu_e} \qquad (44)$$

where
$$\sigma_{i,e} = \eta en\mu_{i,e} \qquad (45)$$

It is seen that for λ equal to unity the flux ratio is just equal to the mobility ratio. For λ different from unity, the flux ratio is between μ_i/μ_e and σ_i because $\sigma_i \ll 1 < \sigma_e$. Thus, for all conditions of interest here, the assumption of $\Gamma_\theta^i \ll \Gamma_\theta^e$ is well justified. The μ_i in the θ equation is actually a different mobility from those for the r- and z- directions because of the general tensor quality of the mobility. This is because ions have infinite path lengths available in the θ-direction, whereas their path is limited to the dimensions of the engine in r and z. In addition, the θ electric field is assumed to be zero, so μ_i^θ is a zero field mobility. [29, 30] For these reasons, the θ mobility should be large compared to those for the r- and z-directions. The Γ_θ^i term can therefore be eliminated in Eq. (38), because $\Gamma_\theta^i B \ll \Gamma_r^i / \mu_i^r$ and Γ_θ^i is

neglected in Eq. 40) because $\Gamma_r^i B \gg \Gamma_\theta^i/\mu_i^\theta$. The value
of eliminating Γ_θ^i from the equations is that an additional
relationship between fluxes is now unnecessary and the
number of parameters in the radial solution is reduced to
one (μ_i). It will be assumed that μ_i is the same for r and
z because of similar electric fields. It is further assumed
that the Einstein relation holds so that

$$D_{i,e} = \mu_{i,e} T_{i,e} \qquad (46)$$

For constant temperatures, the θ equations [(40) and (41)]
can now be solved for Γ_r^e as

$$\Gamma_r^e = \frac{1 + \sigma_e}{\sigma_e} \Gamma_r^i \qquad (47)$$

Note that σ_e is a function of r so that Γ_r^e is a changing
function of Γ_r^i in addition to being non-ambipolar. Using
Eqs. (38), (39) and (47) with the convention

$$E_r = -\frac{\partial V}{\partial r} \qquad (48)$$

where V is the plasma potential, we find

$$(49)$$

$$-\frac{\partial V}{\partial r} = \left[\frac{D_i\left(1 + u_e^2\right) + D_e(\sigma_i - \sigma_e) + 2\sigma_e D_i}{\mu_i\left(1 + u_e^2\right) + \mu_e(\sigma_e - \sigma_i) + 2\sigma_e\mu_i}\right]\frac{1}{n}\frac{\partial n}{\partial r}$$

where

$$u = \mu B$$

We define a new variable

$$x = \frac{n(0)}{n} = \frac{\sigma(0)}{\sigma} \qquad (50)$$

and integrate Eq. (49) to obtain

$$\frac{\Delta V^r}{T_e} = a_1 \ln x + a_2 \ln\left(\frac{1 + a_3 x}{1 + a_3}\right) \qquad (51)$$

where

$$\Delta V = V(x) - V(1)$$

$$a_1 = \frac{1}{\mu} \left(1 - \frac{\mu_e}{\mu_i} - 2 \frac{T_i}{T_e} \right) \tag{52}$$

$$a_2 = \frac{1}{\mu} \left[\frac{T_i}{T_e} (\bar{\mu} + 2) + \left(\frac{\mu_e}{\mu_i} - 1 \right) \right] \tag{53}$$

$$a_3 = \frac{1 + u_e^2}{\sigma_{eo} \bar{\mu}} \tag{54}$$

$$\bar{\mu} = 1 + \frac{\mu_e}{\mu_i} \tag{55}$$

Under most conditions $\mu_e / \mu_i \gg 1$ so the constants become

$$a_1 = -1 \tag{56}$$

$$a_2 = 1 + \frac{T_i}{T_e} = \bar{T} \tag{57}$$

$$a_3 = \frac{\mu_i B^2}{\eta e n (0)} \tag{58}$$

The radial solution in Eq. (51) using the constants of Eqs. (56), (57) and (58) is compared to experimental data in Section III.

The axial potential distribution is easier to find. By using just the z-direction equations [(42) and (43)] and a relation between the fluxes

$$\Gamma_z^e = \gamma \Gamma_z^i \tag{59}$$

and Eqs. (45) and (46), the axial electric field is found to be

$$E_z = \left(\frac{D_i \alpha - D_e \beta}{\mu_i \alpha + \mu_e \beta} \right) \tag{60}$$

where

$$\alpha = [\gamma + \sigma_e (\gamma - 1)] \tag{61}$$

$$\beta = [1 - \sigma_i (\gamma - 1)] \tag{62}$$

Integration of Eq. (60) gives the axial potential in the form

$$\frac{\Delta V^z}{T_e} = b_1 \ln x + b_2 \left(\frac{1}{x} - 1 \right) \tag{63}$$

$$\Delta V^z = V(x) - V(1)$$

and

$$b_1 = \frac{\gamma \dfrac{D_i}{D_e} - 1}{1 + \gamma \dfrac{\mu_i}{\mu_e}} \tag{64}$$

$$b_2 = (1 - \gamma)\sigma_{io} \, \overline{T} \left(1 + \gamma \frac{\mu_i}{\mu_e} \right) \tag{65}$$

As before, when $\mu_e/\mu_i \gg 1$ the constants become

$$b_1 = -1 \tag{66}$$

$$b_2 = (1 - \gamma)\sigma_{io} \, \overline{T}$$

This solution will also be discussed with the experimental data.

As indicated previously, the ion mobility will be determined by matching the radial solution Eq. (51) to experimental data. This value of μ_i will then be used to fit the axial potential solution Eq. (63). Both solutions require the resistivity due to electron-ion collisions which is given by [8]

$$\eta = \frac{6.53 \times 10^3}{T_e^{3/2}} \ln \Lambda, \qquad \text{ohm} \cdot \text{cm} \tag{67}$$

where T_e is in $^\circ K$. The simplified plasma potential equations are presented for each engine comparison, since the a and b constants depend on the electron and ion temperatures in each experiment. The measured density distributtion is relatively accurate, so that with the solution for the plasma potential, the characteristics of the plasma can be firmly predicted. The assumption of constant temperatures will be discussed with the experimental data. To include a variable electron or ion temperature, an energy equation for each species would be required.

C. Axial Ion Flux

The ion flux at the grid structure of the engine is important because it determines the ion beam current that can be extracted. The ion flux in the axial direction in the plasma is given by Eq. (42) using (59) as

$$\Gamma^i_z = \mu_i \left[nE_z - T_i \frac{\partial n}{\partial z} \right] \left[1 + \sigma_i (1 - \gamma) \right]^{-1} \quad (68)$$

Using the definition of the potential, we find

$$\Gamma^i_z = -\mu_i \left[n\frac{\partial V}{\partial z} + T_i \frac{\partial n}{\partial z} \right] \left[1 + \sigma_i (1-\gamma) \right]^{-1} \quad (69)$$

with Eqs. (63) and (66), Γ^i_z becomes

$$\Gamma^i_z = - \mu_i T_e \overline{T} \frac{\partial n}{\partial z} \quad (70)$$

The form of Eq. (70) allows Γ^i_z to be easily evaluated.

III. PLASMA MEASUREMENTS

The measurements made in three operating electron bombardment ion engines are now presented. Since a primary objective of this paper is to evaluate the plasma theory, previously reported measurements are used as much as possible. [18, 31, 32]

In the remaining discussion the terminology "conventional" will refer to an engine geometry in which the cathode is in the center of the engine and the anode is annularly shaped. Two engines of this type will be discussed: one a cylindrical shape and one conical. The cylindrical engine has been operated on mercury and the conical engine has been operated on cesium. The third engine, also operated on cesium, will be referred to as the "reversed current" engine because the cathode and anode geometry is inverted compared to the conventional geometry.

A. Experimental Method

All measurements were made with single movable Langmuir probes instrumented to plot the current-voltage traces automatically. Since the general Langmuir probe theory is covered completely in a number of references [33, 34] it will not be discussed in this paper.

The equations used to reduce the experimental data are presented here for reference [6]. The Maxwellian electron density is calculated using

$$n_m = \frac{i_{sm}}{eA} \left(\frac{2\pi m_e}{kT_e} \right)^{1/2} \tag{71}$$

where

i_{sm} = Maxwellian electron current at the plasma potential

A = probe area

The primary electron density, when present in the plasma, is determined from

$$n_p = \frac{i_{sp}}{eA} \left(\frac{8m_e}{\epsilon_p} \right)^{1/2} \tag{72}$$

where i_{sp} = primary electron current at the plasma potential. The assumption of a monoenergetic group of primaries, for the mercury plasma, rather than a distribution of primary energy decreases the accuracy of the reduced data. The cesium data appear to be entirely Maxwellian and thus no data reduction problem occurs. The probe design is the same as in Ref. 6 and uses a 0. 020-in. -diameter tungsten wire with approximately 0. 15 in. extending beyond the quartz sheath.

B. Cesium Measurements

The two engines operated on cesium are shown schematically in Figs. 14 and 15. The Langmuir probe positions are not shown on the figures, but will be evident from the data points presented later. The reversed geometry will be discussed first, since the measured electron temperatures were relatively constant and this engine most closely approximates the assumptions of the analysis.

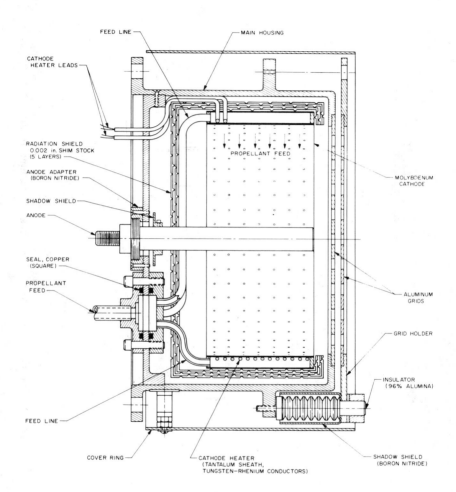

Figure 14. Reversed arc current cesium electron bombardment
ion engine schematic diagram.

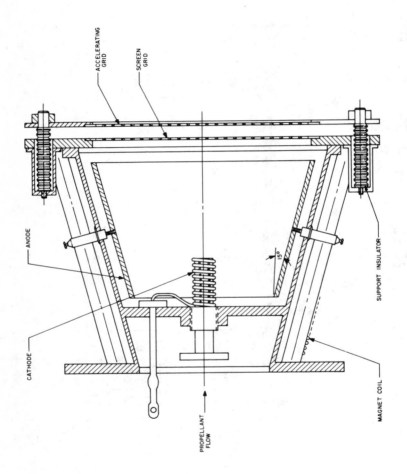

Figure 15.   Conical cesium electron bombardment ion engine schematic diagram.

1. Reversed Current Engine

The data presented here are used only in conjunction with the model; a more complete description of the measurements is presented in Ref. 32. The electron temperature was found to be constant radially as indicated by Fig. 16. This figure shows that all probe traces fell on the same initial straight line and indicates a radially decreasing ion density and plasma potential. Axial measurements of electron temperature are shown in Fig. 17 for three typical operating conditions and also show a relatively constant electron temperature distribution. The radial ion density distribution data for five axial

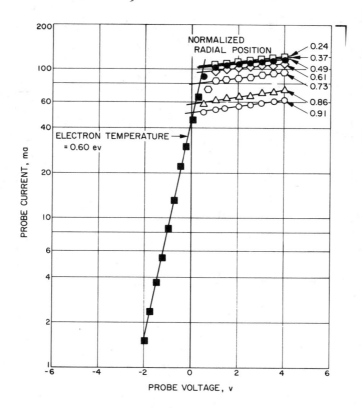

Figure 16. Typical Langmuir probe semilogarithmic plot in cesium for seven radial positions.

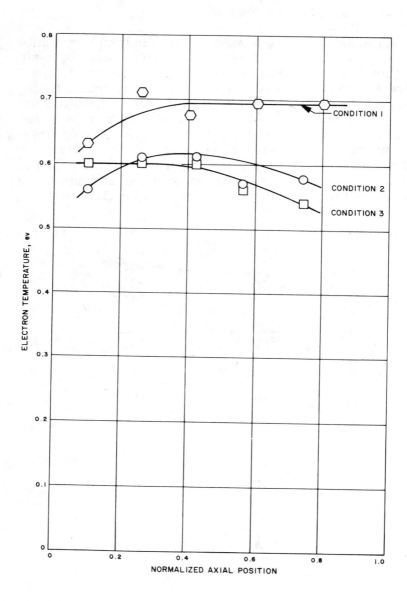

Figure 17.   Maxwellian electron temperature axial distributions
for three typical conditions.

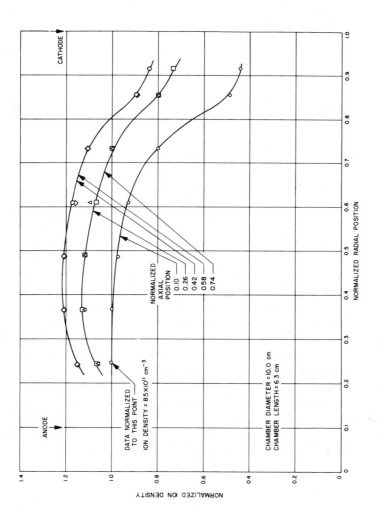

Figure 18.   Normalized ion density radial distribution for five axial locations in the reversed current engine.

positions and one operating condition are shown in Fig. 18. The conditions chosen for applying the potential solutions are

$$T_e = 0.7 \text{ ev} \qquad T_i T_e = 0.1$$
$$n(0) = 10^{12} \text{ cm}^{-3} \qquad n_0(0) = 10^{11} \text{ cm}^{-3}$$
$$B = 5 \text{ gauss}$$

The radial potential solution Eq. (51) reduces to

$$\Delta V = 0.7 \left[1.1 \ln\left(\frac{1 + a_3 x}{1 + a_3}\right) - \ln x \right] \qquad (73)$$

and was found to fit the experimental data as shown in Fig. 19 for $\mu_i = 68 \text{ m}^2 \cdot \text{volt}^{-1} \cdot \text{sec}^{-1}$ and a value of a_3 of 1.10. The axial solution reduces to

$$\Delta V = 0.7 \left[1.5 \times 10^{-2} (1 - \gamma)\left(\frac{1}{x} - 1\right) - \ln x \right] \qquad (74)$$

The ion density of Fig. 18 is used to compute x and the axial plasma potential is shown compared to the experimental data in Fig. 20. Note that the axial solution is essentially independent of γ because of the small coefficient (0.015). It is expected that γ would be between about 0.5 and 0.8 because the axial electron flux serves only to maintain neutrality for the ions lost in recombination at chamber surfaces. The relatively poor agreement of the axial solution with the measurements, in this case as well as those to be discussed, is attributed to variations in plasma conditions during the measurements. The experimental setup allowed complete sets of radial traces to be taken within a few minutes while axial sets took nearly an hour. Thus, the radial data are consistent, but much scatter occurred in cross plotting these data.

2. Conical Engine

The measurements taken in this engine were initially reported in Ref. 18. The Maxwellian electron temperature radial distribution for one operating condition is presented in Fig. 21 for five axial positions. The corresponding ion

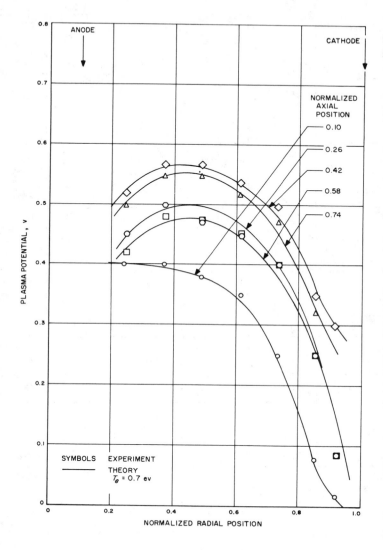

Figure 19. Plasma potential radial distribution for five axial locations in the reversed current engine (measured with respect to anode potential).

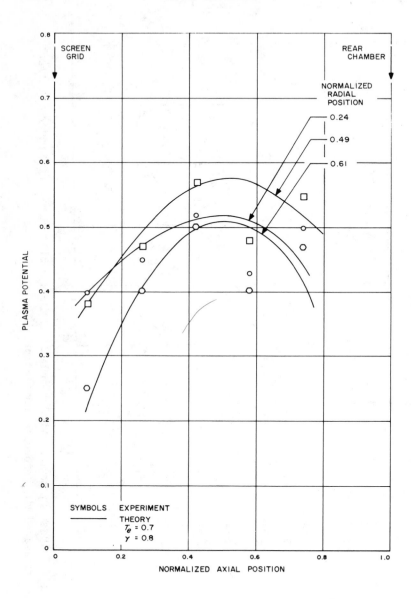

Figure 20. Plasma potential axial distribution for three radial locations in the reversed current engine (measured with respect to anode potential).

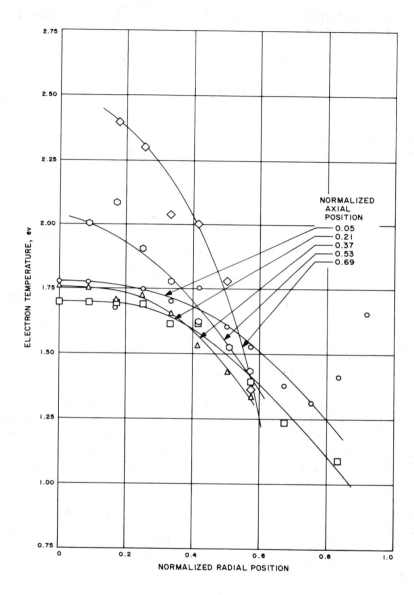

Figure 21. Maxwellian electron temperature radial distribution for five axial locations in the conical engine.

density distribution is plotted in Fig. 22. The conditions used in the plasma potential solutions are

$$T_e = 1.5 \text{ ev} \qquad T_i/T_e = 0.05$$

$$n(0) = 4 \times 10^{11} \text{ cm}^{-3} \qquad n_0(0) = 4 \times 10^{10} \text{ cm}^{-3}$$

$$B = 7 \text{ gauss}$$

Note that since the model assumed constant temperatures, average temperatures are used above. The radial solution simplifies to

$$\Delta V = 1.5 \left[1.05 \ln \left(\frac{1 + a_3 x}{1 + a_3} \right) - \ln x \right] \qquad (75)$$

This solution fits the experimental data for a value of $\mu_i = 43 \text{ m}^2 \cdot \text{volt}^{-1} \cdot \text{sec}^{-1}$ giving $a_3 = 1.33$ and is shown in Fig. 23. The axial solution reduces to

$$\Delta V = 1.5 \left[1.5 \times 10^{-3} (1 - \gamma) \left(\frac{1}{x} - 1 \right) - \ln x \right] \qquad (76)$$

As before, this solution is independent of γ but fits the data relatively well as shown in Fig. 24.

C. Mercury Measurements

The engine used in the tests with mercury was previously shown schematically in Fig. 1 and is a conventional geometry type. The mercury data used in this paper were also reported in Ref. 18. The measured primary and Maxwellian electron energy and temperature distributions are shown in Figs. 25 and 26, respectively. The corresponding normalized primary and Maxwellian electron density distributions are shown in Figs. 27 and 28. In applying the model to mercury, it is necessary to neglect the primary electrons. Thus, the Maxwellian electron density and an average Maxwellian temperature are used. The conditions assumed are

$$T_e = 5.0 \text{ ev} \qquad T_i/T_e = 0.015$$

$$n(0) = 4 \times 10^{11} \text{ cm}^{-3} \qquad n_0(0) = 4 \times 10^{10} \text{ cm}^{-3}$$

$$B = 10 \text{ gauss}$$

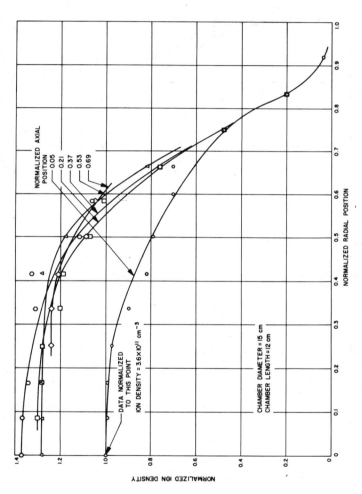

Figure 22. Normalized density radial distribution for five axial locations in the conical engine.

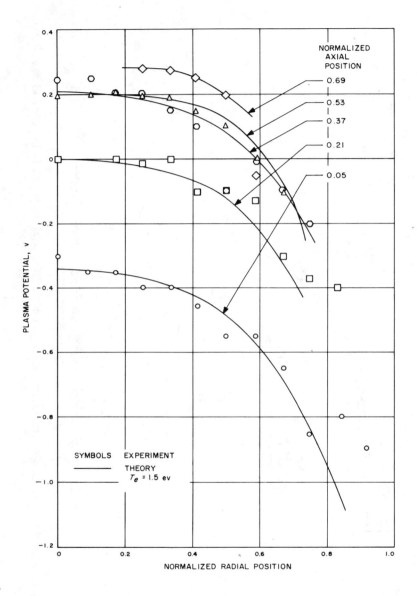

Figure 23.   Plasma potential radial distribution for five axial
locations in the conical engine (measured with respect to anode
potential).

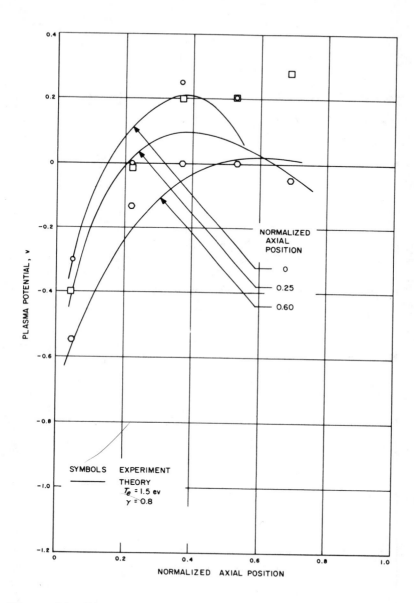

Figure 24. Plasma potential axial distribution for three radial locations in the conical engine (measured with respect to anode potential).

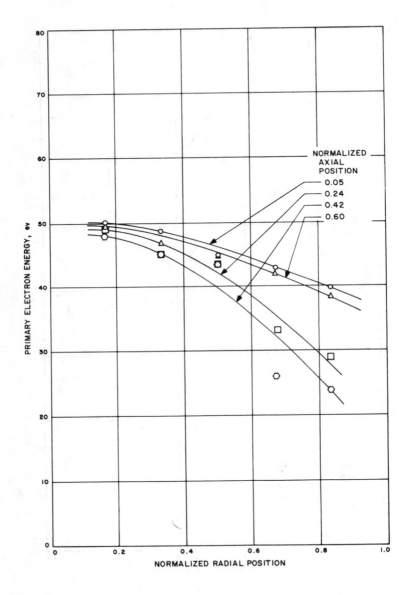

Figure 25.   Primary electron energy radial distribution for four axial locations in the mercury engine.

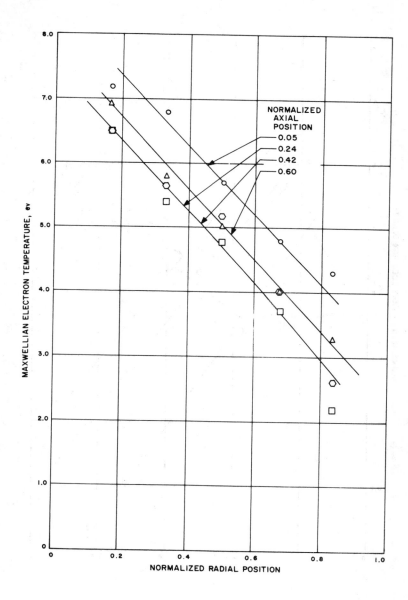

Figure 26. Maxwellian electron energy radial distribution for four axial locations in the mercury engine.

T. D. MASEK

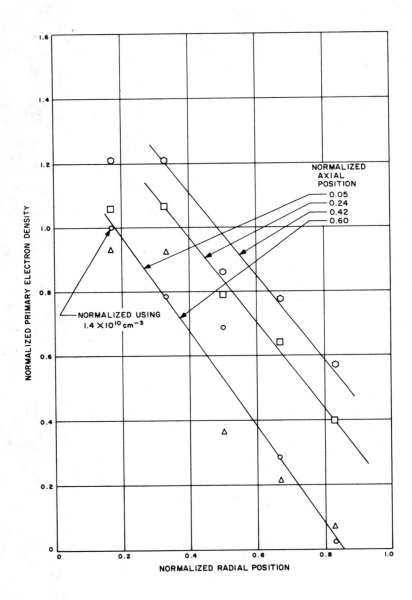

Figure 27. Normalized primary electron density radial distribution at four axial locations.

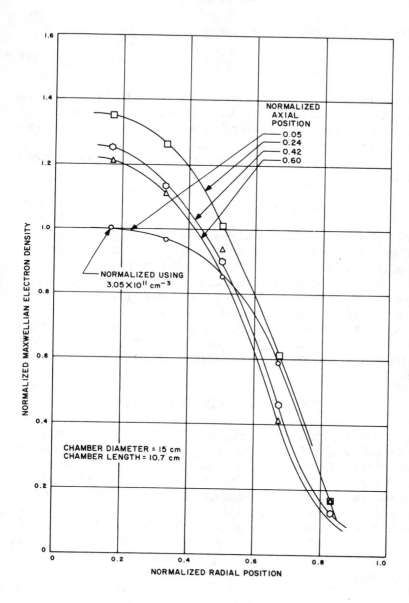

Figure 28. Normalized Maxwellian electron density radial distribution for four axial positions in the mercury engine.

The radial solution now becomes

$$\Delta V = 5 \left[1.02 \ln\left(\frac{1 + a_3 x}{1 + a_3}\right) - \ln x \right] \qquad (77)$$

and the solution is shown fitted to the data in Fig. 29. The mobility is found to be $\mu_i = 6m^2 \cdot volt^{-1} \cdot sec^{-1}$ and $a_3 = 1.75$. This is a rather low mobility, but it is shown that it produces approximately the measured ion current from the engine. The equation for the axial plasma potential is

$$\Delta V = 5 \left[2 \times 10^{-5} (1 - \gamma)\left(\frac{1}{x} - 1\right) - \ln x \right] \qquad (78)$$

This solution is again obtained by use of the measured Maxwellian ion densities and is shown compared to the experiments in Fig. 30. Note that the validity of μ_i is not tested by the axial potential solution because of the small value of the coefficient of the term in which it appears. The solutions, Eqs. (77) and (78), are seen to agree well with the measured points. This tends to justify the neglect of primary electrons in the analysis. Further reference to neglecting the primary electrons is made in Section V.

IV. ION BEAM MEASUREMENTS

Ion beam current density measurements have been made with a Faraday probe using the engines described previously. Both radial and axial distributions have been measured, but only the radial distributions near the engine will be discussed in this paper. It has been found in this work that the beam distribution changes considerably within a few inches of the engine, and thus only the measurements near the grid can be validly related to the plasma. The axial change in beam distribution has been reported previously in Refs. 31 and 35. A difficulty with the Faraday measurements near the engine is that the individual ion beams from each grid hole cause the data to be extremely irregular, so the beam density near the grid is approximated by fairing a curve through a plot of the maximum probe readings. The area under a curve formed

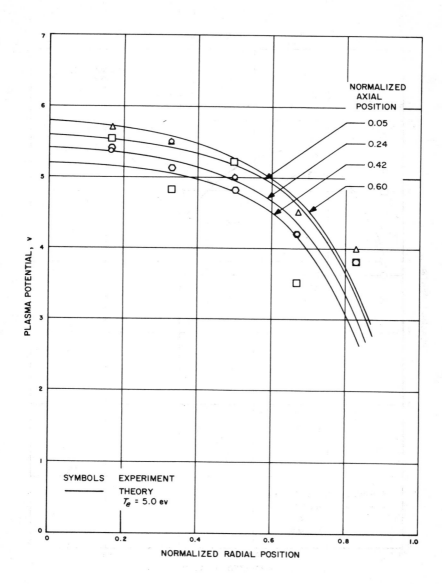

Figure 29. Plasma potential radial distribution for four axial positions in the mercury engine (measured with respect to anode potential).

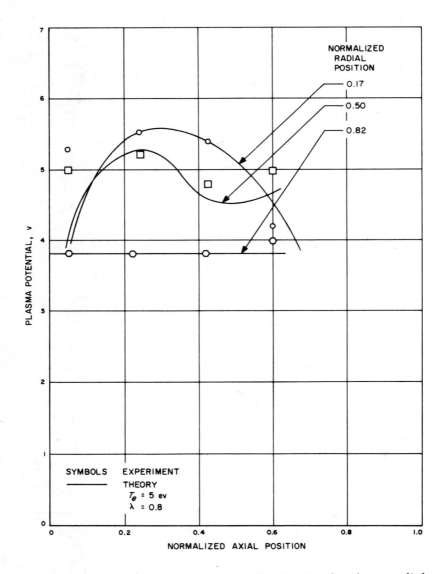

Figure 30.　Plasma potential axial distribution for three radial positions in the mercury engine (measured with respect to anode potential).

in this way is greater than the measured beam current because the ion beams leaving the engine only cover one-fourth to one-half of the grid area. Measurements taken far enough away from the engine to provide a continuous curve integrate to the correct beam current.

A typical original recording of the Faraday probe approximately 0.28 in. from the accelerating grid is shown in Fig. 31. The smooth curve is an estimate of the beam current density leaving the engine. These data were taken with the reversed current engine, but the raggedness is typical of all the data taken near the engines. The estimated beam current densities near the accelerating grid for the three engines studied are shown in Fig. 32. The plasma conditions for these are approximately the same as those discussed previously and are close enough to allow a comparison with the model.

A comparison can now be made between the Faraday probe measurements and the ion flux predicted by Eq. (70). Using the constants presented before, and the mobility determined by the radial potential solutions, the ion flux equations at the center of the engine are:

Reverse current

$$j_i = -8.4 \times 10^{-14} \frac{\partial n}{\partial z} \tag{79}$$

Conical

$$j_i = -1.0 \times 10^{-13} \frac{\partial n}{\partial z} \tag{80}$$

Mercury

$$j_i = -4.9 \times 10^{-14} \frac{\partial n}{\partial z} \tag{81}$$

where $\partial n/\partial z$ has units of cm^{-4}. The slopes $\partial n/\partial z$ can be estimated from Figs. 18, 22, and 29 to find $\partial n/\partial z = 5 \times 10^{10}$, 5×10^{10}, and 6×10^{10} cm^{-4}, respectively. When these values are used in (79), (80), and (81), we find current densities of 4.2, 5, and 3 mamp cm^{-2} for the reversed current, conical, and mercury engines, respectively. These values agree extremely well with the typical observed current densities of Fig. 32. This agreement indicates that the model is self-consistent and that it is possible to obtain consistent values of the "effective" ion mobility by matching the model and experiment.

T. D. MASEK

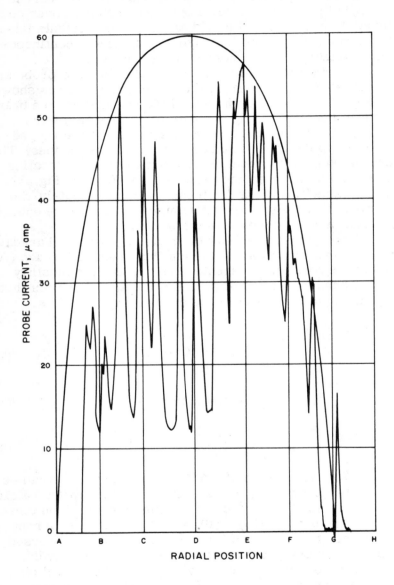

Figure 31. Typical Faraday probe trace 0. 28 inches from reversed current engine accelerating grid.

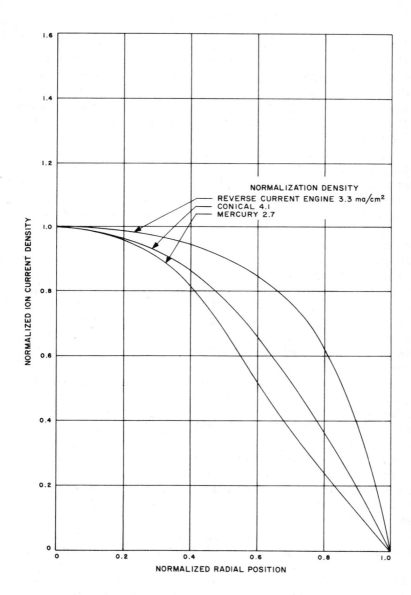

Figure 32. Typical normalized beam current density distributions for three engines.

V. DISCUSSION

Review of the preceding analysis is in order. Several of the important questions concerning the complete solution of the plasma equations can now be discussed. The assumptions, (1) neglect of primary electrons, (2) constant temperatures, (3) accounting for the ion acceleration term in the mobility, and (4) constant magnetic fields, should be assessed in this regard.

The major difficulty in solving the general plasma equations results from the primary electron group. Although this group does not appear directly in the solutions presented here, there is no guarantee that primaries do not contribute significantly to the experimental ion density through ionization. In fact, the ion production rates of Section II suggest that primaries play a large role in ionization, at least near the cathode. Since the cesium plasma is apparently free of primary electrons, a method for determining the effect of primaries is suggested. The complete solution for the ion density using the flux continuity equations could be obtained for cesium with and without ion production. If ion production throughout the plasma contributes to the ion density, primaries must be accounted for in the mercury solutions. On the other hand, if the production term does not contribute significantly to the ion distribution, the primaries could justifiably be neglected. If production in the bulk of the plasma is not important, ionization must be taking place near the cathode with transportion throughout the chamber by diffusion. The determination of the ion production process has far reaching implications on the position of the cathode, the method and position of propellant injection, and the geometrical relationship between propellant injection and the cathode.

The neglect of the ion acceleration term, with its effect included in the empirically determined mobility, is now justified by the fact that the solution works. The general numerical solutions can also be obtained using this same method by choosing mobilities which make the plasma potential ion density and axial ion flux solutions agree with measurements. This procedure should be adequate to produce closed form solutions since three conditions must be satisfied.

The use of average constant temperatures in the present solution is reasonable because the variation in temperature is generally much less than the variation in ion density. This allows derivatives of temperature to be neglected with respect to derivatives in density. Numerical solutions could account for temperature variations by using an assumed variation or by use of an energy equation. It would appear that average temperatures are adequate for practical purposes.

The assumption of a constant magnetic field was necessary to obtain simple analytical solutions. Numerical solutions could easily account for field variations providing the field remains axial, but additional fields would greatly complicate the equations and would couple the r, θ, and z momentum equations.

VI. CONCLUSIONS

This study has presented a framework for analyzing the plasma characteristics of the electron bombardment ion engine. A number of conclusions can be drawn from the previous discussion and analysis.

1. A model for the electron bombardment engine has been formulated. This model accounts for all important factors in the operation of the engine. That is, it includes arc current through Γ_r^e and Γ_r^i, the magnetic field, ion production which effectively includes the arc voltage, ion beam current, propellant distribution through the neutral density and geometry with the proper boundary conditions.

2. Analytical solutions presented in this work indicate that much useful information could be obtained by numerically solving the plasma equations and fitting the solutions to experimental data. It is concluded in this regard that meaningful closed form solutions could not be obtained, at least initially, without experimental data. Therefore, extrapolations through the use of assumed mobilities must be carefully considered.

3. The effect of primary electrons on the ion density must be further investigated. The method proposed sed accomplish this task would also add considerable understanding to the ion production process which is vital to the operation and efficiency of the engine. The reason the effect of primary electrons could not be determined in this study is that experimental ion densities were used and primaries did not enter into the calculations.

4. Additional probe measurements should be made with emphasis on reducing scatter in the axial measurements. This means that all data must be obtained rather quickly in the plasma and in the beam to assure consistent measurements.

5. The effects of magnetic field distribution, propellant feed distribution, cathode and anode position, and chamber geometry can be investigated once numerical solutions can be generalized to eliminate the fitting process. This would allow systematic engine optimization and would provide a better understanding of the electron bombardment engine.

REFERENCES

1. Kerrisk, D. J., "State-of-the-Art of Electric Propulsion - 1965," in AAS Science and Technology, Vol. 6, Space Electronics Symposium, C. M. Wong (Ed.), 1965.
2. "Solar Powered Electric Propulsion Spacecraft Study," Hughes Aircraft Company, Space Systems Division, JPL Contract No. 951144, Final Report, December 1965.
3. "Solar Powered Electric Propulsion Spacecraft Study," Electro-Optical Systems, Inc. To be published.
4. Speiser, R. C. and Branson, L. K., "Studies of a Gas Discharge Cesium Ion Source," ARS Paper 2664-62, 1962.
5. Kohlberg, I. and King, H., "Low Current Density Ion Engine Development," Final Report, Ion Physics Corporation, Contract NASA-1684, January 1963.

6. Strickfaden, W. B. and Geiler, K. L., "Probe Measurements of the Discharge in an Operating Electron Bombardment Engine, " AIAA Jour. 1, 1815 (1963).
7. Langmuir, I. and Compton, K. T., "Electrical Discharges in Gases, Part II, Fundamental Phenomena in Electrical Discharges, " Rev. Mod. Phys. 3, 191 (1931).
8. Spitzer, Lyman, Jr., Physics of Fully Ionized Gases, Interscience Publishers, New York, 1962.
9. Sutton, G. W. and Sherman, A, Engineering Magnetohydrodynamics, McGraw-Hill Book Company, New York, 1965.
10. Sovie, R. J. and Dugan, J. V., Jr., "Energy Required for Ion Production by Electron Bombardment in Helium, Argon and Cesium, " NASA TMX-52064, 1964.
11. Gryziński, Michal, "Classical Theory of Electronic and Ionic Inelastic Collisions, " Phys. Rev.115, 374 (1959).
12. Arnot, F. L. and Baines, G. O., "Elastic and Inelastic Cross Sections of the Mercury Atom, " Proc. Roy. Soc., A151, 256 (1935).
13. Bleakney, W., "Probability and Critical Potentials for the Formation of Multiply Charged Ions in Mercury Vapor by Electron Impact, " Phys. Rev. 35, 139 (1930).
14. Brode, R. B., "The Quantitative Study of the Collisions of Electrons with Atoms, " Rev. Mod. Phys., 5, 257 (1933).
15. Crown, J. C. and Russek, A. "Electron-Alkali-Atom Interaction Potential Elastic-Scattering Cross Section, " Phys. Rev. 138, A 669 (1965).
16. Sohl, G., Reid, G. C., Barcatta, F. A., Zafran, S. and Speiser, R. C., "Ion Rocket System Research and Development, Electro-Optical Systems, Inc., " Final Report, NASA Contract NAS3-5250, December 1965.
17. Reader, P. D., "The Operation of an Electron Bombardment Ion Source with Various Gases, " in Electron and Ion Beam Science and Technology, 1st Inter. Conf., Robert Bakish (Ed.), John Wiley and Sons, Inc., New York, 1965.

18. Masek, T. D. and Kerrisk, D. J. , "Plasma Character-
    istics for Mercury and Cesium Bombardment Ion
    Engines, " Space Programs Summary No. 37-32, Vol.
    IV, Jet Propulsion Laboratory, Pasadena, California,
    1965.
19. Kerrisk, D, J. , "Potentialities of Electron Bombard-
    ment Ion Engines for Electric Propulsion, " IRE
    Trans. Space Electron. Telemetry 8, 188 (1962).
20. Gryziński, Michal, "Classical Theory of Atomic Col-
    lisions, I. Theory of Inelastic Collisions, " Phys. Rev.
    138 A 336 (1965).
21. Tate, J. T. and Smith, P. T. , "Ionization Potentials
    and Probabilities for the Formation of Multiply Charged
    Ions in the Alkali Vapors and in Krypton and Argon, "
    Phys. Rev. 46, 773 (1934).
22. Moore, C. E. , "Atomic Energy Levels, " Circular 467,
    Vols. I, II, III, (1949), (1952), (1958), National
    Bureau of Standards.
23. McFarland, R. H. , "Gryziński Electron Impact
    Ionization Cross-section Computations for the Alkali
    Metal, " Lawrence Radiation Laboratory Report
    UCRL-12268, 1964.
24. Golant, V. E. , "Diffusion of Charged Particles in a
    Plasma in a Magnetic Field, " Usp. Fiz. Nauk 74, 377
    (1963), Soviet Physics Uspekhi 79, 161 (1963).
25. Hoh, F. C. , "Low-Temperature Plane Diffusion in a
    Magnetic Field, " Rev. Mod. Phys. 34, 267 (1962).
26. Wada, J. Y. and Knechtli, R. C. , "Measurements of
    Electron-Ion Recombination in a Thermal Cesium
    Plasma, " Phys. Rev. Letters 10, 513 (1963).
27. Allis, W. P. and Buchsbaum, S. J. , "Plasma Theory"
    in Notes on Plasma Dynamics, Summer Session,
    M. I. T. , Vol. 1, 1959.
28. Ecker, G. , "Enhanced Interaction in the Positive
    Column, " Phys. Fluids, 4, 127 (1961).
29. Chanin, L. M. and Steen, R. D. , "Mobilities of Cesium
    Ions in Cesium, " Phys. Rev. 132, 2554 (1963).
30. Kovar, F. R. , "Mobility of Mercury Ions in Mercury
    Vapor, " Phys. Rev. , 133, A681 (1964).

31. Kerrisk, D. J. and Masek, T. D. "Plasma Non-uniformity and Grid Erosion in an Electron Bombardment Ion Engine," AIAA Jour. 3, 1060 (1965).

32. Masek, T. D., "Plasma Investigation in a Reversed Current Electron Bombardment Ion Engine", AIAA 5th Elect. Prop. Conf., San Diego, Preprint 66-246, March 1966.

33. Langmuir, I., and Mott-Smith, H. M., "Studies of Electric Discharges in Gases at Low Pressure," Part I through V.; G. E. Rev. 27, 449, 583, 616, 726, 810 (1924).

34. Mott-Smith, H. M., and Langmuir, I., "The Theory of Collectors in Gaseous Discharges," Phys. Rev. 28, 737 (1926).

35. Sellen, J. M., Jr., Forbes, S. G., Kemp, R. F., "Advanced Ion Beam Diagnostic Techniques," AIAA Preprint 2067-61, 1961.

ELECTRON BEAMS
IN RECORDING AND
INFORMATION STORAGE

Electron Beams in Recording and Information Storage

The rate of information accumulation in the last few decades has increased virtually as an exponential function and this trend is likely to continue. The need of locating this information and its retrieval today becomes more important than ever before, and the problems of successfully effecting this continue to increase in complexity. Magnetic recording systems have carried the burden of information recording, storage and retrieval to date. The packing density limit capabilities of these magnetic systems have slowly been attained and the need for even higher packing densities is at hand. Electron beams offer some exciting possibilities in this area though considerable problems must be overcome prior to ability to use these with greater frequency and for accomplishment of more down to earth tasks. The papers in this section of the proceedings cover several aspects of the area of electron beams for recording and information storage. The references provided with them should be a useful guide for further studies as would references given at the end of the introductory remarks at the proceeding section.

(Editor)

Charging in the Electron Beam Discwriter

E. S. Barrekette and J. A. Duffy

IBM Watson Research Center
Yorktown Heights, New York

INTRODUCTION

Read-only digital memories, relying on silver halide emulsions as storage media have been in use for a decade. They were proposed by King [1] and others and have since been employed in translation and information retrieval systems. Until recently the photostore, [2] based on photoscopic discs, was the only fully operational photo-digital memory. Discs were recorded optically in a system employing an intermediate 70 mm film master in a two-step reduction of masks onto the disc proper. The process was inordinately slow, requiring more than 24 hours to record 6×10^7 bits on a disc.

In order to improve the recording process, Thornley et al [3] proposed and proved the feasibility of direct recording with an electron beam on photographic film. Electron beams offer the advantages of resolution, ease of control in intensity and position, and high energy density; unfortunately these are accompanied by the disadvantages arising from the need to record in vacuum and from the effects of accumulated surface charges. More recently a discwriter based on direct recording with a laser [4] has been proposed. This system, has the obvious advantages of eliminating the demountable vacuum system, but does not have the potential for high resolution enjoyed by the Electron Beam Discwriter.

Based on Thornley's [3] work, the Electron Beam Discwriter, described in this paper, was built. Several major, somewhat interrelated problems were encountered and corrected before the system could be relied upon to produce high quality discs with a good yield. The most difficult and persistent of these were charging and cleanliness. Nonuniform charging of the film resulted from several causes including the focusing grid, the cleaning brush, dirt, and the platen conductivity. Sufficient charge buildup occurred to cause track displacement and even track overlap, as well as severe variations in the optical density of the recorded information. Finally, dirt particles prevented small portions of the emulsion from being exposed. All these problems were catastrophic since information was lost either by being obscured by overlapping tracks or dirt, or by the inability of the reader servo system to follow overlapped tracks or those with insufficient density. The measures taken to improve the reliability of the discwriter by eliminating these primary causes of unacceptable discs are described in this paper.

THE SYSTEM

Information is recorded serially in concentric circular tracks each having 67, 212 bits. Each bit is represented by a pair of marks, black and white, whose order determines whether the bit is zero or one (Fig. 1). This code was chosen [2] to facilitate servo control of the reading spot in the photostore. The average light reaching the sensor depends on the position of the scanning spot, which consequently can be controlled so that it is centered between the black and white borders.

In order to avoid the problems associated with image rotation (particularly the dependence of rotation on lens excitation), and at the same time to gain simple control of the size of marks, the "paint-brush" approach, illustrated in Fig. 1, was adopted. The advantages of this technique outweigh the disadvantage associated with the slower recording rate, which is almost two orders of magnitude lower than that achievable with shaped beams. The recorder and its control and data transfer systems are shown in Fig. 2. It is a demountable electron column

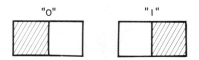

"O"   "I"

TWO MARKS ARE USED TO RECORD
ONE BIT OR A BINARY CHARACTER OF INFORMATION

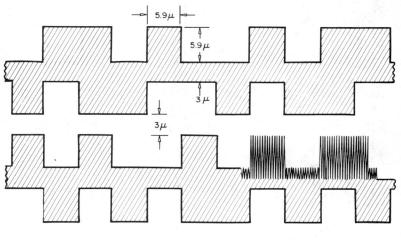

5.9μ

5.9μ

3μ

3μ

PORTIONS OF FOUR TYPICAL TRACKS
OF THE DICTIONARY
SHOWING "PAINTING" TECHNIQUE

Figure 1. Portions of Four Typical Tracks of the Dictionary
Showing "Painting" Technique.

shown schematically in Fig. 3. It consists of a slightly
modified Canalco column incorporating a 5 mil tungsten
hairpin cathode and two magnetic lenses. The gun is
operated at 12 kv with a $0.6\,\mu$ spot and a current density
of 1 A/cm^2. Modifications to the gun include beam blanking plates, electrostatic deflection plates and custom magnetic deflection coils. [3]

The flexible photographic discs are placed on a platen
supported on a commercially available preloaded precision bearing which is housed within the vacuum chamber.

Figure 2(a). Electron Beam Discwriter. (b). Console, Tape Drive and Buffer for the Electron Beam Discwriter.

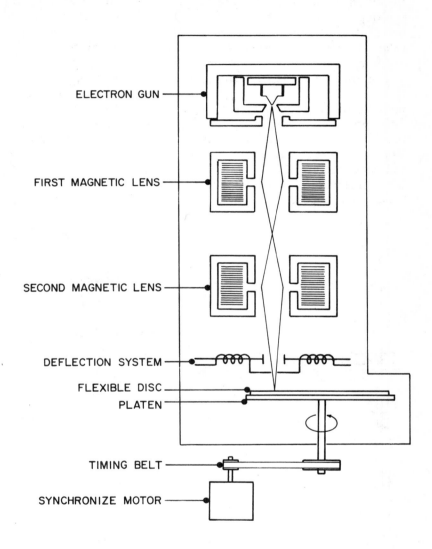

Figure 3. Schematic of Electron Beam Column.

In order to insure, that the area to be exposed was within the depth of focus of the beam, the disc is held down on the platen by an aluminum disc and a retaining ring (Fig. 4) leaving an exposed annulus of film under the column. Motive power is provided by a 900 rpm synchronous motor; it is transmitted to the bearing by a timing belt pulley system rigidly attached to the bearing outside the vacuum system, and driving the platen at 225 rpm. Vacuum is provided by a commercial system incorporating a Welch 15 cubic inch roughing pump and a Veeco four inch diffusion pump, with a cold trap providing a vacuum of about 5×10^{-6} mm Hg.

Information to be record is obtained from a magnetic tape. The information is transferred into a core buffer,

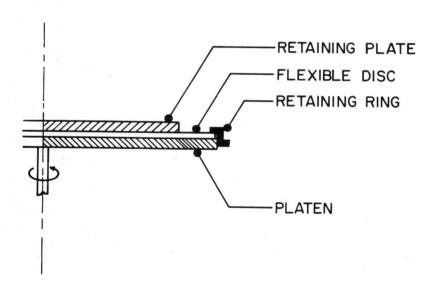

RETAINING PLATE

FLEXIBLE DISC

RETAINING RING

PLATEN

Figure 4. Detail of Disc Retainer.

a full track at a time. This transfer is initiated by a
pulse on a magnetic track located on the periphery of the
platen. This signal also controls the blanking of the
beam. The plates were incorporated in the system specifically for this purpose, thus avoiding the transients in
the high voltage power supply which ordinarily occur with
the usual grid bias on-off control. The next arrival of
the trigger pulse turns the beam on and initiates the
writing process. A second magnetic clock track with
precisely 67, 212 pulses also surrounds the platen. Each
pulse from this track calls one bit from the buffer to the
column controls. Clearly, this clock track insures that
there will be no overlap or break at the track closures
even if the angular velocity of the platen is not absolutely
uniform.

A block diagram of the recording system is shown
in Fig. 5. A description of the buffer is to be published. [5].

Actual recording is then accomplished in the following manner. The rotation of the disc yields mechanical
deflection along the tracks and the deflection coils and
plates provide the transverse deflection. During recording, the current in the coils is kept constant, while a
data-modulated 15 MC RF signal is applied to one of the
plates with the other grounded. The envelope of this
signal is a single cycle of a square wave whose phase is
a function of the bit to be recorded. The black and white
marks are thus "painted" as in Fig. 1. With the beam
blanked, while the buffer is being loaded with data for the
next track, and the current in the coils is kept fixed, the
polarity of the plates is automatically reversed. Thus a
pair of tracks sharing a single black border is recorded.
After an even number of tracks has been recorded, the
current in the coils is automatically stepped to correspond to the position of the next pair of tracks and the
polarity of the plates is again reversed. This process
continues until a band of 58 tracks has been written, at
which time the process stops and the entire column has
to be moved manually to the position of the next band.
Altogether 50 bands can be written in the present system.

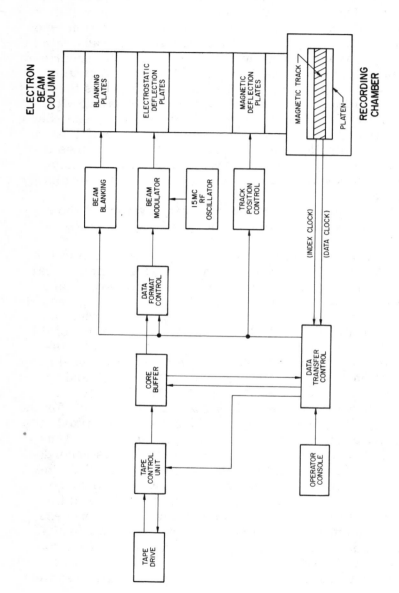

Figure 5. Block Diagram of Electron Beam Discwriter System.

A full Russian dictionary of 6×10^7 bits requires only 18 bands.   At 250,000 bits/sec such a dictionary can be recorded in less than 45 minutes including pump-down and processing.   A portion of a good disc is shown in Fig. 6.

DIRT-INDUCED HOLES

A major cause of unacceptable discs is the presence of dust particles on the emulsion during recording causing a high number of holes (Fig. 7), i. e. , small areas within the information bands where no marks are recorded.   The discwriter was located in a normal laboratory environment where the discs could easily become contaminated. Furthermore, the film was packaged in boxes of 25 sheets in contact with each other.   When the sheets were separated static charges appeared on the emulsion attracting

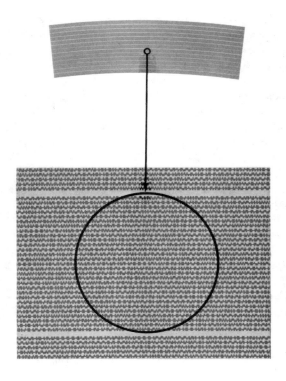

Figure 6.   Portions of a Good Disc.

dust. These charges were eliminated by interleaving the sheets of film with soft paper and storing them in a humidifier. It was found that once a disc was placed in the recording chamber, vacuuming the surface with a standard Hoover dust brush removed all but the smallest dust particles whose size was about one mil. Surprisingly the emulsion is very hard and careful brushing did not cause scratches. However, by the time the chamber was closed new dust particles from the surrounding atmosphere collected on the surface. Thus it was necessary to enclose the gun column in a box which was maintained under positive pressure by means of fans driving in filtered air. This, together with vacuuming the discs prior to recording is sufficient for a high yield of "hole free" discs.

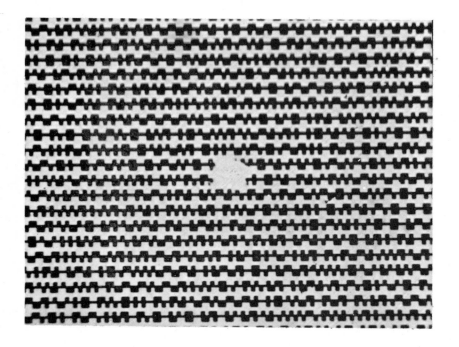

Figure 7. "HOLE" Caused by Dust During Exposure.

In a further effort to improve cleanliness, a camel's hair brush was placed in contact with the emulsion within the chamber in such a way as to clean the disc in the vicinity of the recording spot.   Although this approach did produce some very fine discs, it also introduced, at random, flares of the type shown in Fig. 8.   These are areas of high charge concentration caused by friction. The magnitude of the charge was sufficient to cause deceleration of the beam resulting in unexposed emulsion, as well as deflection of the beam resulting in data tracks which were displaced readily away from the unexposed center.

"Holes" can be tolerated by the system to some extent.   The two mark per bit format and the parity bit

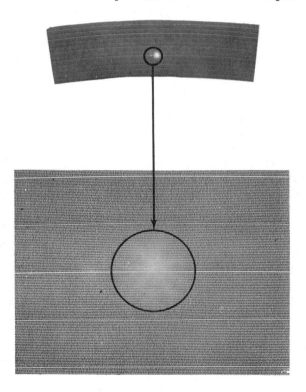

Figure 8.   Flare Caused by Charging Due to Friction.

incorporated in each character allow for some error correction. Thus an acceptable performance can be expected if the "holes" are sufficiently small and sparse so that the track following servo, the reader clock (generated by the data), and the error-correction codes all function properly.

THE CAUSE AND CURE OF OVERLAPPING TRACKS

After performing moderately well for a short period the discwriter developed a strange undesirable malady. It would appear at random in one or more places on some discs but not on others. It would mysteriously disappear for as many as ten consecutive discs and then reappear. A typical example is shown in Fig. 9. Either within a band, or at the boundary between two bands, a group of anywhere from two to twenty tracks would overlap each other over arcs which ranged in length up to one inch.

Careful examination of discs in the sectors where this failure occurred showed that although tracks were circular, the inner tracks developed a slight displacement inward, which grew in magnitude with decreasing track radius. This behavior continued inward until at some point, after anywhere from 75 to as many as 1,000 tracks, the inward displacement would suddenly disappear and subsequent tracks would overlap the displaced ones at the bulge.

The bulge, in some cases reached a maximum excursion of 0.007" before it disappeared in an overlap. In other cases the bulge would increase monotonically in size all the way through the innermost band.

This failure was at first thought to be due to nonuniform charging, but it continued to appear at random even when the glass platen was replaced by an aluminum one which should have minimized any stray field due to charge build-up. Furthermore it was unlikely that an electrical breakdown could occur in the film allowing the inner tracks to resume a circular shape.

Since there was some indication that the bulge was synchronized with the rotation of the disc there was a

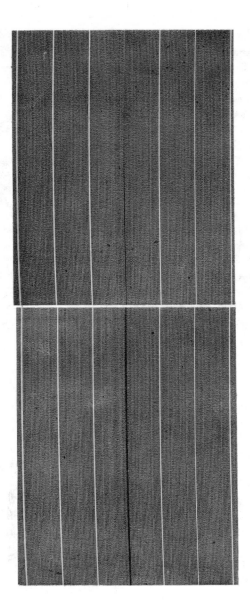

Figure 9. Unsatisfactory Disc Due to Overlapping Tracks.

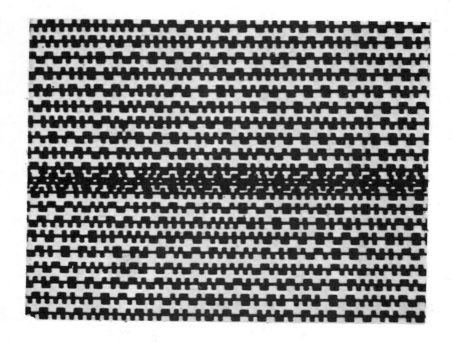

Figure 9(c)

finite possibility that it was of mechanical origin or due to stray noise in the deflection system associated with the beginning of track trigger pulse.

The mechanical system was ruled out after it was established that even with very violent vibrations runout was limited to less than 0.0015 inches. The electrostatic deflection system was also ruled out. Even though the two tracks of a track pair are written with signals of opposite polarity applied to the plates, the pairs were not separated, both tracks being displaced inward by amounts whose difference, if there was any, was imperceptable.

The deflection coils were exonerated when it was discovered that the tracks bulged outward when a disc was written from the inside outward, the signal in the coils having the same sign, but stepped in the reverse direction. Charging thus becomes the prime suspect. To explain the disappearance of the field and associated overlapping tracks, a theory was advanced that outgassing from the film resulted in entrapped bubbles under the disc. These could push the disc away from the platen allowing a field to build up which could deflect the beam away from the recorded area and hence inward. If the entrapped gases could escape, the film would again come in contact with the platen, the stray field would be reduced substantially, and subsequent tracks would be circular.

To test this theory an aluminum platen was prepared with an undercut annulus wide enough to encompass an entire dictionary and about 0.032 inches deep. Radial undercuts were also made so that the annulus could be evacuated with the rest of the chamber.

A portion of a dictionary recorded on the undercut annulus is shown in Fig. 10. The density in the image decreases inward in the first three bands, the bands increase in width from the standard 25 mils to 27.7 mils, and the first two band spacings are also greater than in a good disc. The remaining bands appear to be normal. No overlaps occurred on the undercut annulus. Clearly the gap between the film and the bottom of the undercut allowed a field to build up which decelerated and deflected the beam causing a loss in density and an increased band width. After three bands are written there is enough force due to the surface charge to cause the film to deflect toward the bottom of the undercut thus reducing the stray field and yielding normal bands. No overlaps occurred since the stray field was circularly symmetric. Over twenty discs were recorded with this platen and no overlapping occurred, thus indicating the problem was one of film contact.

Figure 11 shows portions of a dictionary recorded over radial grooves in an aluminum platen. In Fig. 11(a) the undercut is 0.032 inches deep and 0.250 inches wide, while in 11(b) the groove is only 0.094 inches wide. As would be expected, an inward bulge increasing with reduced radius and density decreasing with radius characterize the areas over the bulges. The innermost bands in

Fig. 11(a) have normal density over the center of the
groove where the disc had the opportunity to deflect
toward the bottom of the groove.   When the 1/4" groove
was filled with epoxy, the symptoms, although there,
were almost indiscernible.   This was also true over
shallow, narrow radial V's.

Track overlaps could be induced in two ways.   In one,
a small dielectric bead (0. 01 inches in diameter) which
was attached to a well shielded solenoid was placed between the film and platen causing a small bulge.   After
several bands were recorded the bead was removed on a
signal to the solenoid.   In the other method several bands
were recorded over the 1/4" groove.   Then a piece of
aluminum whose top was level with the surface of the
platen was inserted into the groove under the area being

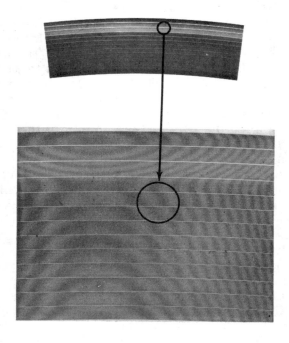

Figure 10.   Disc Recorded Over an Undercut Annulus Showing
Variation in Density.

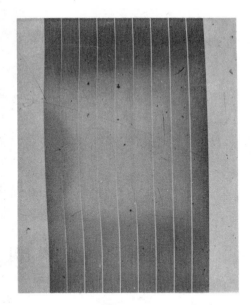

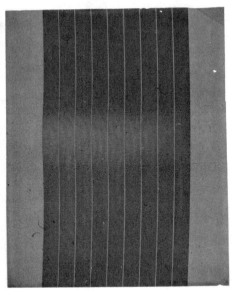

Figure 11. Disc Recorded Over Undercut Radial Grooves Showing Variations in Density and in Inward Bulge.

Figure 12. Overlapping Tracks Induced by Means of a Conductor Inserted into a Radial Groove After Several Bands were Recorded.

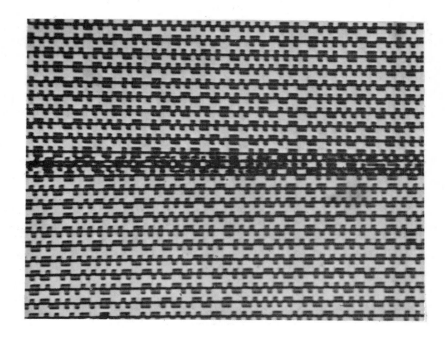

Figure 12(c)

recorded, again by means of an activated solenoid. In both cases, as would be expected there was a developing bulge which was terminated in overlapping tracks, either when the bead was removed, or when the conductor was inserted.

These experiments established the desirability of recording on shallow narrow radial grooves. The platen now in use had radial V-grooves 0.010" deep, 0.026" wide, 1/2° on centers. Thus, although it is not absolutely radially symmetric, the grooves are too narrow to allow for charge build up, and sufficiently numerous to permit outgassed bubbles to escape.

EPILOGUE

Since the new platen was installed no track overlap has occurred. Today, the primary cause of rejected discs is operator error. The other cause of rejected discs is dirt, but here too the operator can be blamed, since care in cleaning the film is accompanied by good results. The discwriter is now serving as the sole source of discs for all photostores and as an experimental tool in evaluating new formats, techniques, and materials for future memories.

ACKNOWLEDGMENTS

The authors wish to thank Dr. R. F. M. Thornley for his valuable suggestions, Mr. P. Pasquarella for recording innumerable discs, and Mr. R. W. Scott for preparing the illustrations for this paper.

REFERENCES

1. G. W. King, G. W. Brown and L. N. Ridenour "Photographic Techniques for Information Storage" Proc. IRE, 41, 1421-1428, October 1953.
2. Final Report on Computer Set AN/GSQ-16 (XW-1) ASTIA No. AD 220204.
3. R. F. M. Thornley, A. V. Brown and A. J. Speth "Electron Beam Recording of Digital Information" IEEE Trans. on Electronic Computers, February 1964.
4. W. M. Drumm "Photo-Optical Recording of Digital Information" Symposium on Photography Information Storage and Retrieval, October 1965.
5. N. H. Kreitzer, "An Electron Beam Recorder Data Transfer System", to be published.

Information Density in Electrostatic Storage

A. S. Jensen and I. Limansky

Westinghouse Defense and Space Center
Aerospace Division
Baltimore, Maryland

INTRODUCTION

Of interest to the electronics system designer is the total amount of information and the density with which it is stored in a storage device. Pragmatically these can be taken as the product of the logarithm of the output signal-to-noise ratio and the total resolution, or resolution density respectively. Thus a signal amplitude equal to the rms noise is taken arbitrarily as a unit of information within a resolution cell. There need be no argument here about whether this unit should be taken as one or three or six times the rms noise since this discussion concerns the device not the system. The system performance needs expressed in terms of error rate or false alarm rate determines what minimum signal-to-noise ratio the system designer will accept. A resolution curve plotted with signal-to-noise ratio as the ordinate will provide the system designer with the data he needs to determine the information that can be stored. However, this curve varies in amplitude and extent with the writing change density, so that a family of such curves is required. In fact, this family of curves forms a three-dimensional surface having axes: resolution, writing change density and signal-to-noise ratio (Fig. 1). This is the performance surface [3] for the storage device.

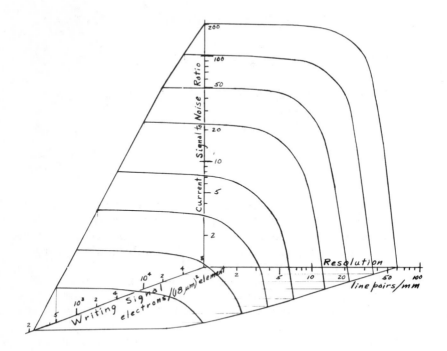

Figure 1. Theoretical Performance Surface

The following discussion pertains specifically to electron charge storage devices such as signal storage tubes and camera storage tubes, and particularly to those that read non-destructively. Relatively minor modifications to the equations will adapt the discussion to display storage tubes and to those which read destructively, such as a vidicon or image orthicon.

LIMITATIONS TO PERFORMANCE

Writing Charge Density

In a camera tube this would be called exposure and would be expressed as photoelectrons per unit area. Usually there is a gain mechanism associated with the writing action, by secondary electron emission or by electron bombardment induced conductivity, so that the written charge is greater than the writing charge. This written charge density charges the dielectric surface through a voltage change inversely proportional to its capacitance per unit area. This voltage difference modulates the reading electron beam according to its reading transfer characteristic. This imposes the limitation since for some voltage difference the reading beam modulation is saturated. Hence the maximum writing charge per area of reading beam is:

$$e\chi_m = (C/A) V_m b^2/\sigma_w = q_m/\sigma_w \tag{1}$$

where

$$q_m = C_j V_m \tag{2}$$

is the maximum written charge per reading beam spot area (Fig. 2).

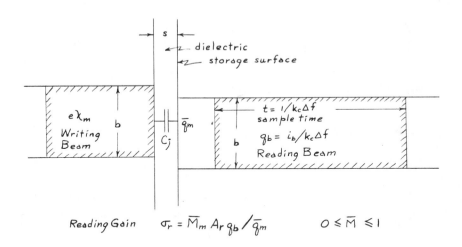

Figure 2

Reading Gain

Though unusual it is perfectly proper to consider the modulation of the reading beam by the stored charge as a charge gain mechanism. The upper cut-off frequency of the video amplifier defines the time per sample in the output signal. With this for a basis there may be defined the charge per sample in any current, [4] for example the reading beam current or the output signal current. Thus the reading beam charge per sample is

$$q_b = i_b / k_c \Delta f \qquad (3)$$

where k_c is usually taken as 2 samples per cycle [4] (Fig. 2). The reading gain can now be defined as the ratio of the signal charge per sample after reading to the stored charge per element, thus:

$$\sigma_r = q_r / q_w = i_r / e \times \sigma_w k_c \Delta f \qquad (4)$$

It is convenient for analysis first to consider separately the electron optic and the spatial aspects of the electron optic and the spatial aspects of the electron beam reading action, thus it comprises two factors: the modulation of the reading beam current by the stored charge, and the spatial signal response.

Modulation of Reading Beam Current

The modulation is the fraction of the reading beam current collected by the storage surface. It is a function of the voltage of the surface, this function being usually called the reading transfer characteristic. Hence the reading signal charge per element,

$$\bar{q}_r = \overline{M} A \, q_b \qquad 0 \leq \overline{M} \leq 1 \qquad (5)$$

and the reading gain can be expressed as

$$\sigma_r = \overline{M}_m A \, q_b / \bar{q}_m \qquad (6)$$

It is at this point that the distinction must be made between destructive and non-destructive reading. If the reading transfer characteristic is measured dynamically during the actual reading, the reading current is actually that integrated over the dwell time (on the beam width for a scanning beam). For destructive reading this is not the same as the instantaneous value. A bar is placed over the letters to distinguish the modulation and maximum stored charge so determined by the integral curve from their instantaneous values. For non-destructive reading both characteristics are the same and no distinction need be made.

For destructive reading a useful concept is the discharge factor, [5] the fraction of the stored charge which is read and erased during the dwell time.

$$\emptyset = q_r/q_w \qquad\qquad 0 \leqslant \emptyset \leqslant 1 \qquad\qquad (7)$$

The modulation is then

$$\overline{M} = q_w \emptyset/q_b \qquad\qquad (8)$$

$$\overline{M} = \bar{q}_m \emptyset/q_b \qquad\qquad (9)$$

For small signals restricted to the linear portion of the instantaneous reading transfer characteristic

$$\overline{M} = M\emptyset/\ln(1-\emptyset) \qquad\qquad (10)$$

This indicates the type of relationship that exists between the integral and the instantaneous characteristics.

Signal Response

The relative signal response is a function of the spatial frequency or the resolution of the input stored signal. It is sometimes called the resolution curve. The signal response is the convolution integral of the reading beam current density distribution, the modulation and the storage charge density distribution. [6-8] The modulation factor must be included in this integral since it is the potential pattern that modulates the reading beam, yet there are important instances where the potential pattern is considerably different from the stored charge pattern. It is in this manner that the thickness of the storage dielectric and beam bending by the strong transverse electric fields between adjacent storage elements affect the resolution.

Three cases of stored charge density distribution are of interest: a square wave vertical bar pattern, a sine wave vertical bar pattern, and a checkerboard pattern which is a sine wave in each of the two dimensions. The square wave response is usually measured since it is easiest to mechanize in the laboratory. This is readily converted mathematically to the one dimensional sine wave response. This latter is very useful for incorporating the storage tube into the frequency response of the system or for analyzing the sine wave response into several contributing components. As with a filter spectral response the point by point product of two sine wave responses is the sine wave response of the two effects acting together. The two dimensional sine wave response is of interest in the consideration of signals of limited extent in both directions, the usual case. It is usually the square of the one dimensional sine wave response.

A storage surface comprising a continuous, uniform film of dielectric on a conducting reference substrate has a limited resolution capability dependent upon the dielectric thickness. [9] The sine wave response has been shown to be:

$$A_s = [1 - \exp(-4\pi Rs)]/4\pi Rs, \quad 0 \leqslant A \leqslant 1 \quad\quad (11)$$

where R is the written signal spatial frequency and s is the dielectric thickness. This is a serious limitation for a signal of which one line pair is spread over a length of the surface equal to as much as ten times the dielectric thickness the sine wave response is only 57 percent. Using the same dielectric thickness, therefore having equivalent writing speed, a structured storage surface such as the grating or Datachon storage target can be made which has a greater signal response out to a spatial frequency at

which the structure is resolved, at which the continuous
dielectric surface would have a signal response of less
than 50 percent.

Strong transverse electric fields between the elements
of a stored charge pattern affect the trajectory of a low
energy reading beam so that it does not read the element
of the storage surface to which it was addressed. [10]
This is known as beam bending, and it is in fact a loss of
resolution. It becomes relatively more serious at higher
spatial frequencies of the stored charge pattern, particularly, for those greater than 20 line pairs per mm. A
continuous dielectric storage surface is much more
limited in resolution by beam bending than is a structured
storage surface.

It is well known that the finite width of the reading
electron beam limits the resolution. The sine wave response (Fig. 3) for a Gaussian reading beam is

$$A_b = \exp\,(-2\pi^2 R^2 \sigma_b^2\,), \qquad 0 \leqslant A \leqslant 1 \qquad (12)$$

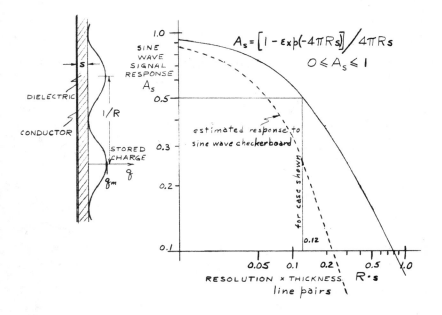

Figure 3. Sine Wave Response of Thick Target

To a first approximation the electron beam current density distribution is Gaussian, though it may have a slightly wider skirt.

Disturbance

Usually more serious than time varying noise are the regular and random shadings that appear in the output signal of a storage tube, the same on every picture or frame read out. Only the regular patterns have yet been amenable to analysis and most are not amenable to elimination even by careful manufacturing techniques. Though they are not included in the mathematical analysis of this paper, they must not be forgotten since they constitute a further limitation to the amount of information that can be stored. There is simply listed here some of the important sources of disturbance: fluctuation in dielectric thickness resulting from the particulate nature of its deposition, photocathode non-uniformity, non-uniform scanning by the reading beam both from noise on the deflection signal and non-linear deflection waveform, non-uniform collection of return beam, fluctuation of gain across surface of first multiplier dynode, modulation of the reading beam as it scans over the storage target structure (screen disturbance), [5] and fluctuation of the work function over the surface of an exposed metal target structure. Note that several of these vary in a statistical manner over the surface so that even though their effect repeats frame after frame, it is still a random effect spatially. Hence, it is no more indefinitely reducible than any other statistical phenomenon. These then constitute limiting effects on the information storage.

Noise

Four sources of noise must be considered: writing charge shot noise, reading beam shot noise, partitioning noise at each action on the signal, and preamplifier Johnson-Nyquist noise.

The partitioning noise is handled by the use of deHaan's [11] analysis, modified to permit the inclusion of the Johnson-Nyquist noise and the beam shot noise and to include the return beam electron multiplier. Four actions on the signal are considered: writing gain, reading gain, multiplier first dynode gain, and gain from each of the remaining multiplier dynodes.

The mean square noise charge per element at the input to the preamplifier can be calculated to be:

$$N^2 = \overline{\Delta q^2} = eq_b\ \sigma_1 \delta^m(\sigma_1\ \delta^m + \delta^m + \delta^{m-1} + \cdots + \delta + 1)$$

$$+ e^2\ X^2 \sigma_w^2\ \overline{M}_m^2\ A^2 q_b\ \sigma_1^2\ \delta^{2\ m}/\overline{q}_m^2$$

$$+ (e^2\ X\ \sigma_w \overline{M}_m A q_b \sigma_1\ \delta^m/q_m)$$

$$\left[\begin{array}{c} (\sigma_w \overline{M}_m A q_b \sigma 1 \delta^m/q_m) + (\overline{M}_m A q_b \sigma_1\ \delta^m/q_m) \\ -\sigma_1\ \delta^m\ +\ \delta^m\ +\ \delta^{m-1}\ +\ \cdots\ +\delta\ +\ 1 \end{array} \right]$$

$$+ 8\pi kTC_i F'/k_c \tag{13}$$

where F' is the noise figure of the preamplifier. The negative sign in the third term comes from using the return beam for the signal path. This equation is for the noise in the same element as the signal, that is, it is the noise "on top of the signal" and not "on the baseline". The first two terms in the equation are the reading beam shot noise. The third term is the signal shot noise, the long parenthesis providing for the partitioning at each action on the signal. The last term is the preamplifier noise.

PERFORMANCE SURFACE

At this same point, the input to the preamplifier, the signal charge is:

$$S = e\ X\ \sigma_w \sigma_r \sigma_1\ \delta^m = e\ X\ \sigma_w M_m A q_b \sigma_1\ \delta^m/\overline{q}_m \tag{14}$$

The current signal to noise ratio can be expressed parametrically as

$$\frac{S}{N} = \frac{\chi}{(\gamma \chi^2 + \alpha \chi + \beta)^{1/2}} \tag{15}$$

where the coefficients γ, α and β can be readily deduced from the noise equation.

$$\gamma = e/q_b \tag{16}$$

$$\alpha = 1 + 1/\sigma_w - \bar{q}_m/\sigma_w \overline{M}_m A q_b + (\bar{q}_m/\sigma_w \overline{M}_m A q_b \sigma_1)$$

$$\sum_{m=1}^{m=m} 1/\delta^{m-1}$$

$$\beta = (\bar{q}_m{}^2/e\sigma_w{}^2 \overline{M}_m{}^2 A^2 q_b) \left[1 + (1/\sigma_1) \sum_{m=1}^{m=m} 1/\delta^{m-1} \right] \tag{17}$$

$$+ 8\pi k T C_i F' \bar{q}_m{}^2/k_c e^2 \sigma_w{}^2 \overline{M}_m{}^2 A^2 q_b{}^2 \sigma_1{}^2 \delta^{2m} \tag{18}$$

This is seen to be the equation of a surface having coordinates S/N (signal to noise ratio), X (the number of writing electrons per element), and the resolution of the writing signal. The resolution enters through the signal response, A, which is a function of resolution as discussed previously. This is the Performance Surface of the storage tube.

Some confusion concerning this surface seems to exist among planners of military and space image systems. Device manufacturers normally quote in their tube data sheets the three intercepts of the performance surface. This is very logical, because it is good mathematics to determine a surface, even a curved surface at least approximately, by its intercepts. But none of these quoted performance figures is attainable except at the complete sacrifice at the other two. Any reasonable operating point on the performance surface has coordinates which are less than the quoted figures by factors of two to ten.

This must be taken into careful consideration when attempting to estimate the effectiveness of a conceptual image system.

The factor $\bar{q}_m/q_b$, the ratio of the maximum written charge per beam width to the charge per sample in the reading beam, indicates that the performance surface is a function of the reading beam current density and an inverse function of the reading data rate. Hence, high performance requires a low reading data rate. This effect reaches a limit about 100 kHz below which the preamplifier becomes more noisy. [12]

STORED INFORMATION

In the plane of signal-to-noise ratio and signal resolution there may be plotted lines of equal information:

$$I = R\log_2 S/N \qquad (19)$$

where I is the linear information density in bits per mm when R is the stored signal spatial frequency in line pairs per mm. On this same plane may also be plotted the projections of the performance surface as a family of curves each for a chosen value of writing electrons per beam width (Fig. 4). For each of these performance curves there is a particular signal spatial frequency for which the stored information is a maximum. In the example chosen this occurs for large signals at a signal spatial frequency somewhat higher than that for which the sine wave response is 50 percent. At maximum writing signal in this example the maximum information density is apparently* 200 bits per mm or 4×10^4 bits/mm².

The example which has been taken for the experimental sine wave response curve and this computed family of performance curves is the Optechon storage camera

---

*For simplicity there has been omitted here the effect of the sine wave response limiting the dynamic range by crosstalk between adjacent elements. This reduces the linear information density by about 15%.

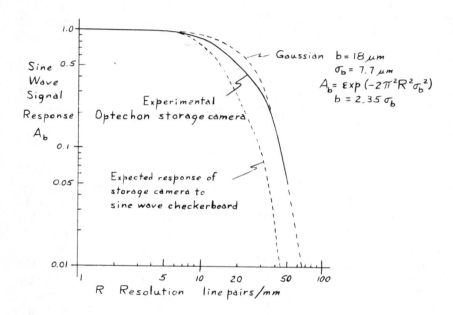

Sine Wave Signal Response A_b

Gaussian $b = 18 \mu m$
$\sigma_b = 7.7 \mu m$
$A_b = \exp(-2\pi^2 R^2 \sigma_b^2)$
$b = 2.35 \sigma_b$

Experimental
Optechon storage camera

Expected response of
storage camera to
sine wave checkerboard

R Resolution line pairs/mm

Figure 4. Signal Response

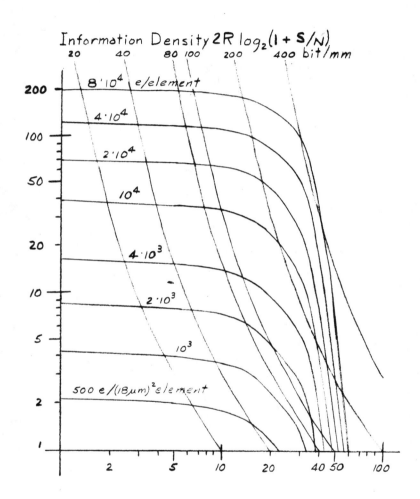

Figure 5. Theoretical Performance and Information Storage

tube. [1,2] It uses the grating storage target [13] to obtain very high resolution, long storage time and good sensitivity.

SYMBOLS

A	signal response (amplitude)
A_b	do, limited by reading, beam width
A_s	do, limited by dielectric thickness
b	reading beam width, taken at half-amplitude of current density spread function; $b = 2.35 \, \sigma_b$ for Gaussian beam
C_i	preamplifier total input capacitance
C_j	capacitance of storage surface per area of reading beam spot
(C/A)	capacitance per unit area of storage surface
e	electron charge, 1.6×10^{-19} C.
Δf	video bandwidth
F'	preamplifier noise figure
i_b	reading beam current
i_r	reading signal current
I	information density, in bits per mm
k	Boltzmann's constant, 1.38×10^{-23} J/°K
k_c	2 samples per cycle of bandwidth [4]
m	number of multiplier dynodes after the first
M	modulation of the reading beam
M_m	maximum modulation without saturation
N	noise at input to preamplifier
q_b	reading beam charge per sample
q_m	maximum stored written charge per area of reading beam spot, for maximum modulation of reading

q_r reading signal charge per sample

q_w stored written charge per area of reading beam

R   resolution, spatial frequency of input written signal, in line pairs per mm

s   storage dielectric thickness

S   signal at input to preamplifier

(S/N)   signal to noise ratio

T   absolute temperature of resistor

V_m maximum voltage change on storage surface, for which reading beam modulation is a maximum

α, β, γ coefficients in parametric equation for signal to noise ratio

δ gain of each multiplier dynode after the first

σ_b standard deviation (radius) of reading beam

σ_r reading gain

σ_w writing (prestorage) gain

σ_1 gain of first multiplier dynode

$\emptyset$ discharge factor

χ number of writing electrons per area of reading beam spot

χ_m maximum number of writing electrons per area of reading beam spot for which the modulation of the reading beam is maximum

REFERENCES

1. W. G. Reininger, A. S. Jensen and W. G. Baran, "Research in Advanced Photoelectric Information Storage", Air Force Avionics Laboratory, Research and Technology Div., Technical Documentary Report RTD-TDR-63-4134, Contract AF33(657)8715, November 1963, ASTIA AD423-982.

2. A. S. Jensen and W. G. Reininger, "Recent Experimental Results of the Photoelectric Storage Tube", Proceedings 1964 National Aerospace Electronics Conference (NAECON) IEEE, pp. 178-184, May 1964.

3. J. A. Hall and A. S. Jensen, "A 3-D Approach to Camera Tube Characteristics for the Systems Designer", Proceedings 1963 National Aerospace Electronics Conference (NAECON) IEEE, pp. 24-29, May 1963.

4. S. Goldman, "Frequency Analysis, Modulation and Noise", McGraw-Hill Book Co., Inc., 1948.

5. A. S. Jensen, "Discharging on Insulator Surface by Secondary Emission without Redistribution", RCA Review, Vol. XVI, pp. 216-233, June 1955.

6. O. H. Schade, "Electro-optical Characteristics of Television Systems", RCA Review, Vol. IX, 4 parts: March, June, September and December 1948.

7. Y. W. Lee, "Statistical Theory of Communication", John Wiley and Sons, 1960.

8. E. H. Linfoot, "Fourier Methods in Optical Image Evaluation", The Focal Press, 1964.

9. I. M. Krittman, "Resolution of Electrostatic Storage Targets", IEEE Transactions on Electron Devices, Vol. ED-10, pp. 404-409, November 1963.

10. R. Theile, "Recent Investigations into the Operation of Image Orthicon Camera Tubes", Jour. Television Soc., Vol. 9, No. 2, pp. 45-59, 1958.

11. E. F. deHaan, "Signal to Noise Ratio of Image Devices", Advances in Electronics and Electron Physics, Vol. XII, pp. 291-306, Academic Press, 1960.

12. R. Theile, "On the Signal to Noise Ratio in Television Storage Tubes", Advances in Electronics and Electron Physics, Vol. XII, pp. 277-290, Academic Press, 1960.

13. A. S. Jensen, W. G. Reininger and I. Limansky, "The Grating Storage Target", Advances in Electronics and Electron Physics, Academic Press, to be published, proceedings of the Third Symposium on Photoelectronic Image Devices, Imperial College, September 1965.

Dove Data Storage and Retrieval
System Presentation

J. F. Dove

Rome Air Development Center
Rome, New York

This presentation relates to an experimental and developmental program to provide a data processing capability for extremely high density storage and rapid retrievel of digital data. The concept was invented by Mr. John F. Dove of Rome Air Development Center and developed by Braddock, Dunn and McDonald, Inc. , with RADC discretionary funds. The Dove Data Storage and Retrieval System is a high energy electron beam for digitally writing information on suitable recording media such as thin metallic or semi-conductor film, tapes, cards, etc. The information is recorded digitally in the form of a "hole" or "no hole" in the recording medium. This recording method is somewhat analogous to punch tape recording except in this case a high energy electron beam is used instead of the mechanical punch. This electronic method allows exceedingly rapid recording with unusually high bit densities. The high bit density is made possible by the use of a narrow electron beam.

The read-out is accomplished by using a lower energy electron beam to illuminate the desired bit location. The same electron gun may be used for both recording and read-out. If there is a hole at the illuminated bit location, then it will be sensed by a collector plate located behind the recording surface. This allows the use of existing beam control and positioning circuitry in the read-out and in the write modes.

DESCRIPTION OF THE SYSTEM

The Dove Data Storage and Retrieval System is an electron tube device which incorporates the features of a rugged, demountable tube and minimum optical aberration. It can produce a spot size of 2.5 microns for a beam current of 100 micro-amps at an energy of 11 kv.

In optimizing spot size, beam control, and resolution, extreme care is required to insure that no magnetic material is placed in the proximity of the beam. This unit has had the small discs of magnetic material on the electrical feed-throughs removed from the immediate environment of the beam to avoid extraneous fields acting on the beam.

Inasmuch as this is an unbaked system, it is possible to provide vacuum-tight mating of the flanges simply by the use of 1/8" wall neoprene elastomers. This feature, is an inexpensive and efficient method of maintaining vacuum levels in the 10^{-6} torr region.

In experiments conducted with the system, to date, two methods have been employed for controlling the drilling operation. The first is accomplished by pulsing the grid to attain the desired current level and driving it back beyond the cutoff at the onset of current to the collector plate located behind the foil. The beam is continuously focussed during this operation. The second method involves starting with a defocussed beam and sweeping the lens current to a value which overfocusses the beam. The current is maintained at a constant level throughout this operation. During this mode of operation the beam is in focus for times which vary from 25 microseconds on upward.

Holes ranging in size from 2 to 11 microns have been drilled in this manner. Drilling times, as short as 2 microseconds and as long as 41 microseconds, have been employed using foils ranging in thickness from 2.5 microns to 6.25 microns. The most successful technique for drilling, however, is the first method described above.

The most consistent set of results was obtained using currents of 60 - 100 micro-amps at an accelerating voltage of 11 kv. A set of 2 to 5 micron holes were drilled

in a nickel foil of a thickness of 2. 5 microns. Drilling
times varied from 7 to 41 microseconds. However,
theoretical studies completed under this program indicate
drilling times of 50 - 100 nanoseconds are practical using
metallic/silicon oxide "sandwich" record media.

RETRIEVAL SUBSYSTEM

The purpose of the retrieval subsystem is to select
and control the read-out of information from the recording media. A method for obtaining access to any word
block in the recording media will be discussed. The
present unsophisticated circuitry was designed to provide
48 bit word access in 4 microseconds. However, with a
slight modification in design the access time has reduced
to $2 \mu s$. Even shorter access times are possible with
more sophisticated circuitry and equipments.

The word retrievel subsystem consists of a
read detector, binary counters, binary address selector switches, address comparators, ramp generators, and sweep control clamping circuits as
major components.

The read detector is a high gain video amplifier which
(a) detects the passage of the electron beam across a word
hole, (b) amplifies this pulse (current gain 5, 000), and
(c) shapes and clamps the pulse to provide a logic level
input to the binary counters.

There are two identical binary counters to count the
logic level pulses from the read detector. The Y-counter
counts pulses associated with beam deflection in the
channel axis. The X-counter counts pulses associated
with beam deflection in the row axis. Each counter is a
seven stage binary counter. Counter design is a conventional type and need not be discussed here.

The binary address selector switches provide the
means to specify access to any desired word block in the
recording media. The address selector switches perform
the command function to stipulate the required motion of
the electron beam across the storage area. For a specified column (Y) and row (X) setting on the address selectors, the electron beam will sweep from a prescribed

reference hole along the column (Y) axis, stop at the
designated Y-hole, then sweep across the row (X) axis
and stop at the designated X-hole. This, then, is the
word block location as specified by the address selectors.

The address comparators consist of logic gates to
compare the address selector switch settings with the
state of the binary counters. When the switch settings
and counter states compare, the comparator generates
a command pulse to hold the electron beam at the designated word block hole location.

The sweep control circuits contain the R-C networks
required to generate the sweep voltage from the ramp
generator. When a comparator command pulse arrives,
a gate in the sweep control opens and disables the ramp
generator input. This action clamps the sweep voltage
at the prescribed level.

The binary counters and comparators were initially
designed using standard logic techniques. Major manufacturers of high speed digital integrated circuits were
contacted to obtain characteristics data for the required
logic devices. By analysis of this data, the Motorola
350 integrated circuit series were selected. The logic
equations for the counters and comparators were then
modified to provide compatibility with the Motorola devices.

The inherent propagation delay of logic components
was a major design consideration. Typical values of
propagation delay for a NOR/NAND logic gate are 6 - 10
nanoseconds. The propagation delay for a flip-flop and is
20 - 30 nanoseconds. Since a word location pulse input
to the counter must be gated into a flip-flop to change the
state of the flip-flop and thus advance the counter, delays
of 26 - 40 nanoseconds will occur. However, by inten-
tionally extending this delay to 50 nanoseconds, the real
time delay can be eliminated. This is accomplished by
advancing the counter so that its initial state is word
block 1. Then, when the first word location pulse enters
the counter, the counter is already at word block 1. The
first word block pulse will trigger the counter, due to
(inherent + intentional) delay, the counter will not advance for 50 nanoseconds. The second word location

pulse enters the counter 50 nanoseconds after the first word location pulse. As a result, the counter will advance to word block 2 at the same instant the second word location pulse arrives at the counter.

The address comparator consists of logic gates. The (inherent + intentional) delay for the comparator is 20 nanoseconds. The time required for the comparator command pulse to disable the sweep control circuit gate, and thereby hold the electron beam at the desired word hole location, is 30 nanoseconds. The combined delay, from the time the switch settings and the counter compare until the time the electron beam stops, is 50 nanoseconds. This is a word sequence access time. Therefore, this delay can be eliminated by advancing the counter so that its initial state is word block 2. This procedure is valid provided special attention is given to the case when word block 1 is selected. Since the initial state of the counter is word block 2, the counter and binary address selector switches cannot compare if word location 1 is selected. A separate gating circuit is therefore provided so that when word block 1 is selected on the switches, the comparator does not interrogate the state of the binary counter. Instead, it interrogates the switch settings only. Sensing the word block 1 has been selected, the comparator generates a command pulse and stops the electron beam. This procedure takes 50 nanoseconds which is the precise time required for the beam to travel from the reference hole to word location hole 1.

The (inherent + intentional) delay in the read detector is 50 nanoseconds. This delay is eliminated since the electron beam leaving the reference hole generates a pulse. The counter cannot distinguish between the reference hole pulse and a word location pulse. The reference hole pulse occurs 50 nanoseconds before the word block 1 hole pulse. By allowing the counter to accept the reference hole pulse as a word location pulse, the delay in the read detector is cancelled.

In summary, a random accessing subsystem has been devised which will provide access from the recording media at a twenty five megahertz rate. Investigations are continuing in an effort to determine feasible means which

may provide even less access time. A two hundred and
fifty (250) Mhz access is possible with sophisticated circuitry.

SUMMATION

The major problem encountered in this development
program has been the behavior of the foils during the
writing operation. Due to the molecular stresses in the
foils which cannot be relieved, the foils have a tendency
to warp this naturally introduces errors in the retrieval
operations. To overcome this problem, a materials
investigation has been conducted, and a series of experiments will be conducted using record media which are
"sandwiches" of bismuth and silicon monoxide.

The present configuration of the system employs a
demountable and dynamically adjustable electron gun. It
is anticipated that this, coupled with the use of a bismuth-
silicon monoxide sandwich record medium will permit a
writing rate (25 mh or greater) which is compatible with
the reading rate. Total storage capacity available in the
present version of the device is 2×10^7 bits and is capable
of immediate expansion to 3.2×10^8 bits. The bit density
is 2×10^7 bit/in.^{2}. Therefore, with the use of tapes or
discs a billion bit or greater capacity is possible. The
use of the device in conjunction with data processing
facilities at Rome Air Development Center dictated a 48
bit word length. This, coupled with a 2 microsecond
random access time will provide a semi-permanent mass
data storage capacity on a scale as large as the largest
core memories, with a random access time which compares favorably. This random access time can be reduced by at least a factor of two by a more extensive use
of integrated circuitry.

The capability mentioned above can be obtained at
only a fraction of the cost of other random such access
systems. This significant contribution to data storage
and retrieval technology can make possible a tremendous
dollar saving to the Military and industry in data processing equipment since present computer memories are quite
expensive. For example, RADC will use this device to
give a 50 thousand dollar computer a million dollar
capability.

Television Recording Using Electron Exposure*

R. F. Dubbe and E. W. Reed

Minnesota Mining and Manufacturing Company
St. Paul, Minnesota

INTRODUCTION

With few exceptions, the presentation means for an electronically generated television signal has been the face of a cathode ray tube with its phosphor screen and glass faceplate. Similarly, the method of making motion picture film from a television signal is to photograph a cathode ray tube as in commercial kinescope or telecine recorders. [1] An excellent review of this type of recording was published in the December, 1965, Journal of the SMPTE, Volume 74, Number 12, page 1069, by A. B. Palmer, titled "The Technical Problems of Television Film Recording". With electron beam recording, one can eliminate the phosphor screen, glass faceplate, and camera lens of present recorders, (Fig. 1) and use electrons rather than photons to record photographic films (Fig. 2). This paper describes an electron beam recorder, and discusses some of the advantages of electron recording with respect to resolution, picture noise, and exposure control. Two possible disadvantages of electron recording are also discussed; namely, the need for

*Revision of papers presented to the Society of Motion Picture and Television Engineers 98th Technical Conference, at Montreal, Canada, November 3rd, 1965. The original papers are published in the Journal of SMPTE, vol. 75, pp.191-197, March, 1966.

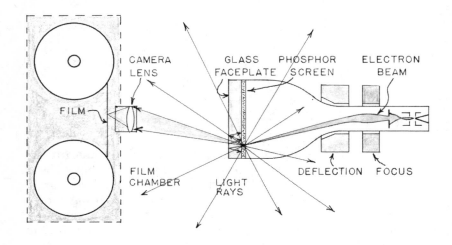

Figure 1. Kinescope Recording

recording the film under high vacuum, and electrostatic charging of the film when subjected to electron bombardment.

The cathode-ray-tube's faceplate flare, along with the phosphor screen grain and associated scattering and absorption losses, are completely eliminated with electron beam recording. Also eliminated, are the problems associated with the camera lens and optical path in general. Theoretically, a considerable increase in resolution and improvement in signal-to-noise would be possible with a correctly designed electron film and electron gun. However, a practical limit exists on how small an electron spot diameter should be recorded. For recording a television raster, adequate optical density is obtained on a 16 mm film negative by having the electron spot fill

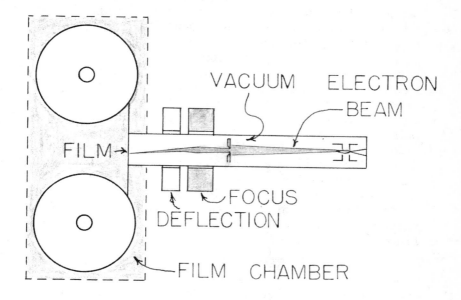

Figure 2. Electron Recording.

the area between the 490 TV lines in the picture area. A
0. 58 mil spot diameter fills the area between TV lines
and permits horizontal resolution in excess of 650
lines. [2]. By making the spot elliptical, approximately
0. 29 by 0. 58 mils, one can best utilize the 525 line vertical resolution (about 490 lines in picture area), and
obtain an increase in horizontal resolution. It is doubtful
if a further increase in resolution could be utilized at
this time due to limitations in TV image tubes and in the
optics of the film projector.

To keep the electron optical system relatively simple
and obtain a small spot size, a single magnetic lens is
placed close to the film target so that a demagnification of
the apparent electron source takes place. A thin deflection
yoke fits between the lens and the film target.

Because the electron gun is not permanently sealed off as in the case of a cathode ray tube but opened to atmosphere when the recorder is shut down, the electron source is a heated tungsten hairpin filament.

The film is kept from exposure during the horizontal scan blanking period and during film pull down by deflecting the beam into a Faraday cage where it is measured. A servo system automatically adjusts the electron gun bias to maintain constant the amplitude of a reference pulse during the blanking interval. Adjustment of the video levels for black and peak white exposure is done by monitoring the beam current on an oscilloscope during the film pull down interval.

This type of television electron beam recorder has made possible 16 mm television recordings free from the fixed noise patterns of phosphor faceplates, a resolution in excess of 600 lines, and pictures free from shutter bar.

ELECTRON OPTICAL SYSTEM

The essential elements in forming and directing the electron beam are shown in Fig. 3. The filament and grid of the triode gun are operated at about 18,000 volts negative to provide the necessary electron acceleration since the film target is most easily kept at zero or ground potential. The filament itself is a .006" diameter tungsten wire bent in the form of a sharp hairpin. The grid and filament structure is readily replaceable. The 0.15 inch spacing of the grid and anode provides a strong field to give a small beam cross-over which acts as the apparent electron source. A .010" diameter aperture limits the size of the beam to reduce spherical aberration. These four elements form the beam which is deflected and focused in the remainder of the optical system.

By the application of a negative voltage to the upper electrostatic deflector, the beam is deflected into the Faraday cage. A negative voltage of about 250 volts is applied during composite blanking of the television signal and pull down of the film. Such a complete shut off of the beam from reaching the film is called "super-blanking". This super-blanking deflection procedure does not disturb the television signal applied to the grid of the electron gun.

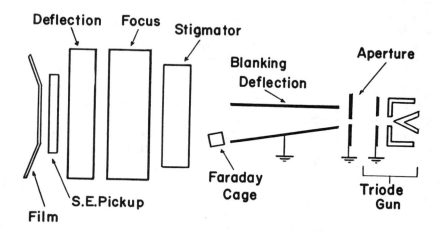

Figure 3.   Electron Optical System.

The stigmator corrects for unwanted astigmatism of
the electron beam usually due to gun asymmetry. Controlled astigmatism is also introduced to mask discrete
raster lines in the recorded film. A single magnetic lens
is used to focus the beam to give a geometric reduction of
the apparent source. Magnetic deflection for the television raster is used because of space and quality requirements. A secondary emission pick up ring is positioned close to the film target and used for focus and
raster size adjustments in a manner similar to that used
in a scanning probe microscope by collecting secondary
electrons emitted from the target area.

VACUUM SYSTEM

Fast start up time or minimum pump down time is achieved by the use of a two vacuum system as shown in Fig. 4. The gun assembly is kept at a high vacuum of approximately 10^{-4} to 10^{-5} mm of Hg by diffusion pumping from the cathode end of the gun assembly. The film chamber is kept at the low vacuum of the fore pump of approximately 0.5 mm of Hg so that outgassing of the film is of minor consequence. A spring loaded pressure plate, similar to the spring loaded shoe in a 16 mm camera is used to hold the film in position against the recording aperture. The film thus forms a seal between the low and high vacuum chambers. Automated valves

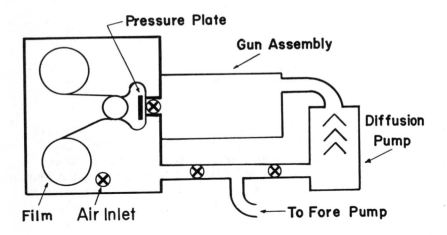

Figure 4. Vacuum System.

allow the gun assembly to be kept at high vacuum during loading, exhaust, recording, and unloading operations.

FILM TRANSPORT SYSTEM

A simplified diagram of the film transport mechanism is shown in Fig. 5. The shuttle mechanism has a film pull down time of about 6 milliseconds with a low acceleration and deceleration cycle. The shuttle cams, drive gear, and sprocket wheel (not shown) are located in the low vacuum chamber while the timing disk, gear reducer for sprocket wheel, and the dc motor are outside the chamber in air.

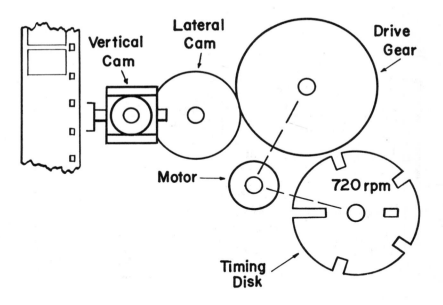

Figure 5. Film Transport System.

THE ELECTRONIC SYSTEM

Figure 6 is a simplified block diagram of the electronic system used in the electron beam television recorder to modulate the electron beam.

Film speed and position is determined by the timing disk on the motor shaft. The motor servo compares the 60 cps output from the timing disk and locks the motor position with respect to the vertical sync derived from the television signal. A 24 cps output from the timing disk initiates the frame exposure by releasing the inhibit gate on a 525 line counter. The output of the counter and the composite blanking derived from the television signal are fed to an OR gate which is part of the blanking amplifier. Thus the electron beam is released from the Faraday

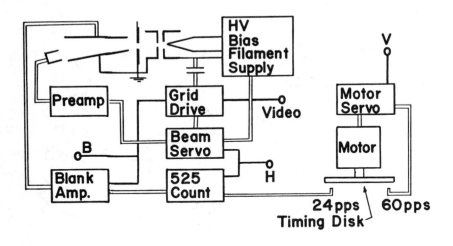

Figure 6. Electronic System.

cage and allowed to expose the film for the duration of one frame only after the timing disk says the film is in position.

The electron beam servo control makes use of the horizontal blanking interval when the beam is available for analysis in the Faraday cage. A reference pulse of approximately one microsecond duration and located in the TV back porch interval is generated and fed to the gun grid. The resultant pulse amplitude from the Faraday cage is compared to a reference voltage and any error voltage readjusts the gun bias to restore the pulse height to its proper amplitude. The reference pulse and video signal are fed to the grid by the grid drive amplifier as is the composite blanking signal to establish the minimum exposure. Monitoring of the Faraday cage after the pre-amp by an oscilloscope allows a measurement of the reference pulse during horizontal blanking and of the video signal during the pull down cycle. With this system, we can now measure directly the actual beam current used for recording. Figure 7 is a simplified block diagram of the remaining electronic components used to shape and position the electron beam.

The stigmator supply has two parts, a variable dc supply and a fixed high frequency ac supply phase locked to the horizontal sync. The dc supply is to reduce the fixed astigmatism caused by gun asymmetry errors. The polarity and amplitude of the dc voltage fed to the parallel bars is adjustable. The high frequency signal is used to provide a type of focus modulation which gives the appearance of breaking the line structure of the recorded raster into a dot like pattern as shown in Fig. 8. This simulated dot pattern is needed in television film chains where the increased vertical resolution in the recording system gives rise to an interference pattern resulting from the rescanned raster lines beating with the recorded raster lines. The oscillator frequency is about 8 mc and is phase locked to the horizontal sync so that the dot like pattern is consistent.

The focus and deflection are both magnetic and conventional transistor supplies are used.

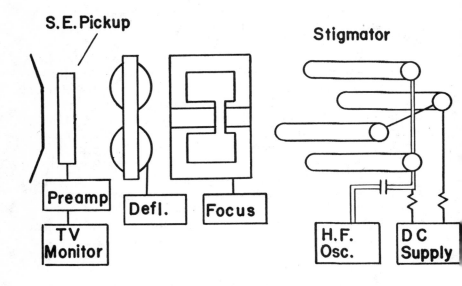

Figure 7. Deflection & Focus.

    The purpose of the secondary emission ring is to aid
in focusing the electron beam. The secondary electrons
emitted from a surface in the target or film plane are
collected by the secondary emission ring, amplified, and
fed to a standard television monitor. With a conductive
target material, generally a spot painted on the beginning
of the film, the variation in the secondary emission presents an electron picture of the surface and beam focus can
be readily adjusted for maximum detail. Once the focus
is set, it need not be readjusted as the focus supply is a
very stable current regulated type.
    A photograph of the laboratory electron beam recorder
is shown in Fig. 9.

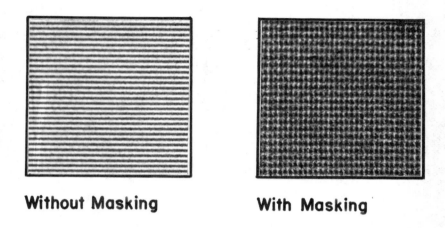

Without Masking   **With Masking**

Figure 8.   Raster Line Masking.

Operation of the electron beam television recorder requires a minimum of mechanical vibration of the film and electron gun. Magnetic and electrostatic effects that deflect the electron beam must also be minimized so that near perfect interlace of the two scanned fields can be achieved.

RESOLUTION

In cathode-ray-tube (kinescope) recorders, the resolution losses are due to the cathode ray tubes phosphor screen, the glass faceplate, the electron beam spot size, the distortions and aberrations associated with focusing and deflecting the beam and the resolution limitations of the photographic film. [1] The phosphor and light optical

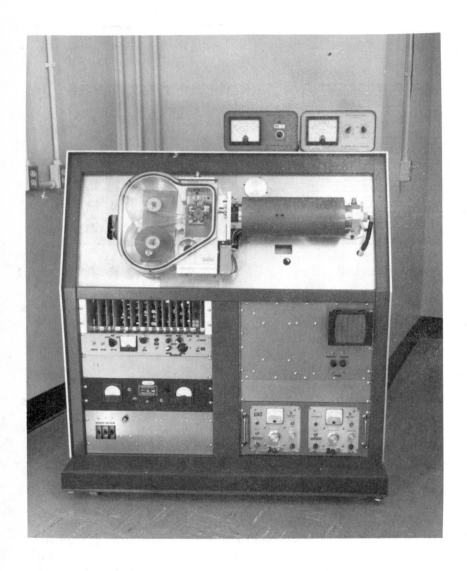

Figure 9.   Electron Beam Television Film Recorder.

limitations are completely avoided with electron recording. In addition, one can optimize the film resolution by
sacrificing sensitivity due to the high energy available.
Any energy source used for TV film recording must be
capable of both high frequency modulation and positioning
(deflection) while contributing sufficient energy to expose
the recording film. At present, the electron beam seems
uniquely capable of this degree of performance, however,
work on laser energy sources may give engineers a choice
in the future. The chief difference between the two systems in Figs. 1 and 2 is the elimination of the following
losses by electron recording:

    1.   Electron to photon conversion in the phosphor.
    2.   The light absorption and scattering in the phosphor.
    3.   The light losses and halations in the glass face-
plate.
    4.   The light losses and distortions in the lens system.
    5.   The overall light losses due to the inefficient
geometry of the system.

Tarnowski and Evans showed that less than 1/300th
of the electron energy in the cathode ray tube of a typical
kinescope recorder ever reaches the film in the form of
light, however, with electron recording, the electron
energy is delivered directly to the film. Therefore, one
can use an extremely slow speed, fine grain film for
direct electron recording; whereas, conventional kine-
scopes require a relatively fast film whose grain structure
noticeably interferes with picture resolution. [3] Figure 10
shows a comparison between the unmodulated TV raster
lines recorded on a conventional kinescope machine using
direct positive kinescope recording film, and the lines
recorded by direct electron exposure on a special 3M fine
grain photographic film designed for electron recording.

PICTURE NOISE

Direct electron exposure, by eliminating the phosphor,
makes possible very low noise TV pictures as shown in
Fig. 11. The noise remaining can be attributed mainly to
the grain of the film and the noise in the electron beam.
Experiments have shown the beam generates mainly shot

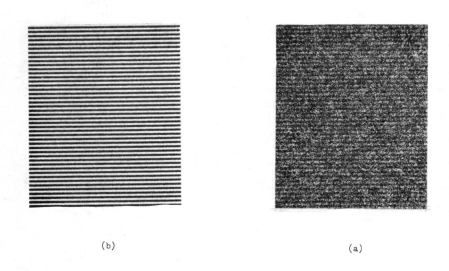

(b)   (a)

Figure 10.   Television Raster Lines Enlarged from a 16 mm
Film Frame. Left: Electron Recording on Special 3M Fine Grain
(Less than 0.1 micron) Electron Recording Film, Right: Kinescope
Recording on Television Recording Film. Line to Line Spacing
in Both Pictures is Approximately 0.00058 inches or 14.7 microns.

noise. It is felt that this noise is low compared to that
contributed by the film grain. K. Hacking has shown that
film grain can be the limiting factor in the signal-to-noise
ratio of the television reproducing system. [4] Experimentally, the grain size of films for electron beam recording can be at least an order of magnitude smaller than that
used for kinescope film (Fig. 10).

Figure 11. Enlarged 16 mm Film Frames Recorded with Television Stairstep. Top, Kinescope Recording on Television Recording Film. Bottom, Direct Electron Recording on Release Positive Film. (Note: Resolution of First and Last TV Lines at Frame Line for Both Systems).

EXPOSURE CONTROL

As engineers in television film recording are well aware, maintaining proper film exposure to insure an adequate gray scale reproduction is a difficult problem. [5] In kinescope recording, the best accepted method has been to read the light output of the cathode ray tube with a light meter. Regrettably, the kinescope beam current cannot be used for establishing exposure conditions, since the phosphor light output is not a linear function of beam current, also, its persistence varies with current, thus

varying the exposure time with varying picture information. Also, the flare of the glass faceplate and camera
lens make exact exposure determination largely a trial
and error procedure even when using the light meter approach.

With electron beam recording, the exposure is directly determined by the beam current density and the
electron penetration for many photographic emulsions. [6]
By proper monitoring of the electron beam current, one
can consistently repeat exposures with the only remaining
variables being film emulsion characteristics and processing. As Evans and Tarnowski demonstrated, [3] films
with radically different sensitivies to light exhibit relatively small sensitivity differences when exposed to electrons. Digby, Firth and Hercock [6] have shown that a
wide range of film emulsions obey the reciprocity law
(D/E curve is linear), when exposed to electrons,
especially when the electrons are of less than 25 kV acceleration. An acceleration of 18 to 20 kV appears to be
a good compromise for a television recorder design,
since it gives sufficient penetration to obtain adequate contrast on suitable emulsions, (Fig. 12) and scattering is
not detrimental for the resolution required.

Since the film emulsion for electron exposure, as
used in television recording, can be relatively simple,
does not vary widely in sensitivity, exhibits little, if any,
reciprocity failure, does not need to be sensitized for the
visible, or near visible region, (nor does the film need
thick emulsion layers, anti-halation layers, etc.), film
and processing variations should be greatly reduced over
conventional kinescope practice. The authors' laboratory
experience with electron beam recording has supported
this assumption.

PICTURE SPLICE

In recording 60 television fields/sec. at a rate of
24 film frames/sec. , half a field between each film frame
is discarded and every other film frame is composed of
two half fields joined within the picture area (Fig. 13).
The meeting point of the two half fields is called the picture

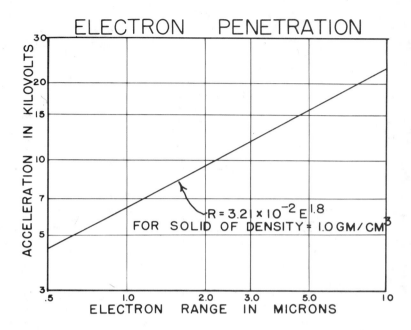

Figure 12.   Electron Penetration, or Range, Versus Acceleration Potential.   The Graph is for a Solid Material with a Density of 1 gm. per cu. cm.   While Silver Halide Emulsions have Higher Densities, Which Yield a Proportionally Shorter Electron Penetration, the Graph Gives Values that Agree Closely with Measured Results in Actual Emulsions. The Electron Scattering Probably Accounts for the Increased Range Over Calculated Values. [6,7]

splice or join-up, and any density discontinuities at this point create a disturbing horizontal line or shading in the picture called "shutter bar". [7, 8]

The four factors generally accepted as creating the problem of uniform exposure at the splice are the light persistence of the phosphor, (Fig. 14) film presensitization, intermittency effects and reciprocity failure, plus the mechanical stability of the recorder and the film during exposure.

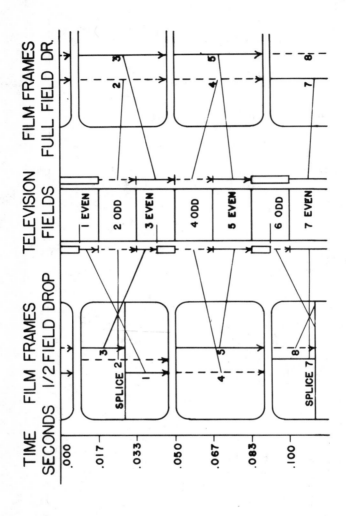

Figure 13. Illustration of the Two Systems Presently Used to Record 60 Interlaced Television Fields Per Second on 24 Film Frames Per Second. Left, Standard Mechanical or Electronic Shutter with 8.3 Milliseconds Pull-Down Time. Right, Vertical Interval Pull-Down with 1.3 Milliseconds Film Pull Down Time (Actual Machines Use about 2 ms. and Sacrifice Some of the Picture Top and Bottom Area).

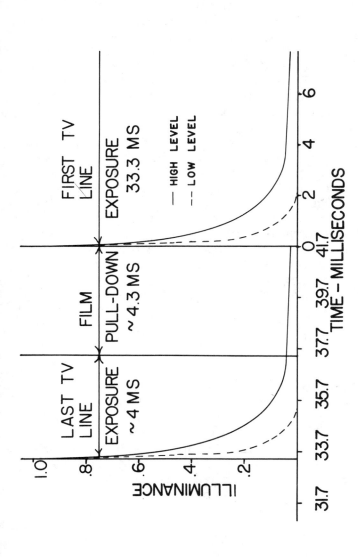

Figure 14. Exposure of First and Last TV Lines in a Film Frame with Light from a Cathode–Ray–Tube Phosphor with Persistence. Shaded Area Under Solid Line Indicates Integrated Exposure at High CRT Light Levels, Area Under Dashed Lines is at Low Levels.

In direct electron exposure, since the phosphor is eliminated, no persistence effect is present, and the exposure is instantaneous. Even the reciprocity failure characteristic of film does not apply for electron exposure. Since the exposure with electrons is instantaneous, almost the entire 8 millisecond vertical blanking interval can be used for film pull-down, permitting a gradual acceleration-deceleration cycle. A long pull-down time greatly alleviates vibration and film stability problems which are so critical in obtaining satisfactory interlacing of the TV fields.

Since electrons have a negative charge associated with them, the photographic film becomes charged during exposure. The charge tends to deflect the oncoming beam, which can cause interlace paring or imperfect join-up, and if large enough, can discharge causing fogging of the film. If the film incorporates a ground plane, such as a thin semi-transparent metallic film, the charge is immobilized and does not give difficulty. Alternatively, the film can be made somewhat conductive (less than 10^8 ohms/sq.) to rapidly dissipate the charge, or conductive surfaces can be placed near the film in the recorder to form a capacitor with the charge until it has time to dissipate. All of the above approaches have proved effective.

SUMMARY

From both theoretical and practical considerations, electron exposure, while adding the complications of vacuum operation and electrostatic charging of the film avoids many of the factors limiting quality in present cathode-ray tube film recorders, and shows promise of producing films with considerably improved resolution, reduced graininess, and greater consistency of results. An electron beam recorder has been developed which demonstrates these capabilities.

ACKNOWLEDGMENTS

The authors' are indebted to Mr. Richard D. Ebbinga and David R. Holdaway for the many contributions they have many in the development of this recorder.

REFERENCES

1. P. J. Herbst, R. O. Drew and J. M. Braumbaugh, "Factors Affecting the Quality of Kinerecording", Journal SMPTE, 58: 85-104, February 1952.
2. Pierre Mertz and Frank Gray, "A Theory of Scanning and Its Relation to the Characteristics of the Transmitted Signal in Telephotography and Television", The Bell System Technical Journal, Vol. XIII, 1934, p. 500.
3. A. A. Tarnowski and C. H. Evans, "Photographic Data Recording by Direct Exposure with Electrons", Journal SMPTE, 71: No. 10, 765-768, October 1962.
4. K. Hacking, "An Analysis of Film Granularity in Television Reproduction", Journal SMPTE, 73: No. 12, 1015-1029, December 1964.
5. Rodger J. Ross, "Film in Television", Journal SMPTE, 67: No. 6, 374-378, June 1958.
6. N. Digby, K. Firth and R. J. Hercock, "The Photographic Effect of Medium Energy Electrons", The Journal of Photographic Science, Vol. 1, 1953, p. 194.
7. F. N. Gillette, "The Picture Splice as a Problem of Video Recording", Journal SMPTE, 58: No. 3, 242-255, September 1949.
8. C. H. Evans, "Shutter-Bar in Television Film Recording", Journal SMPTE 70: No. 11, 898-903, November 1961.

Photographic Development of Electron and Ion Beam and U.V. Light Recordings with Preferential Metal Deposition

H. G. Wehe

Bell Telephone Laboratories
Murray Hill, New Jersey

An alternative long title gives the essence of the matter in one sentence. This title is - "Experimental Use of an Electron Beam, Ion Beam, U. V. Light, Spark & Glow Discharges for Rapid Photographic Recording, Printout, and Copying on Light Insensitive Materials Using Preferential Metal Deposition, and Requiring No Silver, No Powders and No Wet Chemical Development. "

The work I am about to describe was a brief recording feasibility study made in 1948 at Bell Telephone Laboratories at Murray Hill, New Jersey. It has been only partially reported to date with part still classified as "Company Private. "

In substance, and for the most part, an electron beam was modulated and scanned under the control of either a T. V. camera or of other electronic input circuits. The beam 'wrote' in vacuum on various plastics leaving an invisible record which was either immediately or subsequently revealed by preferential metal deposition. Thus the 'beam' modified the accommodation or sticking coefficient of the recipient for subsequent metal deposition. Another way of expressing this is to say that the 'beam' at times enhanced and at times retarded nucleation of the metal deposition.

I have with me for your examination sample recordings which have been stored in an ordinary filing cabinet for over seventeen years with no noticeable deterioration. Also available for your examination is a sample showing strong brilliant interference colors sometimes produced

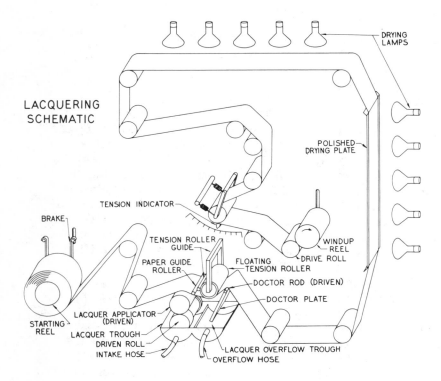

Figure 1. Lacquering Schematic.

Figure 2. Author With Apparatus for Preferential Metal Deposition.

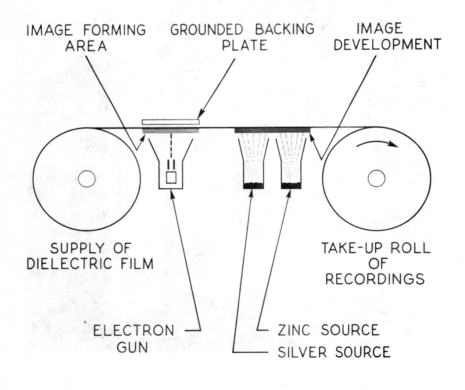

Figure 3.   Schematic of Electron Beam Recording.

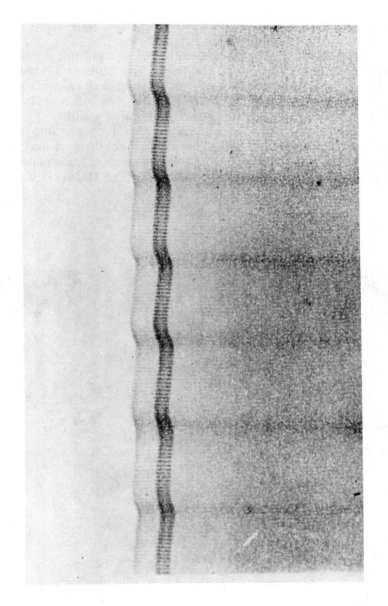

Figure 4. Electron Beam Recording of 2,000 Cycle Tone with 60 Cycle Ripple.

by metal deposition. I am sure many of you are acquainted with such deposits. This sample was not produced under electron beam control which has been used so far to obtain only metallic appearing deposits, blackish deposits, and pastel colored deposits.

Before describing processes and equipment, I wish to express a hope that needs for these processes have developed sufficiently that now research and development can again proceed rapidly. There is much yet to be learned in this interesting and potentially valuable field.

The equipment used was of the ordinary garden variety now found in many laboratories. In describing it and the results obtained, there will be some unavoidable repetition of previously published information. (See References.)

Figure 5.   Simultaneous Record of Both Electron Beam 'A' and and Ion Bean 'B'.

The roller coating lacquering equipment was small enough to fit in a laboratory hood. (Fig. 1.) Note the film supply, the lacquer applicator and doctoring, drying lamps, film windup, etc. Various lacquers were 'roller coated' on the surface of thin Kraft capacitor paper 2-3/4" wide for use in the preparation of experimental metallized paper capacitors. Since this material was readily available, it mainly was utilized as the recipient of the electron beam and other recordings revealed with preferential metal deposition.

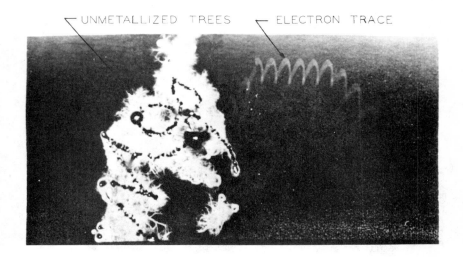

Figure 6. Spark Writing from Magnesium Wire on Plastic.

The vacuum equipment for deposition of metals was pumped to 10^{-4} to 10^{-5} torr with oil diffusion pumps supported by mechanical pumps. In the chamber was equipment for transporting lacquered capacitor paper at speeds ranging from 40 to 800 feet per minute. (Fig. 2.) Incidentally the speaker is shown as he appeared about twenty years ago.

An electron gun (either electrostatic or electromagnetic) was cut from a cathode ray tube and placed in the chamber usually preceding the location of resistance heated metal vaporizers. (Fig. 3.)

Figure 7. Spark Writing from Tin Wire on Plastic.

Glow discharge from a wire was attained with the aid of a few hundred volts and a poor vacuum.   UV light was provided with a lamp used for examining minerals.   Spark writing was done with a tesla coil type of leak detector using various wire tips.   Small amounts of hydrogen and of oxygen were introduced into the vacuum chamber to partially control the residual atmosphere.   Infra red light, soft x-rays, and alpha particles were also tried for recording purposes.   Magnets were used in an attempt to deflect spontaneous electrostatic discharges in the vacuum chamber.   The lacquer surfaces were modified for reception of vaporized metal by rubbing and by the addition of liquid chemicals.

Figure 8.   Actinic Light Recording on Plastic.

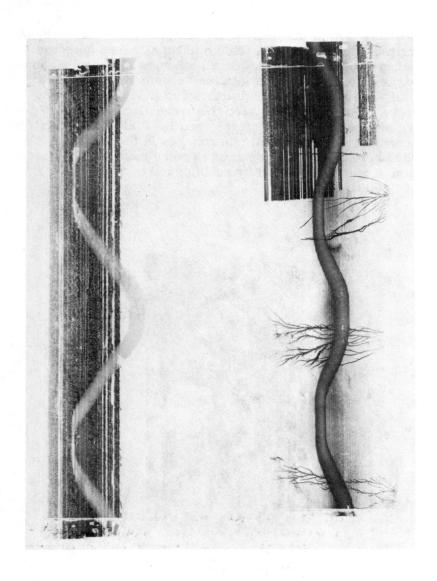

Figure 9. Effect of Rubbing Plastic.

With this equipment, certain feasibilities were demonstrated:

1. An electron beam at 400 to 700 V with about a milliampere of current focused to approximately a five mil spot was easily able to control both the position and amount of subsequent metal deposit with a single pass of the beam scanning at a linear rate of 6,000 inches per second.   This is equivalent to about an 8-1/2" by 11" page of printing and pictures per second with 70-line-per-inch resolution or newspaper picture quality. (Fig. 4.) The dark border indicates a capability of megacycle modulation.   In all the 'recording' illustrations which are positive photographic prints from camera negatives

Figure 10.   Effect of Liquid Chemicals Applied to Plastic.

made with light transmitted through the metallized record, black means metal deposit, gray means less metal, and white shows the absence of metal deposit.

    2.   An ion beam in vacuum likewise was revealed with vacuum deposits of a fractional monolayer of silver (or of copper or of molybdenum) followed by several hundred Å of zinc (or cadmium). (Fig. 5.) Note that the ion beam is deflected to a lesser degree and in the opposite direction to that of a simultaneously recorded electron beam.   This is due to positive polarity and the greater mass of the ions.   Also in this instance, the ion beam's recorded path repelled the developing metal deposits.

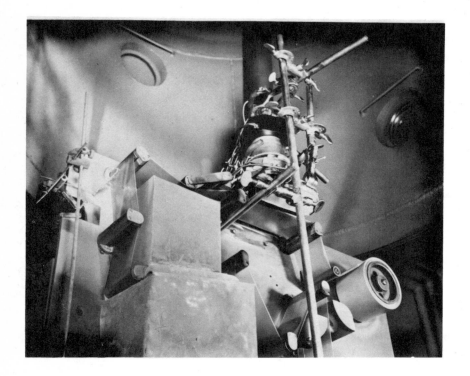

Figure 11.   Setup for Recording Television Test Signal.

3. Spark writing with a magnesium tip (on tesla coil) is shown in Fig. 6.   The result of using a tin tip is shown in Fig. 7.   Notice that tin gave a smoother recording light on a dark background.

4. Actinic light applied by flood lighting through a mask enhanced the subsequent metal deposition.   (Fig. 8.) The location of holes in the metal mask can be seen.

5. Rubbing a lacquer surface (as by a roller which stuck instead of revolving freely) greatly enhanced subsequent metal deposition.   (Fig. 9.)   Traces of metal may have been rubbed from the roller, the rubbing may have disturbed an adsorbed gas film, or perhaps generated surface charges.

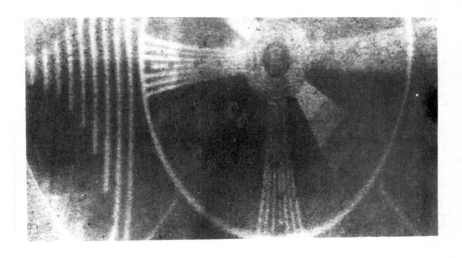

Figure 12.   Electron Beam Recorded Television Test Signal.

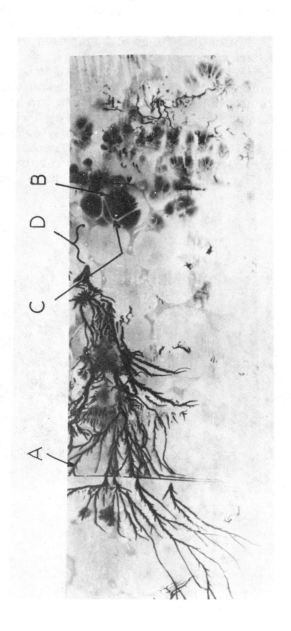

Figure 13.   Both Positive and Negative Trees on Same Polyethylene Terephthalate Plastic Strip.

6. Some liquid chemicals applied to the lacquer surfaces decreased subsequent metal deposits. The chemicals were streaked across the plastic with a small brush.
The exact nature of the chemicals is still considered
'Company Private'. (Fig. 10.) The electron beam path
is the wavy light trace with a dark edge, the 'waves' being
produced by hand twisting a potentiometer at four or five
cycles per second to move the impinging electron beam
back and forth as the lacquered paper moves forward.

7. A T. V. picture was transmitted from one building
to another and electron beam recorded. Figure 11 shows
the mounting of the electromagnetically controlled gun,
and Fig. 12 shows the T. V. test image recorded. The
picture was sent by my colleagues Messrs. F. W.
Reynolds and G. R. Stilwell, now both retired from Bell
Telephone Laboratories.

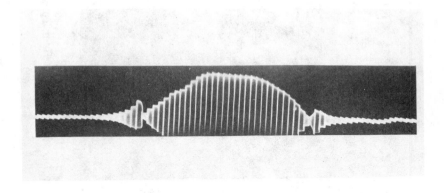

Figure 14. Recording on Cellulose Nitrate Lacquer on Kraft
Capacitor Paper.

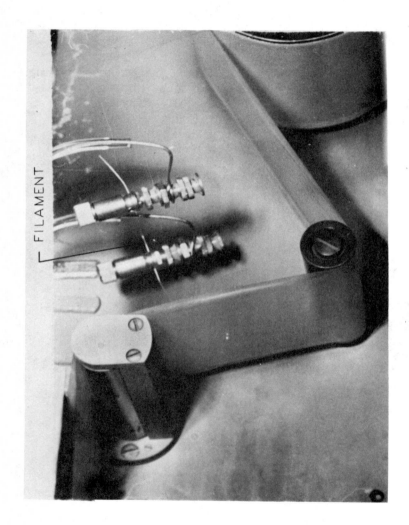

Figure 15.   Placement of Bent Tungsten Filament.

8.   Preferential metal deposition may be useful in studying the surfaces of polyesters.   Figure 13 shows both positive and negative Lichtenberg trees with both enhanced by the metals.   This indicates a chemical rather than a charge effect of the electrostatic discharges.   Note the unmetallized potential hollow at the base of the negative Lichtenberg discharge paths.   The negative paths are short straight lines instead of the longer branching positive 'trees'.

Also are revealed the outlines of surface crystals about one-half an inch in diameter (only a few atom layers thick) which is some 10, 000 times larger than might be expected with such thin films.

Figure 16.   Herringbone Record from Bent Tungsten Filament.

Since polyesters already carry an invisible recording of electrostatic discharge patterns due to static discharge during rereeling, and since these patterns are revealed with the preferential metal deposition, it is fortunate that my first attempts at electron beam recording did not use this material. Instead, fresh lacquer surfaces were used free of recordings until intentional records were made, the experiment being successful at the first attempt.

9. Cellulose, cellulose acetate, cellulose acetate butyrate, polystyrene, and polyesters gave enhanced metallization on the electron beam path.

10. Cellulose nitrate (Fig. 14) showed prohibition of metal deposits on the beam path.

11. A bent tungsten filament shown in Fig. 15 gave a herringbone recording shown in Fig. 16. This appears to consist of multiple gas focused images of the filament. The alternating dark, gray and white pattern is believed to be due to an AC ripple swinging the 400 V negative potential of the filament alternately above and below the crossover voltage of secondary electron emission from the plastic. Perhaps preferential metal deposition is a new tool for studying secondary electron emissions.

12. Residual hydrogen retarded and residual oxygen enhanced metal deposition. Infra red light, soft x-rays, and alpha particles applied at the intensities used had no visible effect on subsequent metallization.

13. Metal deposits atom by atom seem capable of finer grain recording than is possible with either dry powder or wet chemical development, neither of which is needed in this process. Also no probing electron beam is needed for readout of stored information.

14. The recordings on an inexpensive recipient are permanent (at least seventeen year life demonstrated) and hence are not subject to accidential erasure.

In summary, electron beams, ion beams, U. V. light, glow discharges and spark writing, chemicals including gases, and mechanical abrasion have been used to modify the sticking coefficient of plastics for the reception of metals vaporized in vacuum to give controlled nucleation for preferential metal deposition. This offers an interesting and potentially profitable procedure for recording outputs from T. V. cameras, from computers and data phones, from copy machines, etc. Mr. R. I. James of A. T. & T. recently at an IEEE convention meeting in New York City said that transmission of business data was the sleeping giant of the communications industry. This method of recording and developing may aid in awakening the giant, especially if color recording should prove to be readily amenable to control.

During the recess, the samples mentioned will be available for examination.

ACKNOWLEDGMENT

I wish to add a word of appreciation to my associates who have been of great assistance in the physical and chemical interpretations of the data reported. Among the most helpful have been Messrs. D. A. McLean, G. T. Kohman, H. E. Mendenhall, L. E. Cheesman, C. J. Calbick, J. B. Johnson, G. R. Stilwell, F. W. Reynolds, E. F. Kingsbury, A. G. Jensen, K. B. McAfee, E. T. Burton, Wm. McMahon, G. Price, B. S. Biggs, and W. O. Baker.

Figures 4, 12, 14 and 16 (with their description) have been reprinted with the permission of Pergamon Press, Inc.

REFERENCES

1. Wehe, H. G. , U. S. Patent No. 2, 883, 257 of 4/21/59, "Electron Beam Recording", assigned to Bell Telephone Laboratories.
2. Wehe, H. G. , "Electron Beam Recording", Bell Telephone Systems Monograph No. 3576 reprinted from "1958 Fifth National Vacuum Symposium on Vacuum Technology Transactions, " pp. 242-246.
3. Wehe, H. G. , "Electron Beam Tape Recording", A Review published in "Proceedings Third Symposium on Electron Beam Technology, " March 23-24, 1961, Boston, Mass. , pp. 249-268; R. Bakish, Editor.

4. Wehe, H. G. , "Electron Beam Control of Nucleation of Thin Films, " Presented (by Invitation) at the Fall Meeting of Vacuum Metallizers Association, September 16, 1965, Barbizon Plaza Hotel, New York City, (unpublished).

5. Wehe, H. G. , "Experimental Thin Film Nucleation Control Methods and Results", Abstract publ. p. 276 in "Journal of Vacuum Science and Technology" September-October, 1965. Paper presented September 29, 1965, at 12th National Vacuum Symposium at Statler Hilton Hotel, New York City, (unpublished).

6. Wehe, H. G. , U. S. Patent No. 2, 503, 571 of April 11, 1950, "Apparatus for Coating Surfaces by Thermal Vaporization at Atmospheric Pressure. " Assigned to Bell Telephone Laboratories.

7. Glenn, Wm. E. , "Recording Information by Electron Beams", Chap. 14 in "Introduction of Electron Beam Technology", 1962, R. Bakish, Editor. J. Wiley & Sons N. Y.

8. Neher, B. W. , U. S. Patent No. 3, 127, 331 of March 31, 1964, "Reverse Current Electrolytic Process. "

9. Kaspaul, A. F. & Erika, E. , U. S. Patent No. 3, 140, 143 of July 7, 1964, "Information Recording".

10. Caswell, H. L. and Budo, Y. , "Formation of Thin Film Circuits Using Preferential Nucleation", Solid State Electronics, Pergamon Press, 1965, Vol. 8, pp. 479-483.

11. Poppa, H. R. , "Progress in the Continuous Observation of Thin Film Nucleation and Growth Processes by Electron Microscopy", Jnl. Vac. Sci. & Tech. , Vol. 2, No. 1 January-February 1965, pp. 42-48.

12. Hellman, C. S. , "Synoptic Compilation of Thin Film Technology Including Ion and Electron Physics", 1962, 541. 375, H47.

13. Wood, E. A. , "Vocabulary of Surface Crystallography", Bell Systems Monograph No. 4783, Reprinted from Jnl. Applied Physics, Vol. 35, pp. 1306-1312, April 1964.

14. Abstracts on "Nucleation, Growth & Structure of Thin Films", (7 invited and 8 contributed papers), Jnl. of Vacuum Science & Technology, September-October, 1965, pp. 271, 272, 275 to 277.

15. "Electron Beams in Recording & Information Storage", Sec. III of First International Conference on Electron & Ion Beam Science & Technology, 1964, R. Bakish, Editor.
16. Dubbe, R. F. and Reed, E., "Television Recording Using Direct Electron Exposure",
17. Germer, L. H., et al, "Low Energy Electron Diffraction", Bell System Monograph, No. 4364.
18. Gobelli, G. W., Lander, J. J., and Morrison, J., "Low Energy Diffraction Study of the Adsorption of Cesium on the (111) Surface of Silicon", Jnl. Applied Physics, Vol. 37, No. 1, pp. 203-206, January 1966.
19. Calbick, C. J., "Interaction of Electron Beams with Thin Films", "Physics of Thin Films", Vol. 2, 1964, Academic Press, New York.
20. Lawless, K. R., "The Growth and Structure of Electrodeposited Films", Jnl. Vac. Sci. & Techn., Vol. 2, No. 1, January-February, 1965, pp. 24-34.
21. Adamsky, R. F., "Nucleation and Initial Growth of Single Crystal Films", Amer. Vac. Soc. 11th Nat'l. Vac. Symposium, 9/30/64, Chicago, Ill.
22. Bauer, E., and Turner, G., "The Influence of Gases on the Growth and Structure of Films", Am. Vac. Soc. 11th Nat'l. Vac. Symposium, September 30, 1964, Chicago, Ill.
23. Vook, R. W. and Witt, F., "Structure and Annealing Behavior of Metal Films Deposited Near 80°K", Am. Vac. Soc. 11th National Vacuum Symposium, September 30, 1964, Chicago, Ill.
24. Zeheb, D., Kreitzer, N. H., and Cullum, D. G., "Exploratory Fabrication Produced with an Electron-Beam Gun System", Second International Conference on Electron & Ion Beam Science and Technology, 4/17-20/66, New York City, R. Bakish, Editor.
25. Dove, J. F., "The Dove Data Storage and Retrieval System", Second International Conference on Electron & Ion Beam Science and Technology, 4/17-20/66, New York City, R. Bakish, Editor.
26. Jensen, A. S. and Limansky, I., "Information Density in Electrostatic Storage", Second International Conference on Electron & Ion Beam Science and Technology, 4/17-20/66, New York City, R. Bakish, Editor.

27. Barrekette, E. S. and Duffy, J. A. , "Electron Beam Disc Writer", Second Int. Conf. on Electron & Ion Beam Sci. & Tech. , 4/17-20/66, New York City, R. Bakish, Editor.
28. Mader, S. , "Metastable Alloy Films", Jnl. Vac. Sci. & Tech. , Vol. 2, No. 1 January-February, 1965, pp. 35-41.
29. Arntz, F. , and Chernow, F. , "Optical and Structural Properties of Oxidized Titanium Films", Jnl. Vac. Sci. & Tech. , Vol. 2, No. 1, January-February, 1965, pp. 20-23.
30. Ehrlich, Gert. , "Adsorption and Surface Structure", Chapt. 7 from "Metal Surfaces, Structures, Energetics and Kinetics", Proc. ASM-AIME Seminar, October 1962. Publ. by ASM, Metals Park, Ohio, (1963).
31. Rhodin, T. N. and Walton, D. , "Nucleation & Growth Processes on Solid Surfaces", Chapt. 8 from "Metal Surfaces, Structures, Energetics and Kinetics", Proc. ASM-AIME Seminar, October 1962; publ. by ASM, Metals Park, Ohio (1963).
32. "Cathode Irradiation Causes Profound Changes in Cellulose", Cellulose Chemistry, Vol. 30, No. 15, p. 1515, April 14, 1952.
33. Cross, B. , "Static Charges on Dielectrics", British Journal of Chemical Physics, Vol. 17, No. 10, pp. 866-872, October 1949.
34. Frankenburg, W. G. (Editor), "Advances in Catalysis", Vol. III, 1951; Academic Press, Inc. , New York City, p. 132.
35. Cockcroft, J. D. , "Condensations of Molecular Streams on Surfaces", Proc. Royal Soc. of London, A119, 1928, p. 293.
36. British Patent No. 449824 on Electrography.
37. Loeb, L. B. , "The Basic Mechanisms of Static Electrification", Science, December 7, 1945, p. 573.
38. Woodside, F. W. , "An Investigation of Ion Defocusing of Ribbon Electron Beams", Thesis, 1963, North Carolina State College, Raleigh, North Carolina.
39. Selenyi, U. S. Patent No. 2,143,214, January 10, 1939.

40. Carlson, U. S. Patent No. 2, 221, 776, November 19, 1940.
41. Carlson, U. S. Patent No. 2, 551, 582, May 8, 1951.
42. French Patent No. 817, 447, May 24, 1937.
43. McLean, D. A. and Wehe, H. G. , U. S. Patent No. 2, 709, 663, May 31, 1955, "Electrical Capacitors", Assigned to Bell Telephone Laboratories.
44. McLean, D. A. and Wehe, H. G. , U. S. Patent No. 2, 754, 230, July 10, 1956, "Method of Making Electrical Capacitors", Assigned to Bell Telephone Laboratories.
45. Behrndt, K. H. , "Limitations of Nucleation Theories", 1966, (unpublished).

ELECRON BEAMS IN
MICRO ELECTRONICS

Electron Beams in Micro Electronics

Much has been done in this area of electron beam applications and considerable background literature is at the disposal of those interested in entering the field. For those who wish additional information beyond the references [1-10] given below the proceedings of the vacuum society meetings as well as those of the international congresses on electron microscopy and the IEEE session on materials and devices should be consulted.

The papers in this section of the text endeavor to cover the main domains which find consequential use of electron beams for micro electronics related tasks. Possibilities with the two earliest applications of electron beams in electronics related tasks, namely their use for evaporation and for thermal machining are well demonstrated as underlying work tools in an automated system for resistor manufacture. This can be considered as a type of system presently finding use in industry. It is also certain that we will see considerable multiplication of such systems. The field of electron beam induced polymerization and electron stimulated chemical reaction are well illustrated by papers discussing this growing area of activities. To be sure these papers are only a sample of considerable activities. Work on carrier combinations in solid state devices under bombardment and correlation with theoretical consideration continues to be an important device performance related task and a paper on this subject indicates the type of activities that are involved.

One of the subjects likely to assume increasingly greater importance here is the utilization of secondary emission for control of material and devices. This approach which is intimately related to the field of scanning microscopy is joining the later which is rapidly becoming one of the sin qua non instrumental approaches for sophisticated quality control of integrated circuitry.

In general it can be said that electron beams in their many ramifications and areas of applications related to electronic and micro electronics devices certainly offer a most exciting growth once the many problems are resolved.

REFERENCES

1. Proc. 1st Symp. Electron Beam Technology, J. Hetherington, (Ed), Boston, Mass, 1959.
2. Proc. Symp. on Electron Bombardment Floating Zone Melting, Serl, Baldock, England, 1959.
3. Proc. 2nd Symp. Electron Beam Techn. , R. Bakish, (Ed), Boston, Mass, 1960.
4. Proc. 3rd Symp. Electron Beam Techn. , R. Bakish, (Ed), Boston, Mass, 1961.
5. Proc. 4th Symp. Electron Beam Techn. , R. Bakish, (Ed), Boston, Mass, 1962.
6. Proc. 5th Symp. Electron Beam Techn. , J. Morley (Ed), Boston, Mass, 1963.
7. Proc. 6th Symp. Electron Beam Techn. , J. Morley, (Ed), Boston, Mass, 1964.
8. Proc. of a Symposium on Electron and Laser Beams, El Kareh, (Ed), University Park, Pa. 1965.
9. Introduction to Electron Beam Technology, R. Bakish, (Ed), J. Wiley & Sons, New York, 1962.
10. Handbook of Electron Beam Welding, R. Bakish and S. S. White, J. Wiley & Sons, New York, 1964.
11. Proc. 1st. Int. Conf. on Electron and Ion Beams in Science and Technology. R. Bakish (Ed), J. Wiley and Sons, N. Y. (1965).

(Ed)

A New Electron Beam Processing Plant for Thin Film Resistors with a Fundamental Equipment of the 80kV-Type

M. v. Ardenne*, U. Heisig*, S. Panzer** and O. Thieme**

Research Institute Manfred von Ardenne*,
Dresden-Weiber Hirsch and
VEB Keramische Werke**, Hermsdorf
East Germany

INTRODUCTION

With the comprehensive development of electron beam equipment for thermal micro-machining and e-b welding pushed forward in 1960, it was intended to make laboratory apparatus available which could be universally employed on a broad scale. Numerous technological studies regarding application of the e-b machining technique for various jobs were undertaken since then with these laboratory apparatus. Consistent with the probing character of these examinations high demands were made of the apparatus themselves with respect to variation of such essential parameters as accelerating voltage, beam current, spot diameter etc. Work-piece adapted equipment, on the other hand, was merely improvised and could be utilized only for small lot machining, without consideration of economy.

For the industrial application of thermal e-b machining the high economy utilization of the method is an essential factor, aside of the quality advances. This is a condition which materially restricts the scope of machining work that will be of interest for industry. One of the applications is the manufacture of electronic components where thin-film machining and e-b welding is of special significance.

THE FORERUNNER OF THE NEW AUTOMATIC PROCESSING PLANT

Previous development work in our Institute has already dealt with the 150 kV laboratory setup for e-b machining and trimming plane thin-film resistor combinations [1]. It has been the intent of this work to study possibilities for automating the e-b trimming of thin-film resistors. Ceramic substrate members of 10 mm x 15 mm were used which had been uniformly coated with a NiCr film having sheet resistance of 200 Ohms per square. Machining with an electron beam was utilized to create tracks in the film for up to three individual resistors which were trimmed to specified values. In consideration of low thermal stress of the substrate accelerating voltages of 25 to 50 kV were employed. At a working speed of about 1 m/sec., only beam currents ranging from 50 to 100 μA were necessary on the workpiece. These studies showed the feasibility of producing close-tolerance resistor combinations under industrial conditions. An example of the probability of obtaining resistors with a specific tolerance is shown for a double-resistor combination on Table I [2].

During the course of this study principally solutions were found for the economical utilization of the suggested method. Consequently the substrate could be machined with a cycling time of 2.4 seconds, which was attainable particularly by using quasi-continuous operating vacuum pressure drop systems and programmed processing. The high working speed of the apparatus could be employed to advantage only in combination with a rapidly operating digital programming set for the deflection and time control of the electron beam.

FUNDAMENTAL EQUIPMENT OF THE NEW AUTOMATIC TRIMMING PLANT

The new automatic electron beam trimming plant suitable to be industrially utilized grew out of the experiences and results obtained during work with the laboratory apparatus. With the improved version it was intended to

Table I.

deviation from mean value	$0\cdots\pm0,1$		$0\cdots\pm0,2$		$0\cdots\pm0,5$		$0\cdots\pm1$		$0\cdots\pm2$		%
rated value	8.2	20	8.2	20	8.2	20	8.2	20	8.2	20	kΩ
percentage	26	7.3	49	23	84	53	97	86	99	100	%

create an electron gun with parameters adapted to micro-machining of thin films, and to establish a clear separa-tion of the completed plant into the fundamental Equip-ment for e-b machining and its supplementary equipment, which had to be tailored to the job and adapted to the work-piece.

For the laboratory apparatus we used an electron gun operating with an accelerating voltage adjustable to 150 kV. This resulted in a relatively high outlay, par-ticularly for the associated high-tension equipment, aside of the electron gun. Constructional volume can be re-duced materially when an electron gun is used with oper-ating parameters specially adapted to thin-film processing, where an accelerating voltage of 20 to 40 kV and beam currents up to 500 µA are adequate. An electron gun

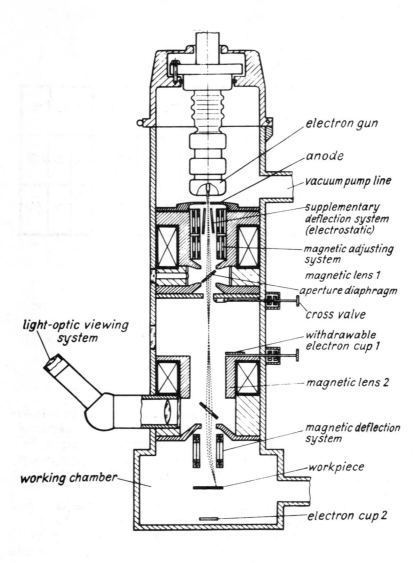

Figure 1.

operating with accelerating voltages up to 80 kV and beam currents up to about 2 mA can be set up without materially increasing the necessary outlay. This has the advantage to considerably extend the application of the plant, where other micro machining and welding jobs can be economically handled with the 80 kV gun.

For the schematic picturization of the new 80 kV electron gun design Fig. 1 is included. The basic physical concept of the two-lens arrangement has been incorporated here also, as it was used for our other apparatus [3, 4]. Among the special features of the electron gun must be mentioned the purely electro-magnetic adjusting system. This provides for centering the electron beam on the aperture diaphragm and to deflect it for the desired inclination around its centre for proper adjusting on the centre of the second lens system, independently of each other. Maximum current through the aperture diaphragm and maximum power density directed on the working plane serve as focusing criteria.

Directly below the anode of the gun an electrostatic deflection system is incorporated which permits blocking and releasing the electron beam with a time constant of 1 μs. With the aid of this deflection system the time control of the beam on the workpiece is handled. Compared to the conventional operation by the control electrode of the gun, this offers the advantage that no short-time changes of the accelerating voltage are caused by the release of the electron beam.

To permit the use of beam deflection machining on conventional substrates of sizes up to about 20 mm x 30 mm in thin-film processing, the lens no. 2 has been designed for an image distance of 175 mm. A magnetic crossed deflection system with astigmatic correction is employed to establish the desired working face. The deflection system is suitable for a cut-off frequency of 6 kc/s.

Observation of the complete working area in direction of the beam is possible by an amplifying stereoscopic light-optical viewer. Using a restricted field of view an amplification of up to about 40-fold can be obtained. As the only light-optical component in the electron gun a plane

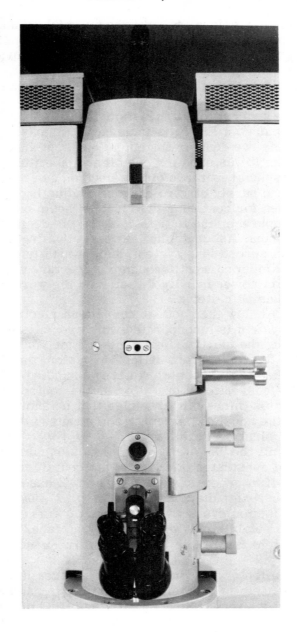

Figure 2. Electron Gun of the 80 kV - 200 W-Type.

surface mirror is arranged on the plane of the pole piece gap of the second lens. It serves to deflect the light beam out of the gun.

In addition to the cross-valve provided for the generally used separation of the electron gun from the working chamber, the gun can also be evacuated separately with the aid of the provided high-vacuum pump set.

Construction of the 80 kV electron gun is illustrated in Fig. 2.

The fundamental equipment includes the electron gun, the vacuum apparatus and the electronic system required for its operation. Current supply for the lens and for the adjusting system, as well as the accelerating voltage are electronically stabilized, with special attention given to long-time stability. Thus, for the accelerating voltage, for example, a stability of 2×10^{-4} is obtained for a period of 30 minutes. In view of the fact of the strong dependability of the machining result on beam current stability, however, this current is also electronically stabilized to a preset desired value in the interest of a high repeatability working conditions of subsequent machined members.

SUPPLEMENTARY EQUIPMENT FOR MACHINING AND TRIMMING RESISTOR COMBINATIONS ON SIZE 10 MM X 15 MM SUBSTRATES

Fundamental equipment for the e-b processing is completed to an automatic plant by the use of special workpiece adapted supplementary equipments. This consists of feed and delivery magazines each holding 720 substrates, the conveying system where transfer blocks travel around a rectangular track, the pressure-drop systems, the working chamber and the specially designed digital programming control unit. This equipment has been used already with previously described laboratory apparatus. Present construction of the mechanical part of these supplements is illustrated in Fig. 3. In deviation of the preceding development, after the substrate is delivered, out of the working chamber the resistors are again measured in normal atmospheric conditions with subsequent

Figure 3. View of the Working Chamber and the Pressure Drop
Stages for the Quasi-Continuous Convey of the Substrates, Including the Mechanical Equipment for Feeding, Conveying, Sorting
to Tolerance Classification and Delivery of the Substrates.

sorting to tolerance classification. During trimming work of the individual resistors the substrate is already connected to the measuring circuits through a respective set of contacts. Repeat inspection seemed necessary because of the small amount of aging the machined films are subject to when delivered into normal atmospheric conditions. This repeat inspection permits the detection of any occurring aging processes, which can be compensated by a suitable adjustment of the reference resistors incorporated in the first testing circuit.

The complete automatic electron beam machining and trimming plant is shown in Fig. 4. It can handle the machining and trimming selectively of single resistors,

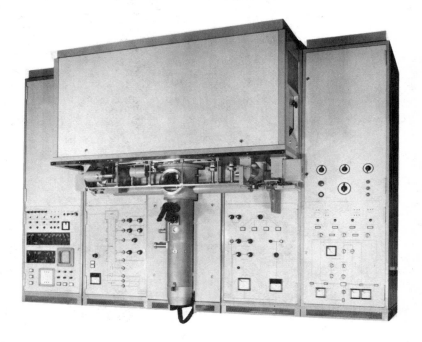

Figure 4. Automatic Electron Beam Processing and Trimming Plant for Plane Thin-Film Resistor Combinations, Consisting of the 80 kV - 200 W Fundamental Equipment and the Supplements for Program Controlled Processing.

double resistors and triple resistor combinations on plane
substrate members of 10 mm x 15 mm.   Consistent with
the cycling time of 2. 4 seconds the automatic plant has
an output of 1, 500 substrates per hour.

When processing NiCr resistor combinations on ceramic substrates the results obtainable with the automatic
plant generally coincide with the data compiled in Table I.
The example of a double-resistor processed in the automatic plant is shown in Fig. 5.

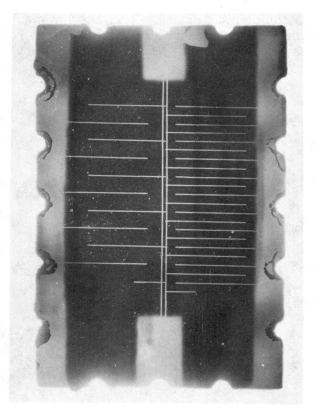

Figure 5. Example of a Resistors Combination Obtained with
the Automatic Plant on a 10 mm x 15 mm Ceramic Substrate
Resistance Values R_1 = 8, 2 kohms R_2 = 20 kohms.

POSSIBILITIES FOR PROCESSING THIN-FILM CIRCUITS

While construction of the supplementary equipment has been designed specially for the automatic processing of resistor combination on 10 mm x 15 mm substrates, the electron gun has from the start been created for processing substrates of sizes up to 20 mm x 30 mm. It was the intent to provide facilities for processing passive thin-film circuits with subsequent development, and using the fundamental equipment of the described automatic setup for the purpose. Suitable adapted supplementary equipment, relating specially to the vacuum pressure drop systems, to handle the larger substrate and the

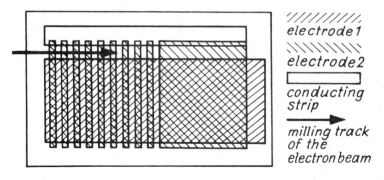

electrode1

electrode2

conducting strip

milling track of the electron beam

Figure 6.

respective programmed control unit are being developed.
For the latter, the principle of the digital control of the
deflection currents is retained.   Compared to the present
unit, the storage volume is extended to 1,024 memory
elements with 32 bits each, while the number of spots
on the working face will amount to $1,6 \cdot 10^7$ [5].   This
will enable the handling of any complicated circuit configuration.

In producing a passive thin-film circuit, our technology envisions the processing of the required resistors
by e-b meandering and trimming.   This will be followed
by the stepwise trimming of the desired capacitors
through removing sections from one of the electrodes
with the electron beam, using a comb-shaped electrode.
An electrode design suitable for e-b trimming is illustrated in Fig. 6.   This trimming technique avoids the
difficult problem of machining the top layer of a multilayer arrangement.

The test sample of an $Al-SiO_2$-Al capacitor trimmed
by an electron beam is shown in Fig. 7.   After vapor
deposition, the basic electrode has been e-b machined
to comb shape first.   This was followed by the deposition
of the SiO_2 film and of the cover electrode layer, and
final trimming handled by removing some portions of
the basic electrode.   Comb-shaped electrodes can
naturally be obtained also by deposition with the aid of
a mask.

Processability of the electrode and resistor materials used on the available glass substrates is a pre-
condition for satisfactory machining and trimming of
passive thin-film circuits.   Glass material must resist
the high temperature gradients which are involved on
the tracks subjected to processing without forming cracks.
Aside of the kind of glass used, the processing result is
essentially influenced by the accelerating voltage and the
'metre-energy', i. e. , input energy per metre cutted
track length.

Tests for the removal of NiCr film on glass using,
an accelerating voltage of 80 kV, 40 kV and 20 kV and a
power level just sufficient for continuous evaporation of
the film, showed the following phenomena.   Using a

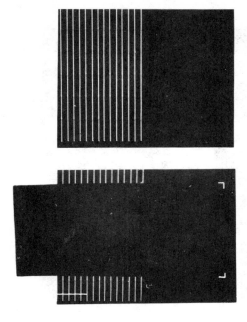

Figure 7. Thin-Film Al-SiO$_2$-Al-Capacitor Step-Wise Trimmed by Electron Beam Machining. (a) Ground Electrode Comb-Shape Machined, (b) Complete Capacitor After Trimming.

relatively unsuitable kind of glass for the substrate, some cracks were observed when employing 80 kV, which reached a length up to several millimetres and which were largely located parallel to the direction of removal. With 40 kV, numerous short cross cracks developed with a length of about 1. 5 times the processing width (see Fig. 8(a). Crack formation could be avoided when using an accelerating voltage of 20 kV, but part of the evaporated layer remained at the processing track in shape of minute droplets (see Fig. 8(b)). With removal width of 30 μm an electric strength of more than 300 volts could be obtained. This shows the acceptability of the process for treating NiCr resistance films.

Figure 8.   Electron Beam Machined Tracks in NiCr-Films on
Glass with Track-Width of 50 μ m.   (a) Cracks Across the
Tracks by Unsiutathe Glass Sorts,   (b) Droplet Formation Caused
by Insufficient Metre-Energy,   (c) Proper Tracks.

A second kind of glass with higher hardness that was tested did not tend to cracking although considerably higher power was employed. On this glass machining was available without droplet formation (see Fig. 8(c)).

SUMMARY

A technical solution for processing resistor combinations on 10 mm x 15 mm ceramic substrates is attained with the described automatic electron beam machining and trimming plant. With the employed cycling time of 2.4 seconds, equivalent to 1,500 substrates per hour, the limit of obtainable production output has not yet been obtained. A considerable reserve can still be used by reducing the mechanical handling time and the full utilization of obtainable working speed. Applying the described pressure drop systems also results in a reduction of unproductive time in effecting the mechanical motion, for example, by conveying two substrates in one transfer block and trimming by a repeat processing program. In this manner the output can be about doubled without materially increasing the supplementary equipment outlay. In consideration of the high basic cost for the electron beam processing plant, an endeavor will be made to avoid unproductive periods as much as possible. A possibility to attain this aim is given by double-track conveying systems of substrates through the processing area, where one substrate is conveyed on one track while the other is machined on the other track.

Assuming a total processing period of 0.4 seconds, with the double-track conveying system an hourly output of about 8,000 substrates, size 10 mm x 15 mm, can be obtained, where at a processing speed of 1 metre per second a resistor of about 1 megohm can be produced on a resistance film of 1 sq. cm. having a resistance value of 400 ohms per square.

For passive thin-film circuits the processing of 20 mm x 30 mm substrates seems profitable for the following reasons:

This working process is compatible with other vacuum processing techniques. It seems to be an alternative of the conventional photo etching method because similarly relative roughly configurated and simple masks can be utilized for deposition of thin films. In addition, the possibility of simple trimming technique permits the production of close-tolerance components in the circuit.

Economy of the electron beam mode for processing passive thin-film circuits can also be considered positive, provided the number of resistors to be processed per substrate is high, for example, ≥ 5 on a size 20 mm x 30 mm substrates.

Another condition to obtain desired economy with this method is that a high number of substrates of similar maximum dimensions has to be processed per year, with the economy limits in the neighborhood of 1 or $2 \cdot 10^6$ processed substrates per year. Because the provided programming control unit can be easily altered, a variety of different circuits can be produced on this number of substrates.

REFERENCES

1. M. v. Ardenne, U. Heisig, S. Panzer, O. Thieme, J. Henneberger: Automatisches Elektronenstrahl-abgleichen von Dünnschichtwiderständen mit kontinuierlichem Durchlauf der Substrate durch die Bearbeitungskammer. Vortrag auf dem IFAC/IFIP-Symposium on Microminiaturization in Automatic Control Equipment and Digital Computers. 21. -23. 10. 65 in München.

2. M. v. Ardenne, U. Heisig, S. Panzer, K. Jessat, G. Bahr, H. Döhler: Continuous Electron Beam Processing Plant for Plane Thin-Film Resistors. Microelectronics and Reliability, in print.

3. M. v Ardenne: Elektronen- oder Ionenstrahlung als Mikrowerkzeug. Nachrichtentechnik 11 (1961) Nr. 8, S. 338-342.

4. M. v. Ardenne, U. Heisig, S. Panzer: Thermische Mikrobearbeitung mit Elektronenstrahlen, Feingerätetechnik 13 (1964), S. 293-301.

5. G. Bahr, H. Döhler: Ein digitales Programm-steuergerät mit Ferritkernspeicher zur Ablenksteuerung von Elektronenstrahlbearbeitungsgeräten, unpublished.

Deposition of Polymer Films by Electron Bombardment

G. W. Hill

British Scientific Instrument Association
Semiconductors & Thin Film Department
South Hill, Chislehurst, Kent, England

INTRODUCTION

The phenomenon of the formation of organic insulating and dielectric layers on a substrate in a vacuum chamber which is subject to electron bombardment in the presence of a partial pressure of an organic vapor has been known for many years. The use of these layers as thin film insulators and dielectrics has been studied by many workers recently. At SIRA we have been investigating this deposition process with a view to the application of these films to low temperature device insulation and normal temperature insulators and dielectrics.

EXPERIMENTAL DATA

Our early work [1] showed that better films would be deposited if a high vapor pressure starting monomer were used with low energy electron beams. The problems of focussing the low energy beams were such that it was decided that polymer film pattern delineation would be best achieved using out of contact metal masks and flooding the substrate with low energy electrons.

The earlier investigations were carried out with a Pierce [2] type flood gun with either a strip filament or one wound in the form of a reentrant spiral. The various deposition processes were carried out in separate plants, the vacuum being broken between depositions.

Metal masks were fitted to a rotary substrate changer for the deposition of vacuum deposited metal electrodes and the middle dielectric layer. This was mounted in a multi-station vacuum plant. Various polymer film test capacitor matrices were deposited in the one pumping cycle for single, double and triple layer capacitors. Typical samples are shown in Fig. 1.

The flood of electrons for the deposition of the polymer dielectric layer was provided by a rotating twelve filament electron gun shown in Fig. 2. [3] The filaments of this gun were lanthanum hexaboride coated rhenium and the rotation was provided by an encapsulated electric motor. The gun was run with the cathode negative and the accelerating anode at earth potential.

Figure 1.   Single and Double Layer Polymer Film Test Matrices.

This gun gave an even spread of electrons over the substrate and when tested in the vacuum plant, about 70% of the gun emission reached the substrate.   This should have ensured a good deposition rate, but subsequent operation of the system gave unsatisfactory deposition rates.   This effect was eventually traced to severe de-focussing of the electron flood when the monomer partial pressure of $1 - 2 \times 10^{-4}$ torr was introduced into the system.   This is shown by the figures in Table I.   The figures shown in Table II for the emission collected by a cylindrical plate surrounding the gun, confirm that the low deposition rate was a function of deflection of the electrons from the gun to substrate path.

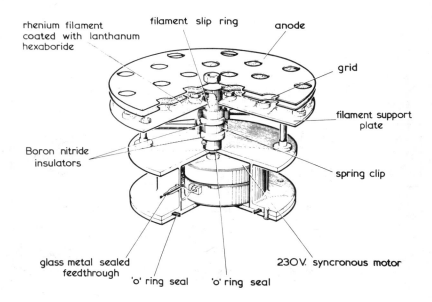

Figure 2.   4" Diameter 12 Filament Rotating Electron Gun.

This problem was tackled by surrounding the gun to substrate volume with a shield at the same potential as the cathode. This enabled a higher proportion of the emitted electrons to reach the substrate during deposition as shown in Table III. Under these conditions the deposition rate was trebled to 60 Å/min.

Polymer films can also be laid down by the formation of free radicals in a plasma discharge, which then cross-link during their sticking time at a substrate. Initially both hot [4] and cold cathode discharges were used [5], but more recently magnetically controlled hot cathode induced plasmas of organic vapors have been used to deposit polymer films. The system used is shown in Fig. 3.

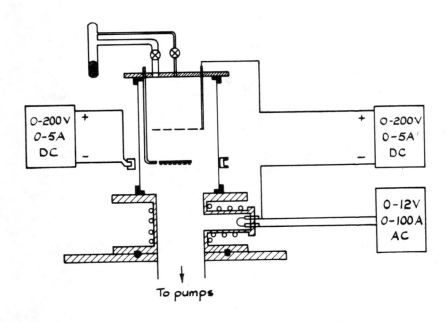

Figure 3. Magnetically Controlled Plasma Polymer Deposition Plant.

Table I. Effect of Monomer Partial Pressure on Substrate Current

System pressure	Gun-plate separation	Plate area	Accelerating voltage	Cathode input current	Plate Current to earth
torr	in	cm²	V	mA	mA
2×10^{-5}	10	80	240	13	9
10^{-4}	10	80	240	18	2.5
3×10^{-4}	10	80	240	45	0.7
2×10^{-5}	10	80	240	13	8

Table II. Effect of Monomer Partial Pressure on Total Gun Output

System pressure	Gun-plate separation	Plate area	Accelerating voltage	Cathode input current	Plate Current to earth
torr	in	cm²	V	mA	mA
2×10^{-5}	10	80 + shield area	260	13	11
2×10^{-4}	10	80 + shield area	260	20	15

Table III. Effect of Negative Potential Shield on Substrate Current Under Operating Conditions

System pressure	Gun–plate separation	Gun potential	Plate area	Accelerating voltage	Cathode input current	Plate current to earth
torr	in		cm^2	V	mA	
2 x 10^{-5}	10	Shield	40	250	17	45 μA
2 x 10^{-4}	10	-250 V	40	250	40	15 mA

The magnetic field concentrates the plasma enabling the discharge to be maintained at a lower pressure (middle 10^{-4} torr range) and it also imparts a directional property to the plasma. These two factors improve the edge definition, at the same time use is made of the higher deposition rate inherent in the plasma deposition.

Following the work published by Christy [6], work was started using MS 704 silicone pump fluid (the UK equivalent of DC 704). Within a few months the monomer was changed to MS 200 fluids with room temperature vapor pressures of 2 torr and 30 torr. These molecules cross-linked more easily and were capable of being pumped from the system when the polymer deposition was finished. These monomers have been used for most of the films whose results are quoted below.

RESULTS AND DISCUSSIONS

Polymer Films as Insulators

Current voltage curves have been derived for many samples and certain general conclusions have been reached.

The room temperature breakdown field of these films is about 5×10^6 v/cm. This breakdown can be either catastrophic or in certain cases when a pulsed potential is applied non catastrophic and repeatable. This latter effect is shown by the top part of the characteristic in Fig. 4. It is necessary to apply pulsed potentials to thinner films since steady potentials cause breakdown at a lower voltage probably due to thermal effects rather than electrical breakdown.

A plot of log current against the square root of the voltage gives a straight line for various films, as shown in Fig. 5. Consideration of the slopes of these linear relations indicate that Schottky emission is the major room temperature conduction mechanism for thicknesses up to about 1000 Å and above this thickness range Poole-Frenkel [7] defect conduction predominates.

At liquid nitrogen temperature the films still show a predominance of the room temperature conduction

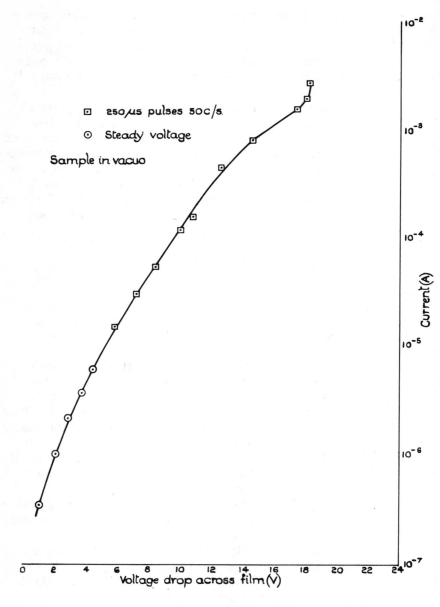

Figure 4.   Continuity of Steady and Pulsed Characteristics.

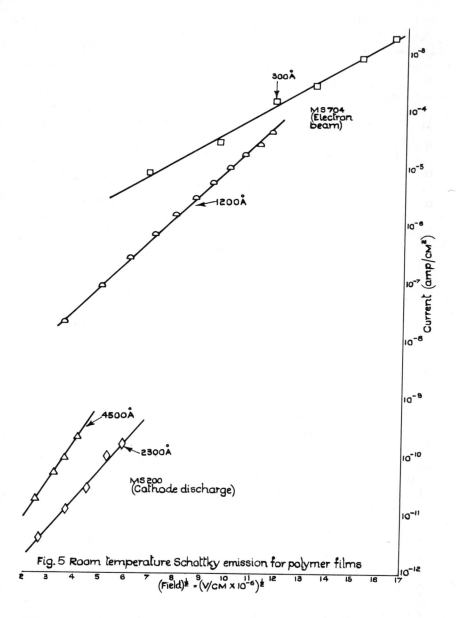

Figure 5.   Room Temperature Schottky Emission for Polymer Films.

mechanisms but at liquid helium temperature tunnelling predominates, particularly for higher fields. The increase in the heat loss from the sample and the lower conductivity at lower temperatures allow higher potentials to be applied at liquid nutrogen and liquid helium temperatures. In fact some films which appear unsatisfactory at room temperature can be perfectly adequate liquid helium temperature insulators at thicknesses preferred by the designers of cryotron circuits.

These films have been compared with other thin film insulators, silicon monoxide, anodized tantalum, anodized aluminum, reactively evaporated alumina and spun on photoresist layers. The general conclusion which can be drawn is that electron beam polymerized organic thin films offer effective thin film insulation at film thicknesses which are significantly less than those used in the other materials.

Polymer Films as Dielectrics

The dielectric constant of these films is approximately 2.8. The dielectric loss is given by a tan δ value of 2×10^{-3} at 1 Kc/s which stays fairly constant up to 500 Kc/s. Correction has been made for the loss introduced by the series resistance of the electrodes.

The capacitive aging of these films has been studied as a function of starting monomer and deposition energy and it has been found that a deposition energy of about 200 eV with a high vapor pressure siloxane monomer (hexamethyldisiloxane) should give polymer film capacitors which are stable to within 5% when exposed to the atmosphere over a period of six months. If a longer chain length starting monomer is used, the dielectric loss increases severely at higher frequencies.

As a preliminary test, sets of capacitors were deposited and after testing 24 were included in the thin film capacitor life test cycle carried out by a member firm of our Association on its own thin film capacitors. The capacitors were maintained at 120°C under a test potential of 25 V (approximately 10^{6} V/cm). After 1000 hrs all the capacitors were still functioning although decreases in capacity of between 5% and 10% were found for most of the samples. This may be due to oxidation of parts of the film or the fact that the higher temperature causes trapped but not cross-linked monomer molecules to slowly desorb from the film.

A total number of about 5000 capacitors have been deposited and tested over a period of six months to give an idea of the sort of yield to be expected from these films. Once suitable deposition parameters have been chosen, the results are best summarized in terms of film thicknesses.

Between 800 Å and 1500 Å the initial yield is 93.7%. Above 2000 Å a 100% yield is expected. Upon aging in the atmosphere the yield is at least 96% for the thinner films. Films which are satisfactory at room temperature have always been satisfactory when tested in liquid helium.

Stress measurements on these films have indicated a very low value of mechanical stress for those films deposited at energies up to 220 eV. Above this figure crazing sometimes occurs, probably due to excessive cross-linking.

The good yield figures, low stress properties and satisfactory dielectric performance of these films make them suitable for use in multilayer capacitors and an investigation is about to start into the use of these films in high capacity/unit area multilayer capacitors. It is proposed to use the magnetically controlled plasma for this work.

In conclusion, the use of electron beams for the in situ polymerization of organic molecules at a substrate offers good insulating and dielectric layers with low pinhole incidence and stress properties. Although the dielectric constant is low, multilayer capacitors deposited in a standard vacuum plant may well be a useful alternative to the need for either wet anodization or rigorous vacuum conditions to achieve high capacity/unit area using high dielectric constant materials.

ACKNOWLEDGMENT

Grateful thanks are made to Chairman and Council of BSIRA for permission to publish this paper. This work was performed under a Ministry of Technology contract.

REFERENCES

1. Hill, G. W. , Microelectronics and Reliability 4 March 1965, p. 109.
2. Pierce, J. R. , J. Appl. Phys. II, 8 August 1940, p. 548.
3. Allam, D. S. , and Stuart, P. R. , J. Sci. Instr. 42, 11, November 1965, p. 812.
4. Da Silva, E. M. , and Miller, R. E. , Electrochem. Technology, 2, 5-6, p. 147.
5. Bradley, A. and Hammes, J. P. , J. Electrochem. Soc. , 110, 1, p. 15.
6. Christy, R. W. , J. Appl. Phys. 31, September 1960, p. 1680.
7. Hirose, H. , and Wada, Y. , Jap. J. Appl. Phys. 4, 9, September 1965, p. 639.

Recent Developments in Fabrications Using an Electron Beam Gun

D. Zeheb, N. H. Kreitzer and D. G. Cullum

IBM Watson Research Center
Yorktown Heights, New York

INTRODUCTION

The present state of the integrated circuitry art may be classified as field integration. Circuit patterns consisting of from a few to a few tens of components are arranged in fixed field formations. These fields are repeated as many times as is possible on the surface of a wafer. After proper processing, the wafer is diced to yield the individual fields. Those that meet specifications are then individually packaged, whereas the defective ones are thrown away.

Future trends in integrated cicuitry lead in a direction which may be classified as wafer integration. Here, fields composing identical or different circuits are placed on the same wafer. These fields are interconnected on the wafer itself to form a complex system.

Both applications require equipment capable of precise recording of fine lines in perfect registration. There, is however, a major operational difference. In the former application, utilization of masks in step and repeat techniques is quite practical and, indeed, used extensively. In the latter, however, each wafer will require its own custom-made mask. Thus, direct operation on the wafer becomes more practical.

Equipment capable of meeting both applications was previously described.[1] For the sake of completeness, a brief summary will be given here.

[1] D. Zeheb, N.H. Kreitzer, and D.G. Cullum, Electron Beam Gun in an Exploratory Fabrication System, IEEE International Convention Record, March 1966.

EQUIPMENT DESCRIPTION

The equipment consists of five major systems. (See Fig. 1)

1. An electron beam gun with its associated lens, power supply, vacuum apparatus, deflection plates, and deflection coils. This system produces a beam of electrons focused down to 0.5μ spot diameter which is made to impinge upon a desired workpiece.

2. A mechanical positioning system, capable of positioning a workpiece to a resolution of five microns and repeatability of better than three microns over a 4 inch x 4 inch field.

3. A main deflection system, which controls the beam position by controlling current in x and y deflection coils. This control is automatic, originating as digital instructions on magnetic tape. Resolution is one part in 4096. Short term stability over a 1/2 x 1/2 inch field is in the submicron range.

4. An auxiliary deflection system using deflection plates. This system is used for measuring the focus of the beam, scanning over registration marks, and controlling line width by high speed modulation.

5. A secondary emission system which consists of a secondary emission detector, a series of amplifiers, and a visual monitor. This system operates on the scanning electron microscope principle and provides a window into the work chamber. The main use of this system is in precise registration.

MASK GENERATION WITH THE ELECTRON BEAM SYSTEM

The generation of a mask requires that a rough drawing be made of the desired pattern on coordinate paper. The "x" and "y" end points of each line are then listed and prepared for computer input. A computer program has been generated to accommodate complex patterns of the

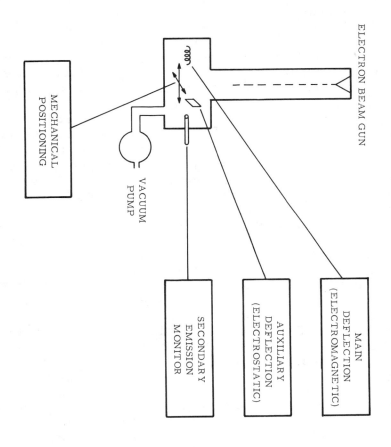

ELECTRON BEAM GUN

MECHANICAL POSITIONING

VACUUM PUMP

SECONDARY EMISSION MONITOR

AUXILIARY DEFLECTION (ELECTROSTATIC)

MAIN DEFLECTION (ELECTROMAGNETIC)

Figure 1. System Block Diagram

type that appear in this paper.

The film used in the electron beam gun for these tests was type DER, a film specifically manufactured by Eastman Kodak Company, Rochester, New York, for electron beam exposure. Heavy writing currents tend to cause considerable charging on the surface of the film resulting in poor registration of subsequent patterns.

In order to minimize this effect, a writing beam current of 3×10^{-12} amperes was used. This current level, at a linear deflection speed of 130 mils per second and a super-imposed 15 micron square scan gives sufficient density in the image without serious distortion. The acceleration potential is normally in the range of 10 to 12 kV The present working distance of one inch from the deflection yoke yields a field of slightly greater than 0.5 inch. The beam diameter, when properly focused, is in the submicron range (0.4 to 0.6 μ). Since present applications involve line widths much larger than the focused beam, astigmatism and beam spreading are not serious problems. Pincushioning, however, does affect the usable field size.

A typical circuit configuration is shown in Fig. 2. The repeated recording of this pattern shows the magnetic deflection stability of the system. Direct comparison of identical lines and blocks between fields has proven the magnetic repeatability to be within previously stated tolerances. Each field in the 5 x 5 matrix was recorded using only magnetic deflection. Mechanical stepping was used for multifield coverage. The narrowest recorded line has a width of 15 microns. In order to demonstrate the short term mechanical stability of this system, two patterns, shown in Figs. 3 and 4, were superimposed in a double pass in the electron beam gun. Pattern 1 was written in four locations on the film; pattern 2 was then written retracing the initial path. Figure 5 shows the resultant recording.

USE OF THE SYSTEM FOR DIRECT FABRICATION

The use of a focused electron beam to produce complex latent images on silver halide emulsion has been demonstrated. A logical extension of this process is to eliminate

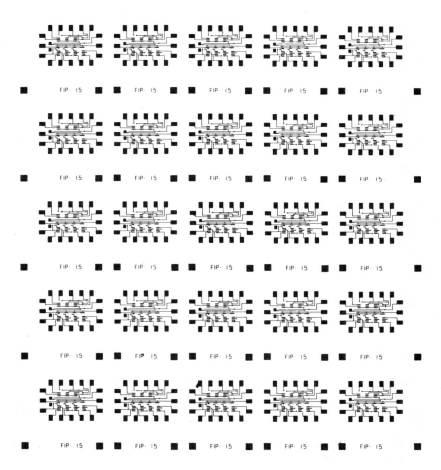

Figure 2. Interconnect Patterns in a 5 x 5 Array.

the mask completely by direct electron exposure of photo-
resist-treated conductive or semiconductive substrate
material. In this manner, one can achieve direct fabrication of integrated circuit structures from digitized information recorded on tape. Thus, the inherent light optic
limitations of the intermediate mask technique can be
eliminated along with the associated time and cost factors.

Of prime importance in the production of any multi-
layered structure is the ability to accurately register
patterns at each level. The registration problem is complicated by the nature of the fabrication process that requires intermediate chemical processing external to the
electron beam gun vacuum chamber, between the various
pattern exposures. Registration, in this system, relies
on the detection of secondary emission from fiducal lines
included in the first exposure for a given structure. The
quantity and positions of these fiducal lines is determined
by the registration accuracy requirement. In all cases,
such registration marks occupy regions of uncertainty
external to the desired field area on the substrate.

Registration can be divided into two basic classes
which, in some cases, may overlap: 1) The case where
one or only a few large fields of exposure are required
with limited accuracy, and 2) The case where many
small fields are required on the same substrate with rigid
accuracy requirements.

In case 1, perimeter registration will usually suffice.
Fiducal lines are recorded on first exposure near the perimeter of the substrate. On subsequent entries, secondary
emission registration is performed at the perimeter of the
substrate. Following this, the desired field area is positioned under the electron beam gun to mechanical accuracy.
In multiaccess applications, mechanical repeatability errors less than three microns can be achieved by always
approaching the desired field from the same initial direction of travel. In case 2, perimeter registration, although
not sufficient by itself, may still be employed for gross
registration, at the start of each operation. Where accurate positioning of many microfields within a single substrate is desired, mechanical accuracies may not be sufficiently resolute or stable for multiaccess exposures. In

this case, each microfield must be provided with a pair of registration marks for individual secondary emission alignment. These fiducal marks are recorded on first exposure in void areas of uncertainty near the corners of each microfield. During subsequent exposures, the areas of uncertainty are positioned to mechanical accuracies under the electron beam. Precise secondary emission alignment to submicron accuracies is performed by scanning the fiducal marks in these areas.

Of critical importance in case 2 is the ability to detect secondary emission from microfield fiducal marks which may have become coated with layers of photoresist and/or metal during intermediate processing. Present indications are that structures covered with photoresist can be detected. The case where fiducal marks must be covered with both metal and photoresist may require an additional processing step to uncover the fiducal marks. This requires further research. Perimeter registration avoids this problem, since it is a relatively simple task to shield a perimeter fiducal mark during the evaporation or coating processes.

In illustration of some of the points which have been discussed, Fig. 6 shows a circuit structure of etched aluminum on silicon. The over-all structure size is about 30 x 50 mils. Since it is desired to re-enter the wafer into the system for a second exposure, fiducal marks have been provided. These marks do not appear in the Fig. 6 photograph. The etched circuit structure was formed by evaporating aluminum on a silicon wafer and coating with a negative photoresist. The resist was then "exposed" with the electron beam, developed and etched. The negative resist prevents etching in the exposed areas.

The following photographs illustrate the response of the secondary electron detection and monitor system to various scanned structures. The photographs were taken directly from the face of a 14" monitor oscilloscope. Each photograph represents a scanned area of about 6 square mils. Figure 7 shows a portion of the circuit structure after etching but before stripping. The resist covered structure resides on clear silicon. Figure 8 shows a portion of the circuit structure after etching and stripping. The clear aluminum structure resides on clear silicon.

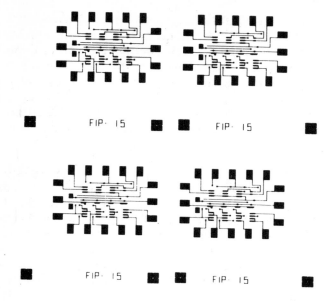

Figure 3. 2 x 2 Array Showing Component Pattern.

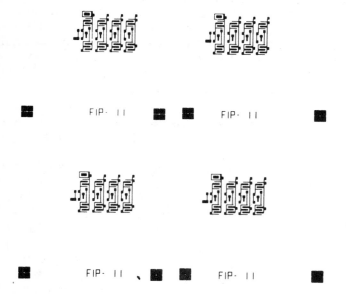

Figure 4. 2 x 2 Array Showing Interconnect Pattern.

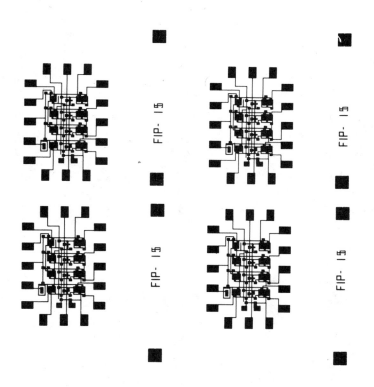

Figure 5.   Interconnect and Component Pattern Overlayed.

Figures 9 and 10 show a fiducal mark covered with resist and another portion of the circuit structure without resist, respectively.

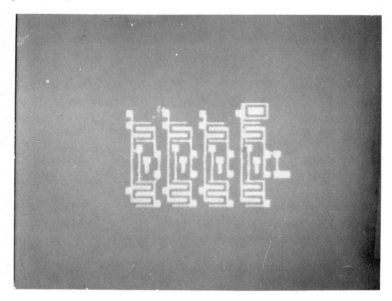

Figure 6. Circuit Pattern of Aluminum on Silicon (40x).

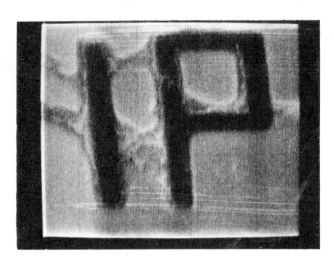

Figure 7. Detail of Unstripped Aluminum on Silicon (400x).

Figure 8. Detail of Stripped Aluminum on Silicon (400x).

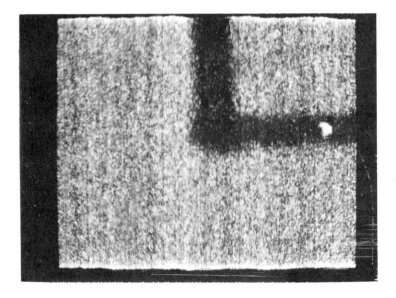

Figure 9. Unstripped Fiducal Mark Aluminum on Silicon.

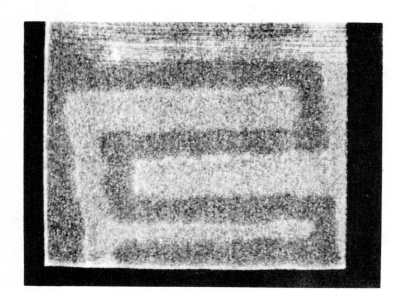

Figure 10. Circuit Detail Aluminum on Silicon (400x).

CONCLUSION

The feasibility of using electron beams as production tools for integrated circuits in particular and for any application which requires precise patterns in general has been demonstrated.

High quality patterns have been obtained on silver halide materials as well as photoresists.

Incorporation of the electron beam gun into an operational system has also been proven practical, indicating the possibility of developing a large scale manufacturing facility exploiting these techniques.

The Preparation of High Resolution Silica Diffusion Barriers by an Electron Stimulated Chemical Reaction

A. F. Beer, J. Kelly, H. N. G. King,
E. D. Roberts and J. M. S. Schofield

Mullard Research Laboratories
Redhill, Surrey, England

INTRODUCTION

The ability of an electron beam to stimulate chemical reactions has been known for some time. Probably the first and best known type of reaction is the formation of insulating films by the polymerization of pump oil in the electron microscope. Pump oil which has diffused into the system condenses on cool surfaces and wherever electron bombardment occurs molecules become cross linked, resulting in undesirable insulating films.

It appears that the polymerization is only one of a wide variety of reactions which can be stimulated by electron bombardment. Shoulders [1] has reported the etching of metal targets with reactive vapors; the deposition of metal layers has been examined by Baker and Morris [2] and more recently by Christy [3], while the deposition of resistive materials [4] and semiconductors would also seem to be possible.

Reactions of this type are potentially suitable for the commercial construction of complex microcircuits, because of the high degree of flexibility. Reactions only occur where there are electron collisions and the type of reaction is controlled by the gases present, so that the processes are ideally suited to automation. However any such target would still seem to be some time ahead, and the aim of the present work is to study a few of the reactions available and their application to the already existing technology.

It was eventually decided that a study of the possibilities of making high resolution diffusion barriers on silicon would be a convenient starting point. A number of devices can be visualized, the performance of which will be grealy improved by the use of diffusion barriers of higher resolution than it is possible to make by conventional photolithography.

The present work, while still at an early stage, is aimed initially at the construction of a high performance M. O. S. Transistor. Present activity can be divided into three main sections:

1. The study of the reactions involved, the composition of the films produced and their properties.

2. Examination of the films in use as diffusion barriers.

3. The study of the high resolution aspects of the process.

This paper describes the apparatus and the experimental results obtained to date.

THE APPARATUS

Two pieces of apparatus are available for use on this project. The first is a relatively simple bell jar equipment fitted with an electron gun and differential pumping system, and is intended for investigation of the reactions on a large scale. The second is a high resolution device, designed for the production of electron images or for use as a scanning electron microscope.

The Bell Jar Apparatus

This apparatus has been designed as a means of producing films a centimeter or more in diameter, such films being suitable for analytical and physical examination. A diagram of the apparatus is shown in Fig. 1. Mounted on the base plate is a simple electron gun, using a tungsten hairpin emitter. The beam passes upwards through a double deflection system and is focussed by a simple electrostatic lens to pass through a limiting

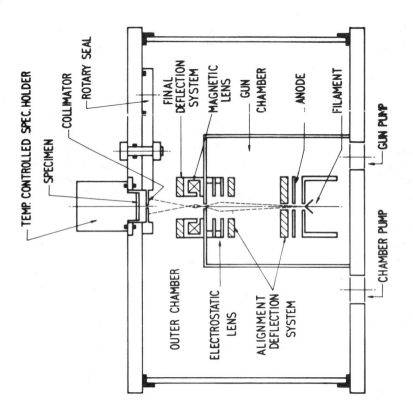

Figure 1. The Bell Jar Equipment.

aperture in the wall of the gun chamber. The focal length of this lens remains substantially constant with changes in voltage and the deflection system is used to align the beam with the lens plates.

In the outer chamber the beam intensity, diameter, and position can be controlled by a small magnetic lens and further deflection system. Gases can be introduced into the vacuum system near to the target and the gas flow can be controlled by needle valves. The specimen can be loaded without letting the main chamber down to air, and beam currents of up to 2 mA and voltages up to 10 kV are available.

The High Resolution Machine

This is a multi-lens electron optical device, capable of producing high resolution electron patterns either by demagnifying the shadow image of a mask illuminated with electrons, or by scanning a fine probe over the surface of the target and modulating its intensity. In the latter context the machine can also be used as a scanning electron microscope. The electron energy is variable between 5 and 50 keV.

A simplified diagram of the optics is shown in Fig. 2. In Fig. 2(a) the machine is shown in use as a probe forming device, using three stages of demagnification, which should produce a probe size smaller than 500 Å. In Fig. 2(b) the system is set up to provide a demagnified image of the mask. The first two lenses provide an illuminating beam, while the two lenses below the object mask focus the image onto the target. The variation obtainable is between x 5 magnification and x 500 demagnification.

A photograph of the device is shown in Fig. 3.

THE PREPARATION OF LARGE AREA FILMS FOR ANALYSIS

Films have been made in a bell jar vacuum chamber by electron beam decomposition of tetraethoxysilane, $Si(OC_2H_5)_4$. This chemical (called TEOS hereafter) is known to decompose on heated surfaces forming a silica

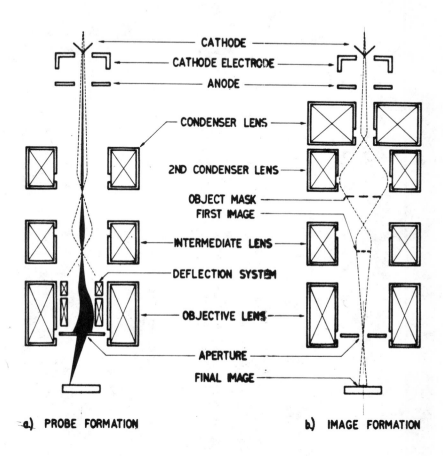

CATHODE

CATHODE ELECTRODE

ANODE

CONDENSER LENS

2ND CONDENSER LENS

OBJECT MASK
FIRST IMAGE

INTERMEDIATE LENS

DEFLECTION SYSTEM

OBJECTIVE LENS

APERTURE
FINAL IMAGE

a) PROBE FORMATION   b) IMAGE FORMATION

Figure 2.   Optics of the High Resolution Machine.

Figure 3.   The High Resolution Machine.

film.   Films can be grown, in this way, on a silicon surface heated above about 250°C in an atmosphere of TEOS and oxygen.

The TEOS is a liquid at room temperature with a vapor pressure of about 1 torr. The vapor was admitted into the vacuum chamber to a pressure of 1 mtorr and is adsorbed on the target surface where it is converted by the electron beam to a silica like film.

Films are deposited at about 1 Å/sec using a current density of 1 mA/cm^2 at 10 kV. Substrates of aluminum, dural, copper and silicon have been used.   The material used should only affect the initial layer of film and no substantial differences have been observed although investigations are continuing (cf. section 5). The majority of films have been grown on water cooled substrates at 20 to 25°C. In preliminary experiments, however, when the substrate was cooled to -30°C the weight of the film deposited increased by about a factor two, while early experiments without cooling showed a rapidly diminishing deposit with increased temperature. This is consistent with an exponential dependence of the time of stay of the adsorbed TEOS upon the temperature of the substrate [5]:

$$\tau = \tau_0 \exp\left(\frac{Q}{KT}\right) \tag{1}$$

where τ = time of stay in seconds
τ_0 = characteristic vibration time of the molecules in the adsorbed state
Q = heat of adsorption per molecule in ergs.
K = Boltzmann's constant
T = substrate temperature in degrees absolute.

Some of the earlier films deposited by electrons above 6 keV had a dark appearance which was not due to contamination from pump oil. It was thought that this might be due to the presence of free carbon in the film formed from TEOS alone. Subsequently films were deposited using increasing proportions of oxygen with the TEOS; the films produced were much clearer and the total weight of film per electron was increased. A graph of weight deposited against the ratio of the partial pressures of oxygen to TEOS is shown in Fig. 4.

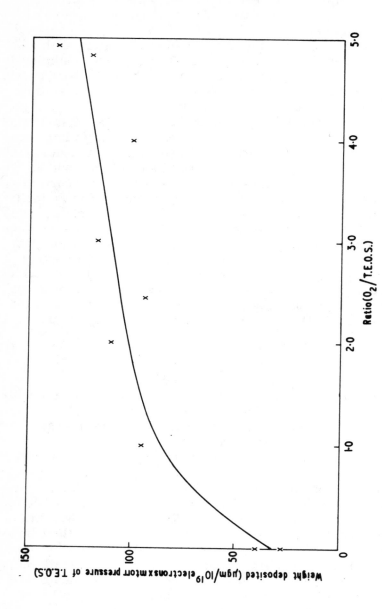

Figure 4. Weight of the Film Deposited Against Oxygen Ratio.

THEORY OF FILM GROWTH

According to the conditions, any one of three quantities can predominate in controlling the rate at which films are deposited. These are the rates of arrival of both electrons and vapor molecules at the substrate, and also their time of stay. Christy [6] has obtained expressions for the rates of film growth which he verified experimentally. These rates reach steady values in a short time after switching on the beam compared to the time for which the films are grown. We have combined his expressions by assuming the adsorption of molecules is proportional to the flux to the uncovered areas of surface (i. e. little self condensation) and obtain the asymptotic rate:

$$R = \frac{v\, F\, \sigma\, f}{aF + \sigma f + 1/\tau} \tag{2}$$

where R = rate of film growth
v = volume of a molecule
F = molecular flux density
f = electron flux density
a = area of a molecule
σ = cross section for the reaction
τ = time of stay.

If the time of stay is short, $1/\tau$ dominates aF and σf and so

$$R = v\, F\sigma\, f\, \tau \tag{3}$$

and the deposition rate is proportional to all three quantities. When τ is large, $1/\tau$ may be neglected and:

$$R = \frac{v\, F\, \sigma\, f}{aF + \sigma f} \tag{4}$$

In the latter case the film growth rate is proportional to whichever quantity is the smaller and becomes independent of the other. At high enough partial pressures of TEOS, when $aF \gg \sigma f$, then:

$$R = \left(\frac{\sigma}{a}\right) vf \tag{5}$$

The growth is proportional to electron current density, and any nonuniformity of the beam appears as a variation in the film thickness. If however, more than sufficient electrons arrive, $\sigma f \gg aF$, and

$$R = v F \tag{6}$$

and there is evidence that film properties alter, perhaps due to a change in the degree of cross linking [7].

In our present experiments it is estimated that:

$$F \approx 1.5 \times 10^{18} \text{ cm}^{-2} \text{ sec}^{-1}$$

$$f = 1.6 \times 10^{16} \text{ cm}^{-2} \text{ sec}^{-1}$$

$$v \approx 5 \times 10^{-22} \text{ cm}^3$$

$$a \approx 6 \times 10^{-15} \text{ cm}^2.$$

It is assumed at 10 keV energy: $\sigma \approx a/100 = 6 \times 10^{-17}$ cm^2. Then $aF \approx 9.0 \times 10^3$ sec^{-1}, while $\sigma f \approx 9.6 \times 10^{-1}$ sec^{-1}. Neglecting σf in the denominator of equation (2):

$$R = \frac{(\frac{\sigma}{a}) \ vf}{1 + \dfrac{1}{aF \tau}} \tag{7}$$

Substituting the above values

$$R = \left(\frac{8}{1 + \dfrac{1}{aF\tau}} \right) \overset{\circ}{A}/\text{sec}.$$

Therefore, comparing this value of R with the measured value of 1 Å/sec, it appears that $\tau \approx 1/7aF$, which is consistent with the temperature dependence observed and gives $\tau \approx 16 \ \mu$ sec. For silicon and many other substances [5] $\tau_0 \approx 4 \times 10^{-13}$ sec, this would give from equation (1) a heat of adsorption $Q \approx 10$ Kcal/mole for TEOS. This is to be compared with 7 Kcal/mole the latent heat of evaporation of TEOS and supports the assumption we made of little self condensation of the vapor on the substrate.

EXAMINATION OF SILICEOUS FILMS

Examination of the films produced is primarily intended to provide information about the nature of the reactions stimulated by electrons with a view to predicting other possible reactions and the composition of the resulting films. For most analytical processes, it is desirable to deal with the free film, and the first experiments were directed to finding a method for removing the film from the substrate without damaging it.

It soon became apparent that satisfactory removal could not be achieved unless the film was adequately supported during the etching process required to remove the substrate. This was done by preparing a sandwich structure as illustrated in Fig. 5. The film was easily separated from the plastics support after the substrate had been etched away. The process has worked satisfactorily with metal substrates, but work is still going on to remove films from silicon substrates.

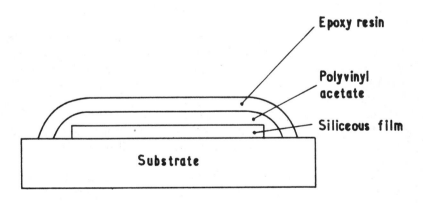

Figure 5. Cross-Section of Film with Plastics Supports Before Etching.

892   BEER, ET AL.

Physical Methods

Films have been examined by infra-red absorption spectroscopy. It has been shown that films removed from copper and aluminum are identical and infra-red spectra are shown in Fig. 6. Spectra obtained by transmission through the film on silicon are also shown, but the peaks may be masked by the silicon substrate itself. It is expected that films on silicon will also be identical, because after the first layer of molecules is deposited, addition of further molecules occurs on the film itself, irrespective of the nature of the original substrate. While this cannot be demonstrated unequivocally until a process for removing films from silicon has been developed, the spectra of films on silicon obtained so far show nothing to indicate a difference from films formed on metal substrates. Possible interpretations of the spectra as tabulated, follows. There is little doubt that thermal oxide film is amorphous silica, the absorption peaks corresponding with published data [8].

Chemical Methods

A number of films prepared with oxygen: TEOS ratio 3:1 have been examined by conventional chemical methods. The silicon content has been found generally to be about 25-30%, and the proportion of siliceous matter about 50%. The latter appears to be a polymer based upon a silicon-oxygen network, but still containing carbon and hydrogen. The infra-red spectra indicated that these are present as ethoxy and acetyl groups, and possible also as vinyl groups.

The remaining portion appears to be carbonaceous material. It is black, and contains carbon, hydrogen and probably oxygen, and exists as a separate compound from the siliceous material. The only analysis yet available for this compound indicates it contains 65% carbon, 6.5% hydrogen, and about 28% oxygen. As practically no deposit is formed in the absence of TEOS vapor, it appears that the carbonaceous material is formed by combination of fragments of aliphatic chains produced from TEOS by the

Wavelengths of Absorption Peaks and Possible Interpretations

Curve A		Curve B		Curve C		Curve D	
Electron beam film on metal		Electron beam film on metal after HF treatment		Electron beam film on silicon		Thermal oxide film on silicon (1000°C)	
Wavelength μ	Groups present	Wavelength μ	Groups present	Wavelength μ	Groups present	Wavelength μ	Groups present
2.7-3.2	O H	2.7-3.2	O H	(3.43)	(Alkyl)		
3.43	Alkyl	3.43	Alkyl				
5.75	SiO OC CH$_3$	5.85	O H				
6.25	Si CH=CH$_2$						
6.70	SiO C$_2$H$_5$						
6.90	SiO C$_2$H$_5$						
7.30	SiO C$_2$H$_5$						
7.75	SiO C$_2$H$_5$						
8.15	SiO OC CH$_3$						
8.45	SiO C$_2$H$_5$			8.4	SiO C$_2$H$_5$		
9.4	SiO			9.35	SiO	9.25	SiO
10.5	SiO C$_2$H$_5$						
12-12.5	SiO			12.2	SiO	12.5	SiO
				16.2	Si	16.2	Si
22.5	SiO			22.0	SiO	21.9	SiO

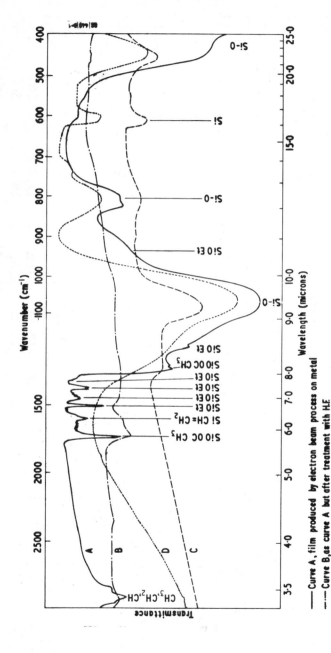

Figure 6.   Infra-Red Absorption Spectra of Various Films.

electron bombardment, followed perhaps by further cross-linking and elimination of small molecules or atoms under the influence of the beam.

Masking Properties

The films grown on silicon from tetraethoxysilane have been tested as masks against diffusion. It has been found that when the films are grown in the presence of oxygen as well, masking is substantially improved. Films 0.2 μ thick, grown using a 3:1 vapor pressure ratio of oxygen to TEOS mask satisfactorily against high concentration boron diffusion at 1000°C, except in the immediate vicinity of any windows opened in the film. If the film is first heated to a temperature of about 700°C for 1/2 hour in a wet Argon (or Nitrogen) atmosphere, the masking is further improved and in fact is fully comparable to the masking of a normal thermally grown oxide. The films so far grown have always produced an n-type skin on the silicon under the film. This is consistent with the film containing a large concentration of positive ions.

HIGH RESOLUTION STUDIES

The advantage of the electron beam process is its ability to produce extremely fine patterns. In this case very fine oxide films can be grown which can subsequently be used as barriers against diffusion as in normal planar transistor technology. A relatively simple experiment has been carried out in an attempt to demonstrate the feasibility of making high resolution patterns by the electron beam approach.

A fine copper gauze was flooded with electrons, and the resulting shadow image was focussed onto a silicon target by a single magnetic lens. The lens and target were arranged to give a 5 to 1 demagnification of the shadow image. TEOS was introduced into the vacuum as was described for the large area depositions, and films deposited.

The results are shown in Fig. 7. The upper photographs are the grids themselves, while the lower ones are

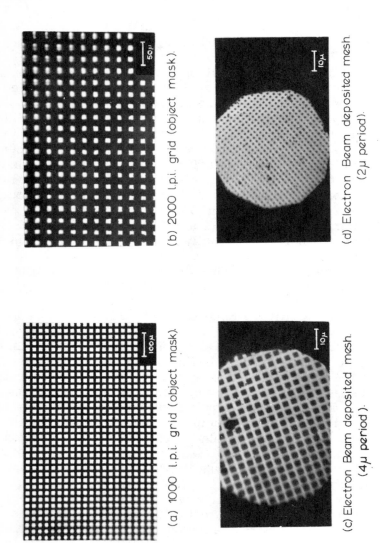

(a) 1000 l.p.i. grid (object mask).

(b) 2000 l.p.i. grid (object mask).

(c) Electron Beam deposited mesh. (4μ period).

(d) Electron Beam deposited mesh. (2μ period).

Figure 7. Samples of Electron Beam Deposition.

the demagnified siliceous patterns. In the case of the fine grid the squares of silica are less than $1\,\mu$ across and are about $0.2\,\mu$ thick. The photographs were made with an ordinary optical microscope and are consequently somewhat lacking in resolution.

These results demonstrate clearly the feasibility of making high resolution patterns, even in relatively thick films. It is difficult to say, at this stage, what the ultimate limit will be, but this may well be determined by electron scattering.

One device in which the fine geometry may be used to advantage is the insulated gate field effect transistor or metal-oxide semiconductor (MOS) transistor [9].

The transconductance per unit length "g_m", of a MOS Transistor (Fig. 8) is given by the approximate formula:

$$g_m = \frac{\mu\,\epsilon}{at}\,V_G^{\,2}$$

where μ = mobility of the carriers
ϵ = dielectric constant of the oxide
t = thickness of the oxide
a = width of channel
V_g = voltage applied to the gate (neglecting any offset voltage)

From this formula it can be seen that for a high g_m a low value of "a" is desirable. This also gives a low value of input capacitance "C" and hence a large grain-bandwidth product. With the resolution obtainable with the electron beam, it is hoped to obtain values of "a" around $1\,\mu$, which would give a marked improvement in the ratio g_m/C over that of conventionally made devices.

CONCLUSIONS

Dielectric films have been laid down on various substrates including silicon by the breakdown of tetra-ethoxysilane with an electron beam. The films have been shown to contain a silica like material still combined with some organic groups together with some organic and carbon content. They have been deposited with a resolution of a fraction of a micron and tests on large area films

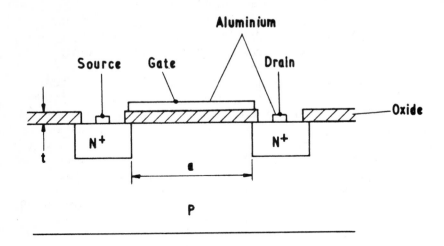

FIG.8 A SCHEMATIC M.O.S. TRANSISTOR

Figure 8.   A Schematic M.O.S. Transistor.

show that they mask satisfactorily after heat treatment at 700 °C, and are in this respect comparable to thermally grown oxide.   It is hoped to exploit the high resolution capability of the technique in an M.O.S. Transistor which should have a performance substantially better than those made at present.

ACKNOWLEDGMENT

We gratefully acknowledge the constructive help and criticism of Mr. D. Baker of the G.P.O. Research Station, Dollis Hill.   We wish to thank Mr. D.H.O. Allen and Mr. J.R.A. Beale for their continued support of the work. We also thank the Directors of Mullard Research Laboratories and the Ministry of Defense for permission to publish this paper.

REFERENCES

1. K. R. Shoulders, "Microelectronics using Electron-Beam-Activated Machining Techniques", Advances in Computers, Vol. 2, 1961. Academic Press.
2. A. G. Baker and W. C. Morris, "Deposition of Metallic Films by Electron Impact Decomposition or Organometallic Vapors", Rev. Sci. Instr., p. 438, 1961.
3. R. W. Christy, "Conducting Thin Films Formed by Electron Bombardment of Substrates", J. Appl. Phys., 33, 5, p. 1884, May 1962.
4. J. M. Hlavin and R. A. Fotland, "The Fabrication of Electronic Components Using Low Energy Electron Beams", Proc. First International Conference, Electron and Ion Beam Science & Technology, R. Bakish (Ed.) John Wiley & Sons, New York, 1965.
5. J. H. de Boer, "The Dynamic Character of Adsorption", p. 30, Oxford University, Clarendon Press, 1953.
6. R. W. Christy, "Formation of Thin Polymer Films by Electron Bombardment", J. Appl. Phys., 31, 9, p. 1680, September 1960.
7. H. T. Mann, "Electrical Properties of Thin Polymer Films", J. Appl. Phys., 36, 7, p. 2173, July 1964.
8. L. E. Howarth and W. G. Spitzer, "Infra-red Properties of Silicon Monox and Evaporated SiO Films", J. Am. Ceram. Soc., 44, 1, p. 26, January 1961.
9. S. R. Hofstein and F. P. Heiman, "The Silicon Insulated-Gate-Field-Effect Transistor", Proc. IEEE, 51, 9, p. 1190, September 1963.

Low Energy Electron Microscopy: Scanning A p-n Junction Diode

E. D. Wolf, R. G. Wilson and J. W. Mayer

Hughes Research Laboratories
Malibu, California

INTRODUCTION

Recently there have been several applications of scanning electron beams to microelectronics and to the surface physics of semiconductors. Most of these experiments utilize a very small diameter (submicron) beam of high energy (generally $\geq$ 10 keV) electrons which is scanned over the surface of the device in a raster-like fashion. The resulting secondary electrons, electron beam induced currents, or target voltages, provide a video signal capable of modulating the intensity of a synchronously scanned cathode-ray tube which may be used to show boundaries of dopant regions, [1, 2] location and depth of p-n junction, [3] dislocations near a depletion region, [4] inversion layers, [5, 6] and other electrical and physical information [7] about the sample being examined.

It is the purpose of this paper to present two different, though complementary approaches to the study of semiconductor surfaces, one of which utilizes a very low energy (0 to 10 eV) and the other a low energy (100 to 300 eV) electron beam, 1 to 5μ in diameter. The very low energy beam method yields the local surface potential directly and quantitatively, and although it is temporarily limited to mechanical scanning of the surface, two-dimensional information is readily obtained. A scanned beam display system is being fabricated. This technique is

similar to the retarding potential method originally used
for metals by Anderson [8] and recently greatly improved
by Haas and Thomas [9, 10].

The low energy technique is similar in approach to
that of Everhart's work but is particularly applicable to the
analysis of shallow junctions. The low energy beam
minimizes radiation effects, the energy dissipation within
the semiconductor surface, and the associated local heating. One of the important features of operation in the 100
to 300 volt mode is the shallow penetration of the beam.
In structures whose junctions are parallel to the surface
and greater in depth than the electron range, only negligible
electron beam induced currents will be measured. Junctions formed by ion implantation can be as shallow as
$0.1\,\mu$. Detection of small localized nonimplanted areas
where the depletion region extends to the surface is possible by using electrons whose range is less than the implantation depth.

TECHNIQUES

The experimental arrangement is illustrated in Fig. 1.
The 5-mil tungsten hairpin cathode was enclosed in a grid
can. The last electrode of the einzel lens had an aperture
diameter of $7.5\,\mu$. More recent data have been obtained
with a 1- μ diameter aperture. As the electrons emerged
from the cathode they were accelerated to ~ 200 volts,
made to converge within the einzel lens, and then limited
by the small aperture which served to define the beam.
Upon passing through the limiting aperture, the electrons
entered a highly retarding (~ 10^4 volts/cm) electric field
region which permitted the decelerating electrons to impinge the target with minimized perturbation of their
trajectories by transverse "patch" fields on the surface.
The target was moved beneath the stationary electron
beam on an x-y stage which was actuated by motor-driven
precision micrometers.

The all-metal vacuum system was sorption and ion
pumped, and maintained a pressure of 1×10^{-10} Torr or
less with bakeout and 1×10^{-9} Torr without bakeout.
(Indium solder connections to the n-type regions of the

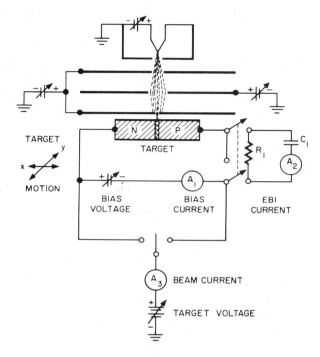

Figure 1.   Schematic of the Experimental Design.

diodes prevented bakeout in some cases.   The lithium diffused junctions were prepared in 6000 Ω -cm p-type silicon and the antimony ion implanted junctions were produced in a 20 Ω-cm p-type silicon.

An ion bombardment gun for sputter-cleaning (not shown in Fig. 1) produced a one-cm diameter beam incident at 45° to the plane of the target surface.

The low energy electron scanning microscope was operated in three different modes; static retarding potential, scanning potential, and scanning electron beam induced (EBI) current mode.   In the static retarding potential mode, the low energy beam remained stationary on the target surface and the beam current was recorded as a function of the target voltage, utilizing a logarithmic picoammeter and an x-y recorder.   The current to the

sample remained essentially constant until the target
potential became sufficiently negative to retard the incident electrons. At this point (i. e., at the knee), the collected current decreased exponentially with increasing
retarding potential.

This behavior is expected from the approximately
Maxwellian distribution of emitted electrons from the
cathode. The retarding potential curves can be expressed
for the ideal* case by

$$I_t = I_{sat}\, e^{-(\phi_t - E_b)/kT_c} \qquad \text{for } E_b < \phi_t \qquad (1)$$

$$I_t = I_{sat} \qquad\qquad\qquad \text{for } E_b \geq \phi_t \qquad (2)$$

where I_t is the beam current collected by the target, I_{sat}
is the saturation current, i. e., all the current emerging
from the limiting aperture, ϕ_t is the local work function
of the target surface and E_b is the beam energy which is
composed of the cathode work function, ϕ_c, and the net
potential energy difference between the cathode and target.
In this case $E_b = \phi_c - eV_f + eV_t$. The V_f term is the
filament voltage at the point of emission and V_t is the
target voltage. Because $\phi_c = 4.52$ eV and $V_f = 1.50$
volts, $E_b = eV_t + 3.02$. T_c is the cathode temperature.
In the absence of an in situ work function reference, a
semi-quantitative value for the surface being studied was
calculated from the extrapolated intersection point of the
saturation current curve with that of the deep retarding
potential curve, i. e., $\phi_t = E_b = eV_t$ (knee) + 3.02.

In the scanning potential mode the target voltage was
fixed at a value near the knee of the retarding potential
curve and the collected beam current was measured as a
function of position on the surface for a given applied

*Several factors are involved and have been discussed extensively
(e. g., Ref. 11 and 12) which cause the experimentally determined curves to fall away at the knee. Not to be excluded is the
effect of non-axial fields on the normal velocity distribution which
may occur in the present environment.

junction bias voltage. At any potential within the voltage
range in which the current exhibited exponential behavior,
the collected current was a very sensitive function of
either the surface potential or the externally applied potential. This mode of operation measured the local surface potential variation.

In the scanning EBI mode, the electrons which
energized from the limiting aperture no longer were retarded, but now experienced an accelerating field to the
target. Secondary electron emission from the target
back to the limiting aperture electrode was suppressed
by this same electric field. The electron beam created
hole-electron pairs. Those pairs created in the junction
depletion region were swept apart creating a measurable
current. Carriers which are created near the junction
and diffuse into the depletion region also contributed to
the EBI current. Utilizing d.c. current suppression,
the EBI current was measured as a function of beam position. In order to eliminate noise and drift in the d.c.
EBI signal, an alternate technique was used. A sinusoidal
potential was imposed on the grid can which modulated
the beam from full-off to full-on and a lock-in amplifier
was a.c. coupled to the signal output and tuned to the drive
frequency (40 cps).

RESULTS

In the retarding potential mode of operation, the work
function difference between two areas on the crystal surface is measured directly from the displacement on the
voltage axis between the deep retarding portions of their
respective curves. This is a direct result of $E_b = \phi t$
at the extrapolated knee and requires the further condition
that the cathode temperature remains constant. Operating
in this mode gave a series of retarding potential curves
for a 20 Ω-cm p-type silicon target which had an antimony
ion implanted n-type region. At least three important
features are indicated by these data which are shown in
Fig. 2. The small differences in work function between
the n- and p-type areas verified the expected low sensitivity
of the work function to dopant concentration [13] . The

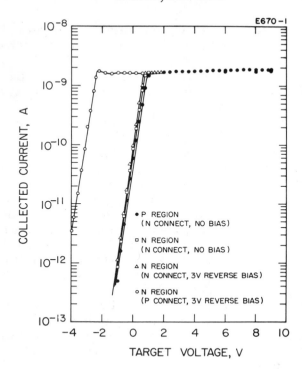

Figure 2.   Retarding potential curves for an antimony implanted
silicon junction diode.

absolute value of the work function was about 3.8 eV which
is considerably lower than 4.7 - 4.9 eV obtained by Allen
and Gobeli [13]. This was attributed to surface conditions
in that cleaved surfaces were not used. The third feature
was the displacement, caused by the external bias voltage,
of the retarding potential curve for the n-region (p-connect,
3 volt reverse bias). The designation (p-connect, 3 volt
bias), means simply that the p-region was at the applied
target voltage, V_t, while the n-region was reverse biased.
In this case, the potential of the n-region was $V = V_t + 3.0$
volts and hence its retarding potential curve was displaced
by 3 volts.

In the scanning potential mode, this type of displacement can be used to define clearly the p- and n-regions
and the intervening p-n junction in low resistivity silicon

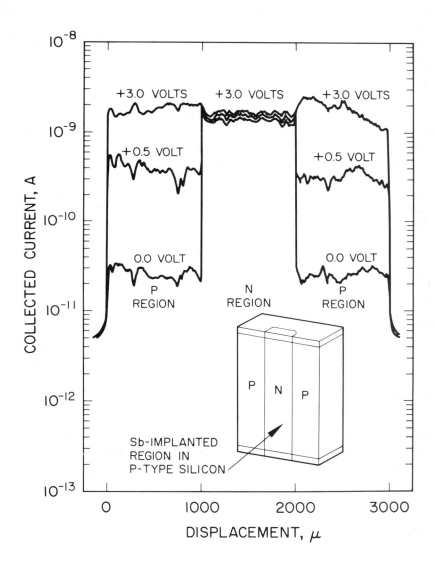

Figure 3.   Incident Beam Current vs Displacement Across an Antimony Implanted Silicon Junction Diode.

as shown in Fig. 3. The beam was scanned from one edge
of the crystal across the implanted region to the other
edge. The implanted region was held at + 3.0 volts and
the p-regions were adjusted to the potential indicated by
appropriate reverse bias voltages. Local current fluctuations were attributed to local imperfections such as
scratches, etch pits, and contaminants on the surface.

The work function of 6000 Ω-cm p-type silicon was
determined to be approximately 5.0 eV which indicated the
probable existence of a thin oxide layer on the surface.
Small departures from this value in this material were due
primarily to preferential surface treatment. Figure 4
shows the external potential drop across a crystal of this
high resistivity material in which there was located a p-n
junction about midway through the small 2-mm cube. The
location of the junction (verified by potential probe methods
and staining) coincided with the pronounced current minimum in the curve. This minimum in the beam current
was caused by a visually detectable oxide growth over the
junction. The oxide charged negatively under electron
bombardment thus reflecting most of the incident electrons.
The n-region was fixed at 3.0, 5.0 and 10.0 volts positive,
respectively, and 7 volts reverse bias was applied at the
p-side. The linear series resistance potential drop was
calculated from the reverse current and resistance of the
p-region (assuming the resistance of the n-region to be
negligible). It is interesting to note that the sharp decrease in the measured current started at those points (as
indicated) in the p-region whose voltage correspond quali-
tatively to the voltage at which the knee occurred in the
retarding potential curves for this material.

Figure 5 shows one further example of detecting externally applied voltage. A one-volt potential difference
was maintained between the two ends of an antimony implanted strip with one end of the implant fixed at the knee
voltage of the retarding potential curve. The beam
traversed the entire length of the implant and the collected
current decreased about one decade as expected from the
retarding potential curve. The decrease was linear (i.e.,
linear using semi-logarithmic representation) over approximately half the implant. The non-linearity near the

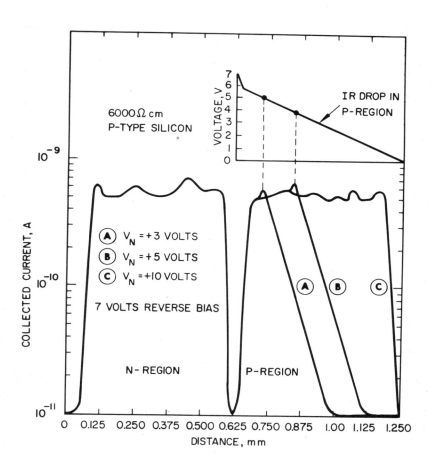

Figure 4. Incident Beam Curent vs Displacement Across a
Lithium-Diffused Silicon Junction Diode.

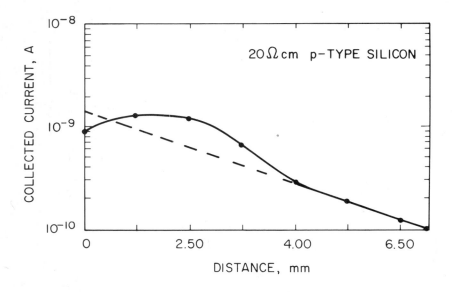

Figure 5. Incident Beam Current vs Displacement Across an Antimony Implanted Region with a 1.0 Volt Potential Difference Applied.

one end was attributed to a nonuniform implantation and/or a surface contaminant.

   Important information is gained from operating the low energy scanning microscope in the EBI current mode. The peak magnitude of the EBI current is shown as a function of beam energy in Fig. 6. These data were taken at the edge of the antimony implanted region near the center of the crystal (see Figs. 3 or 7). Three volts reverse bias was applied and the beam was scanned across the depletion region from p-type to n-type. An "effective" energy for hole-electron pair generation in silicon was estimated to be ~ 5.3 eV. This value is appreciably larger than the predicted value of 3.6 eV and does not take into consideration surface recombination and other

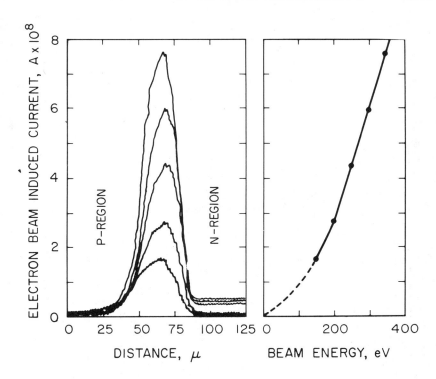

Figure 6.   Electron Beam Induced Current vs Displacement and Beam Energy for an Antimony Implanted p-n Junction.

energy loss mechanisms which become important at low beam energies. A beam diameter maximum was estimated by assuming a gaussian distribution of electrons within the beam.   The displacement between 90% and 10% of the EBI current maximum on the n-side of the junction gave an upper limit of ~ $10\,\mu$.   This agreed approximately with both the limiting aperture diameter and also the lower resolution limit obtained when a 2000-lines-per-inch nickel mesh was traversed.

The location and uniformity of depletion regions adjacent to an antimony implanted region are shown in Fig. 7.   The conditions for the scan were 10 volts reverse bias, a 40-cps modulated 200-volt electron beam, $4.5\,\mu$/sec scan rate, and a large separation ($125\,\mu$)

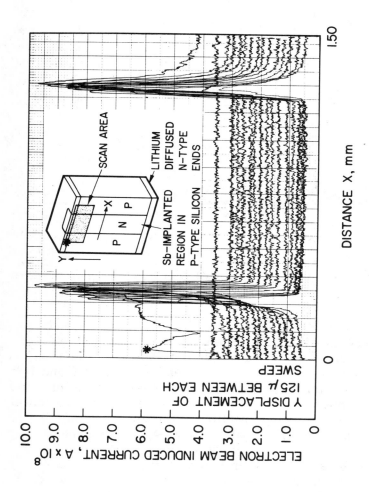

Figure 7. Two-dimensional Scan of Electron Beam Induced Current vs Displacement for an Antimony Implanted Silicon Junction Diode.

between scans in order to cover a major portion of the
implanted region. The starred scan was made at the
lithium diffused junction as indicated. A finer mesh scan
in this region revealed the slightly convex advance of the
lithium into the p-type region. Significantly absent are
protruding p-regions within the implanted region. These
so-called "pipes" can occur locally when the incoming ion
beam is stopped by dust particles and other surface contaminants before penetrating the lattice. EBI current
from imperfections less than about 0.5 μ in diameter (if
present) were lost in the background noise. Note that the
current in the implanted region is comparable to that in
the p-material (away from depletion region). The pairs
generated in the implanted region did not diffuse to the
underlying junction. At increased beam energies, there
was a spatially uniform increase (see Fig. 6) in the current for beams incident on the implanted region as compared to the base material.

SUMMARY

Low energy electron microbeam techniques for
studying semiconductor device surfaces are described.
As a means of illustrating the methods employed, antimony implanted and lithium diffused junctions in p-type
silicon were analyzed. The local surface potential was
measured, thus establishing the work function distribution
of the surface as well as detecting externally applied potentials such as junction bias and series resistance potential drops. The location and uniformity of p-n junctions
were studied by measuring the electron beam induced
current in and near the depletion regions. Imperfections
in shallow ion implanted areas were sought, but not detected. A beam diameter of about 10 μ was demonstrated.

The retarding potential technique offers the unique
ability to determine quantitatively the local surface potential. The method would seem to offer advantages as a
basic research tool for studying phenomena on cleaved,
well defined, surfaces. Because the electron energies
are low, the information obtained is related to the electric
potential distribution just outside the surface. This

technique is particularly applicable to those processes which affect the first few atomic layers of the surface. The investigation of surface states and kinetic processes such as adsorption and diffusion appear feasible.

Hole-electron pair generation by low energy electron bombardment offers one very important and unique feature. This is the analysis of shallow ion implanted regions. Detection of imperfections within the implanted areas and the measurement of junction depths appear to be possible. Both the surface potential measurements and the EBI measurements will be useful inspection tools for implanted devices during certain stages of their formation.

ACKNOWLEDGMENTS

The authors wish to thank Drs. G. R. Brewer, T. E. Everhart, and C. A. Mead for several helpful discussions. The experimental assistance of P. Coane, J. Montross, and H. Dunlap is gratefully acknowledged.

REFERENCES

1. C. W. Oatley and T. E. Everhart, J. Electronics 2, 568 (1957).
2. T. E. Everhart, K. C. A. Smith, O. C. Wells, and C. W. Oatley, Proceedings of the 4th International Conference on Electron Microscopy, Berlin, 1958, p. 269.
3. T. E. Everhart, O. C. Wells, and R. K. Matta, Proc. IEEE 52, 1642 (1964).
4. W. Czaya and J. R. Patel, J. Appl. Phys. 36, 1476 (1956).
5. D. Green and H. C. Nathanson, Proc. IEEE 53, 183 (1965).
6. H. Higuchi and M. Maki, Japan J. Appl. Phys. 4, 1021 (1965).
7. T. E. Everhart, O. C. Wells, and R. K. Matta, J. Electrochem. Soc. 111, 927 (1964).
8. P. A. Anderson, Phys. Rev. 47, 958 (1935).
9. G. A. Haas and R. E. Thomas, J. Appl. Phys. 34, 3457 (1963).

10. G. A. Haas and R. E. Thomas, Surface Sci. $\underline{4}$, 64 (1966).
11. C. Herring and M. H. Nichols, Rev. Mod. Phys. $\underline{21}$, 185 (1949).
12. H. Shelton, Phys. Rev. $\underline{107}$, 1553 (1957).
13. F. G. Allen and G. W. Gobeli, Phys. Rev. $\underline{127}$, 150 (1962).

Reflection Electron Microscopy of Electrically Active Solid Surfaces

H. Köhler*

Zentralinstitut ELTRO GMBH, Schloss Langenzell,
Germany

INTRODUCTION

Reflection electron microscopy, utilizing primary back scattered electrons, can be a powerful technique in general solid surface inspection, and particularly in inspecting electrically active solid state devices. As a matter of fact, results obtained from observing electrically active solid state devices in the reflection electron microscope do supplement similar work done with electron beam scanning machines. This was neither generally recognized nor expected, for the impressive results of electron beam scanning experiments obtained from monitoring low energy secondary electrons seemed to give little chance to obtain similar results with high energy primary back scattered electrons.

Thus it appeared to be of interest to investigate the potential of conventional reflection electron microscopy in imaging the "electrostatic state" of solid state devices. It became soon apparent that indeed significant contrast variations were obtained from solid state devices imaged with and without electrical bias applied. However, quan-

*This work was carried out at Fairchild Semiconductor, Division of Fairchild Camera and Instrument Corporation, Palo Alto, California.

titative interpretation of the observed contrast variations appears to be somewhat involved. This paper deals with some results obtained from attempts to interpret reflection micrographs of electrically active thin film capacitor configurations as well as biased p - n junctions.

INSTRUMENTATION

A detailed description of the instrumentation used has been given elsewhere (see Ref.). Therefore, only a brief reiteration of the instrument principles involved is given here.

The reflection electron microscope used consists of a Hitachi HU-11 electron microscope equipped with a long focal objective lens, and with a commercial permanent magnetic condenser lens whose optical axis is tilted in reference to the optical axis of the HU-11 electron microscope.

A specially designed specimen stage provides in addition to the convential translational motion in a x-y plane (in Fig. 1: A-B plane) specimen tilt angle ϕ (rotation about axis A-A), and azimuth control (rotation about axis B-B). Figure 1 is an illustration of these motions as well as of the specimen orientation.

A somewhat novel, but necessary, feature of this reflection electron microscopy set up is the incorporation of a low energy, secondary electron gun. With this gun, an electron beam is "sprayed" over the specimen area irradiated by the primary beam. Empirically this permits the inspection of poorly or non conducting specimen surfaces without the need for coating the specimen surface with a thin metal film. The secondary gun as used consists of a primitive home made triode structure utilizing Hitachi tungsten hairpin filaments. Both the total electron beam current and accelerating potential of this gun were selected for maximum effect and varied from case to case.

Figure 2 shows the HU-11 electron microscope in operating position for reflection electron microscopy. The primary electron gun structure is tilted at 30°. This orientation remained constant throughout our experiments.

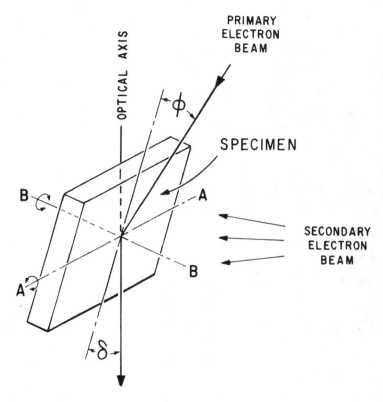

Figure 1.   Illustration of Specimen Orientation and Specimen
Rotations.

Depending upon the surface imaged, the specimen tilt was
varied from less than 1° to about 15° angle between the
primary incident electron beam and the specimen surface.
It appears obvious that the image contrast variations
obtained from electrically active devices are depending
upon the primary accelerating potential.   To provide
some flexibility in the choice of the primary accelerating
potential, the HU-11 high voltage transformer 50 kV
primary winding was attenuated by a variac.   Thus it was
possible to select and work with accelerating potentials
to as low as 20 kV.

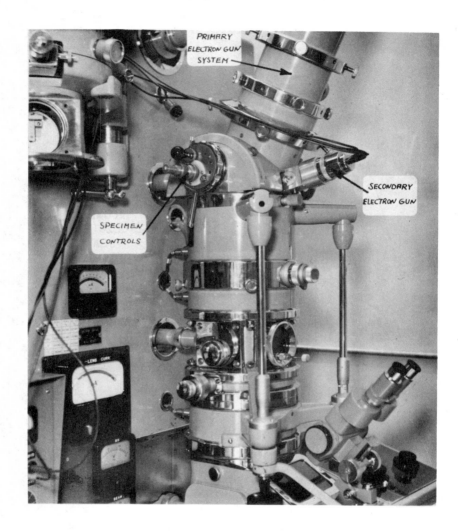

Figure 2. HU-11 Electron Microscope with Reflection Stage in Operating Position.

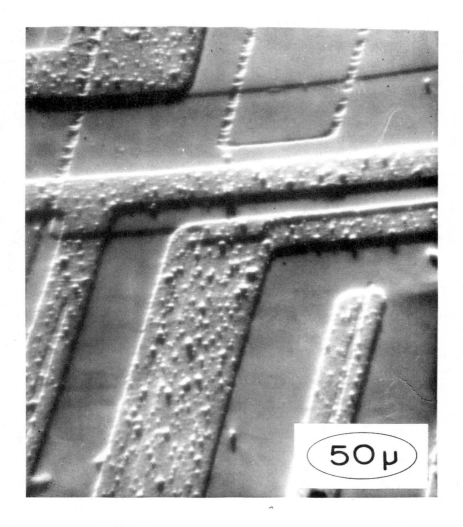

Figure 3. Section of an Integrated Microcircuit.

Naturally, for decreasing primary beam current and potential, increasing exposure times have to be used. In some applications, exposures to more than 3 minutes were needed.

Figure 3 is shown as a demonstration of the image quality obtained with the instrumentation described. It is a section of an integrated amplifier.

OBSERVATIONS ON CAPACITOR CONFIGURATIONS

As mentioned above, reflection contrast variations caused by biasing solid state devices were observed at an early stage. Figure 4 shows a section of an integrated differential amplifier; Fig. 4(a): no bias applied; Fig. 4(b): with bias.

Naturally, this and similar observations immediately raised questions about the quantitative relationship between contrast changes, primary electron beam parameters, and electrostatic bias. In an attempt to obtain well defined electrostatic field configurations for the purpose of

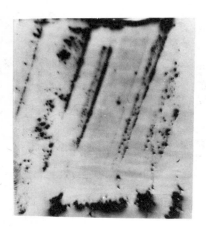 

Figure 4. Contrast Changes in a Section of an Integrated Amplifier, (a) No Bias, (b) Electrical Bias Applied.

calibrating the expected contrast changes, two different thin film capacitor geometries as illustrated in Fig. 5 were made.

Using suitable potential differences between the capacitor electrodes, both with the straight edge and with the wedge shaped capacitors, fields from 10^3 V/cm to about 9 x 10^4 V/cm were generated. These field magnitudes approach those obtained in solid state devices and they are, therefore, suitable for calibration purposes.

With the 2 capacitor geometries the following sequence of reflection electron micrographs was taken:

    a. no electrical bias

    b. positive bias applied to one electrode, and the sequence of biasing modes as illustrated in Fig. 6 applied

    c. same as b., except bias reversal.

In addition, micrographs were taken for various primary electron beam accelerating voltages (20 to 50 kv) and for various specimen tilts ϕ (from 1° to 15°).

The biasing modes as illustrated in Fig. 6 were used in order to eliminate possible ambiguities in the expected field distributions which could be expected with the substrate material choosen (Epitaxial Si; $\rho > 20$ Ω-cm). However, for all biasing modes used, no relative contrast changes were found. Therefore, no further clarification of the field distribution seemed to be necessary.

Based on the experimental results and their photometric analysis, the following were concluded:

    I. Across the gap between the capacitor electrodes, contrast changes caused by electrostatic bias are observed. They are proportional to the electric field generated in the gap.

This is illustrated in Fig. 7 which shows a straight edge capacitor, imaged at $\phi = 3°$ and $U_{PRIM} = 30$ kv. Figure 7(a) shows the capacitor with no bias applied. Figure 7(b) shows the capacitor with $U_{BIAS} = 135$ V. Figure 7(c) is as Fig. 7(b) except the bias reserved. Similarly, Fig. 8 shows a wedge shaped capacitor without, and with bias applied.

    II. Without any detailed knowledge of the bias conditions applied, immediate differentiation between positive and negative biasing polarities is possible. Thereby the positive polarity can clearly be identified as such.

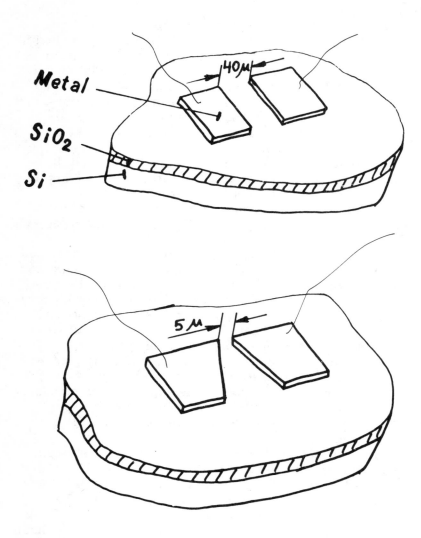

Figure 5. Illustration of Experimental Thin Film Capacitor
Geometries.

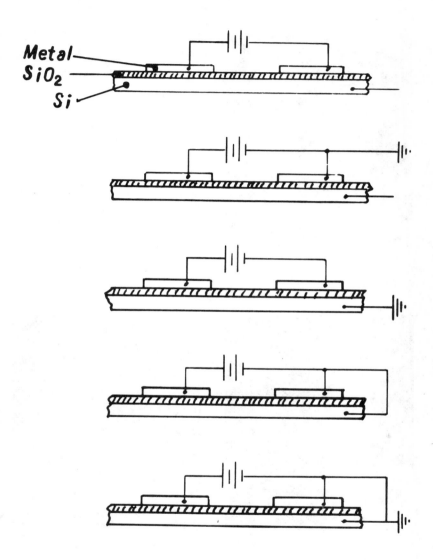

Metal
SiO₂
Si

Figure 6. Illustration of the Bias Modes Used.

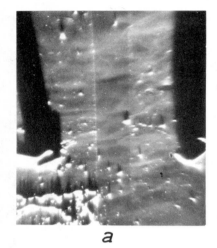

$U_{prim} = 30\ KV$

$U_{cap.\ bias} = 135\ V$

$\phi = 3°$

a

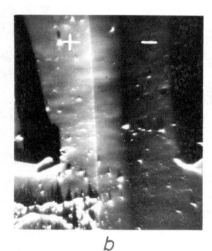

b

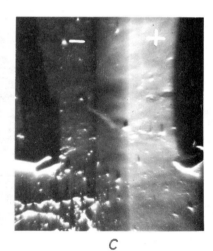

c

Figure 7.   Contrast Changes on the Straight Edge Capacitor, Caused by Electrical Bias: (a) No Bias, (b) 135 V Bias, (c) Some as b; Except Reverse Polarity.

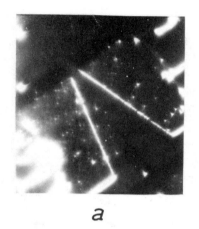

$U\,prim. = 40\,KV$

$U\,cap.\,BIAS = 200V$

$\phi = 3^{\circ}$

a

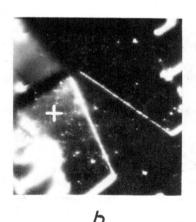

b

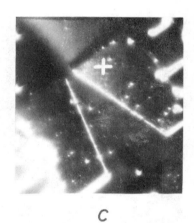

c

Figure 8. Contrast Changes on the Wedge Shaped Capacitor,
Caused by Electrical Bias: (a) No Bias, (b) 200 V Bias, (c) Some
as b; Except Reverse Polarity.

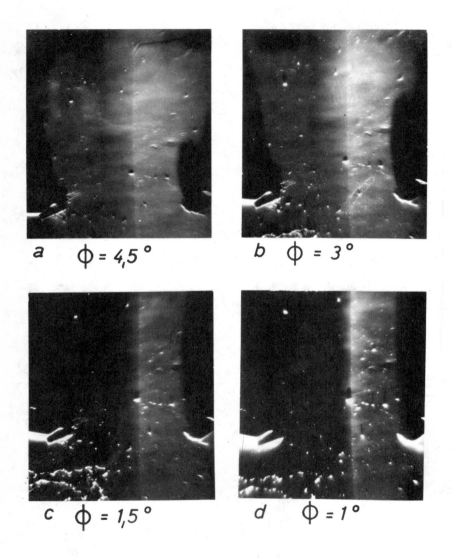

Figure 9. Influence of Specimen Tilt on the Bias Caused Contrast:
(a) $\emptyset = 4,5^{\circ}$, (b) $\emptyset = 3^{\circ}$, (c) $\emptyset = 1,5^{\circ}$, (d) $\emptyset = 1^{\circ}$.

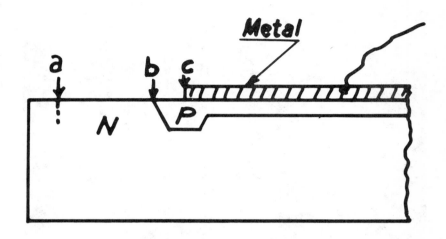

Figure 10. Illustration of the Cross Section of the Zener Diodes Used.

III. The magnitude of the contrast changes obtained is directly proportional to the specimen tilt angle ϕ, and inversely proportional to the primary beam potential.

Figure 9 shows a straight edge capacitor at constant bias (U_{BIAS} = 135 V; U_{PRIM} = 30 kV), and varying speciment tilt; Fig. 9(a): ϕ = 4.5°; Fig. 9(b): ϕ = 3°; Fig. 9(c): ϕ = 1.5°; Fig. 9(d): ϕ = 1°.

OBSERVATIONS ON ACTIVE p-n JUNCTIONS

In one of the first attempts to apply the reflection electron microscopy technique to practical problems of the solid state device design engineer, a series of reflection micrographs was taken from Zener diodes with the intent to obtain some information about the depletion layer.

Several Zener diodes of identical breakdown (76 V) were selected and the protective silicone oxide layer was removed from the junction region. Figure 10 is an illustration of the cross section of the diodes used.

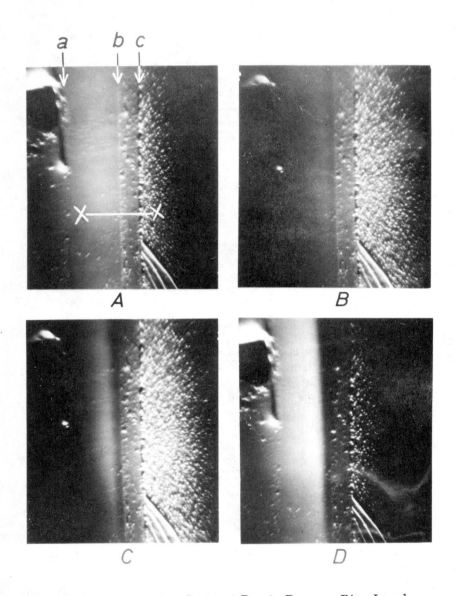

Figure 11. p–n Junction Contrast Due to Reverse Bias Levels:
(a) No Bias. (b) 22.5 V Reverse Bias, (c) 45 V Reverse Bias,
(d) 67.5 V Reverse Bias.

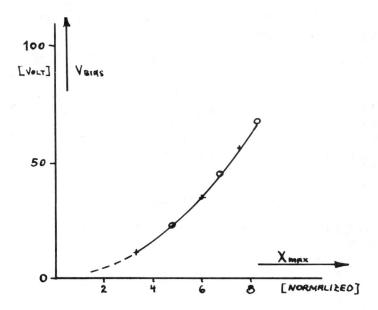

Figure 12.   Position of Maximum Electric "Junction Field"
Plotted as Function of Reverse Bias Magnitude.

Reflection micrographs of the biased junction region
show contrast changes as can be seen in Fig. 11.   Figure
11(a):   no bias;   Fig. 11(b):   22. 5 V reverse bias;   Fig.
11(c):   45 V reverse bias;   Fig. 11(d) 67. 55 V reverse bias.
For identification, the letters in Fig. 11(a) refer to the
identical ones in Fig. 10.

The pictures show dark fringes extending from the
metallurgical junction (line b in Fig. 11(a)), into the N-
type material.   These fringes obviously are regions of
negative polarity.   Photometer scans along X-X were
made and the band widths plotted vs reverse bias levels.

Figure 12 shows a plot including the values of Figs.
11(b) through 11(d).   The resulting relationship

$$X = K \cdot V_{BIAS}^{1/2}$$

corresponds indeed to the depletion layer vs bias dependence of a step junction.

ACKNOWLEDGMENTS

The author expresses his sincerest gratitude to Dr. G. Moore who created the working environment which made this work possible; to Dr. H. Sello for stimulating discussions; and to Mr. D. Mattern and Mr. R. Warncke for their endurance and assistance in securing much of the material published.

REFERENCE

Versatile Electron Microscope Reflection Stage and its Application.

H. Köhler and G. Cooper

Rev. Sci. Instr. Vol. 36 No. 7 1005 (1965).

Measurement of the Mean Energy for Electron-Hole Pair Formation in Silicon by Low-Energy Electron Bombardment

C. B. Norris, Jr. and J. F. Gibbons

Stanford Electronics Laboratories
Stanford University
Stanford, California

INTRODUCTION

It seems well established that, when single-crystal silicon is bombarded by high-energy electrons, electron-hole pairs are created at the average rate of one pair for every 3.5 to 3.6 eV of kinetic energy initially in the bombarding electron, and that this value is essentially independent of initial electron energy. Specifically, Koch, Messier, and Valin [1] obtain ε pair = 3.53 ± 0.07 eV for bombardment with 279 keV electrons. However, for the stopping of lower-energy electrons in silicon, previous experimental results have not been as conclusive. Vavilov [2] gives ε pair = 4.2 ± 0.6 eV, based on bombardment with 10 to 30 keV electrons, while Brown [3] finds that ε pair = 4.7 eV for bombardment with 19 keV electrons.

In the low-energy experiments of Vavilov and Brown, the measurement of ε pair was accomplished by initially generating electron-hole pairs in the space-charge neutral body of a p-n diode. Transport of minority carriers by diffusion to the depletion region of a reverse-biased junction then gives rise to an increase in reverse-bias junction current. The number of pairs generated per bombarding electron was obtained by comparing the increment in reverse-bias junction current, corrected for recombination losses which the minority carriers suffer in reaching the high-field region, to the beam current. This correction

933

is based on measured values of low-level carrier lifetimes and is necessary because of the difficulty of fabricating a good junction near enough to the surface to obtain
generation directly in the depletion region from low-
energy bombardment.

However, even for arbitrarily low beam currents, it
seems likely that the local density of carriers in the region
of bombardment ionization is sufficiently great to invali-
date the use of a low-level lifetime in making the corrections for recombination necessary to obtain $\mathscr{E}$ pair with
this experimental arrangement.

In contrast to the experimental results we have mentioned, the simple theory given by Shockley [4] for
electron-hole pair creation in semiconductors by energetic particle bombardment predicts that

$$\mathscr{E} \text{ pair} = 2.2 \, \mathscr{E}_i + r \, \mathscr{E}_R$$

where

$\mathscr{E}_i$ = Band Gap Energy

r = # of phonon scattering events, assumed to
involve only phonons of energy $\mathscr{E}_R$, per
ionizing collision.

$\mathscr{E}_R$ = Energy of Raman Phonons

For silicon, evaluation of these quantities from independent observations gives

$$\mathscr{E} \text{ pair} = 3.6 \text{ eV}$$

Shockley's result is independent of the energy of the
bombarding particle so long as this energy is much greater
than energies characteristic of the band structure, which
should be true for particles having energies down into the
low keV region.

It is therefore of interest from a purely physical
standpoint to attempt more accurate determination of $\mathscr{E}$
pair. Furthermore, electron-hole pair creation in semiconductors by low-energy electron bombardment is the
basis for a class of high-gain, high-speed active devices
employing modulated or deflected electron beams and

reverse-biased p-n junctions. Accurate predictions of the characteristics and properties of these devices requires knowledge of ε pair, making it of interest to investigate the difference between expected and observed values of ε pair for low-energy electron bombardment.

In order to obtain a more accurate measurement of ε pair in silicon, it was proposed to fabricate the devices to be bombarded so as to minimize the corrections required for recombination. Since the range of a 10 keV electron is of the order of 1 micron in silicon, this result may be accomplished by fabricating a junction a distance of the order of 1000 Å from the device surface.

The fabrication of such diodes has been accomplished in the manner we describe in Section II. In Section III we consider energy losses of the bombarding electrons in reaching the depletion region of these diodes, and in Section IV we show that carriers generated in the bulk silicon are collected with negligible losses due to recombination or gains due to high-field multiplication. Section V deals with experimental apparatus, procedures, and raw data, and in Section VI we present the reduced data allowing determination of ε pair.

DIODE FABRICATIONS

The diodes employed in these measurements were fabricated simultaneously on a piece of Monsanto n^-/n^+ epitaxial silicon.

Basic Process

Microcircuits techniques were employed to obtain uniform devices with protected junction edges. Following thermal growth of a layer of SiO_2 on top of the 7.5 ohm - cm n-type epitaxial layer, circular windows 70 mils in diameter were etched in the oxide using standard photolithographic techniques. An aluminum film nominally 1000 Å in thickness was evaporated through a mask onto the exposed silicon and enough of the surrounding oxide to form a reliable contact area and insure protection of the junction edges.

Film thickness was determined by weighing, before and after removal of the film, small glass plates placed next to the silicon wafer during evaporation. The mass thickness obtained in this way represents the originally evaporated Al and the $Al_2 O_3$ that forms on exposure to air. The determination of film thickness was carried out after completion of the alloying process described next.

Alloying Operation

Without exposure to air, the evaporated Al film was alloyed into the lightly-doped n-type silicon exposed by the oxide windows. At the maximum temperature reached in this operation the Al and Si form a molten alloy whose composition may be obtained from the phase diagram for the Al-Si system. On cooling, the dissolved silicon begins to recrystallize on the substrate, at each point doped with Al to a level determined by the solid solubility of Al in Si, which depends on the temperature of the system when re-crystallization occurs at the point in question. For the present situation we find from the data of Trumbore[5] that the doping level of the p^+ recrystallized Si is roughly constant and of the order of $10^{19}/cm^3$. The recrystal-lization continues until the eutectic temperature and eutectic concentration are reached, at which point the Al-Si eutectic freezes.

From these considerations we may calculate the structure in the region of alloying knowing the original Al film thickness and the maximum temperature of the alloy-ing operation. For Tmax = 700°C, we find the thickness of the p^+ recrystallized layer as

$$t_{p^+} \cong 0.12 \, t_{Al}$$

and the thickness of the Al-Si eutectic layer as

$$t_{Al-Si} \cong 1.15 \, t_{Al}$$

where t_{Al} is the Al film thickness before alloying. The fractional increase in the mass per unit area of the original Al film is approximately 0.128.

Diode Structure

The results of this fabrication procedure is the formation of a step p^+ - n^- junction of the order of t_{Al} from
the surface. The structure of the resulting diodes, calculated as outlined above for the measured film thickness
with correction for oxidation from the data of Vernon [6].,
is shown in Fig. 1. It is assumed that, on exposure of the
alloyed diodes to air, a layer of oxidation forms at approximately the same rate as on pure Al. The mass-
thickness of the diode dead zone obtained from the above
considerations is 33.5 ± 2 $\mu g/cm^2$.

These diodes exhibit excellent electrical characteristics, with reverse leakage that is negligible compared
to 10 μA, the lowest bombardment-induced reverse current
employed in these experiments, for reverse voltages of
the order of 10 volts.

ELECTRON-BEAM ENERGY LOSSES

We now consider the effects of the dead-zone on the
incident electron beam. It is useful for this purpose to
define a quantity e_T such that the energy entering the
bulk silicon per unit time is

$$\frac{de_{in}}{dt} = \frac{I_B}{q} e_T \quad . \tag{1}$$

e_T would be the mean energy of electrons transmitted
through the dead zone if the current from bombarding
electrons entering the bulk silicon were equal to the incident beam current. With this definition,

$$e_{pair} = \frac{e_T(e_B)}{N(e_B)} \quad , \tag{2}$$

where $N(e_B)$ is the average number of electron-hole
pairs generated per bombarding electron of energy e_B.
Evaluation of $N(e_B)$ from measurements of bombardment-induced diode current will be considered in the following section.

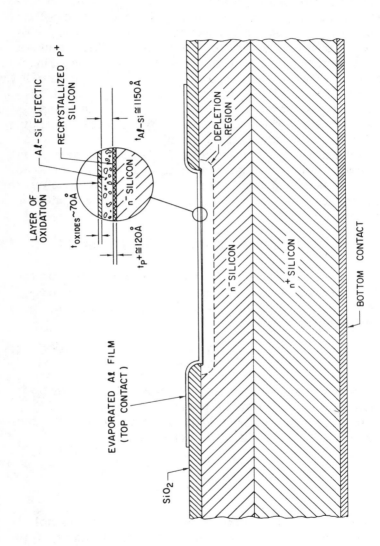

Figure 1.   Diode Structure.   (Not to Scale).

Backscattering

In relating $\mathcal{E}_T$ to $\mathcal{E}_B$, we must consider beam energy losses arising from backscattering as well as from energy dissipation in the dead zone. As shown in the data compiled by Sternglass [7], for solid elements of atomic number between 6 and 29 the fraction of incident particles backscattered is approximately independent of electron bombardment energy from 1 to over 100 keV and the mean energy of backscattered electrons is closely equal to $0.5\mathcal{E}_B$ for bombardment energies between 2 and 32 keV.

As the backscattered fraction is a slowly-increasing function of atomic number, we estimate the backscattering coefficient of the composite structure under consideration from the data for aluminum. In this way we obtain from the data of Sternglass [7] and Holliday and Sternglass [8] an average beam energy loss from backscattering, $\mathcal{E}_R$, that varies between $0.057\,\mathcal{E}_B$ and $0.070\,\mathcal{E}_B$ as $\mathcal{E}_B$ varies from 4 to 14 keV.

Transmission Losses

We next consider the dissipation of beam energy in the dead zone. Since Kanter [9] and Holliday and Sternglass [10] as well as other authors have shown that stopping power data as a function of mass-thickness is approximately independent of atomic number, we may estimate the energy loss in the composite $Al-Si-Al_2O_3-SiO_2$ dead zone from published data for aluminum. For the dead-zone mass thickness determined earlier, we employ the data given by Kanter [11] for electron energy dissipation within thin aluminum foils and the backscattering corrections described earlier to obtain the graph of $\mathcal{E}_T$ vs. $\mathcal{E}_B$ given in Fig. 2.

Although these dead-zone corrections are adequate for the present purpose, we remark before continuing that the dead-zone actually causes slightly more energy loss than estimated above. Kanter's data is for energy dissipation within thin, self-supporting foils and is corrected for the backscattering that occurs from each foil. As may be seen from the work of Kanter [12] and Holliday and

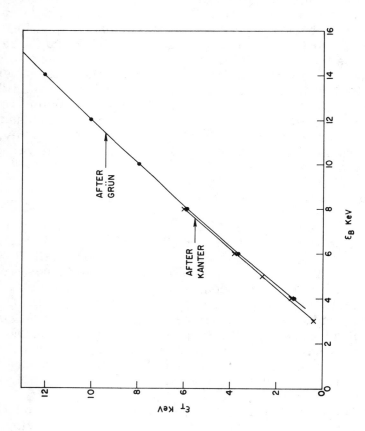

Figure 2.   Beam Energy-Loss Corrections for 33.5 $\mu g/cm^2$ Diode Dead Zone.

Sternglass [8] a substantial fraction of the backscattered electrons originates at depths greater than the dead-zone considered here. For given conditions of bombardment we thus have more electrons entering a supported foil than an unsupported one with a resulting increase in the total energy absorbed by the foil. This effect is not significant in the present situation.

An alternate estimate of electron beam energy losses in the dead zone may be made from the data obtained by Grün [13] for the stopping of low-energy electrons in gases. On the assumption that beam electrons dissipate energy in the dead zone according to the normalized depth-dose functions in this reference, we employ these data and electron mass-thickness ranges in aluminum given for various energies by Schlonland, [14] Holliday and Sternglass, [15] and Kanter [16] to estimate the average beam energy dissipated in the dead zone. With corrections for backscattering applied as before, we obtain for the dead-zone under consideration the relation between ℓ_T and ℓ_B as shown in Fig. 2.

The agreement between dead-zone corrections derived from the data of Kanter and Grün is excellent.

FACTORS AFFECTING COLLECTION OF BOMBARD-MENT-GENERATED CARRIERS

We consider now the measurement of $N(\ell_B)$, the average number of pairs created per bombarding electron of energy ℓ_B. We refer for simplicity to a diode constructed as in Fig. 1 with matters arranged so that the depletion region extends past the maximum depth of bombardment ionization.

Junction Characteristics

On the assumption that the space charge from carriers in the depletion region is negligible in comparison to space charge from ionized impurity atoms, we obtain from the first-order theory of the one-dimensional step junction the approximate charge density, electric field, and potential as shown in Fig. 3. The corresponding algebraic

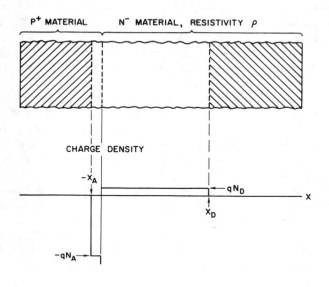

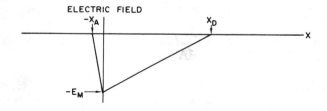

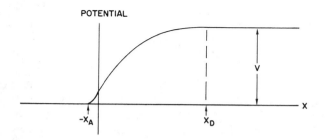

Figure 3.   Step p-n Junction.

analysis yields, for the present case of an abrupt p^+ - n^- junction in silicon, the convenient formulae

$$\frac{x_A}{x_D} = \frac{N_D}{N_A} \sim 10^{-4} \ll 1$$

$$x_D \cong 0.52 \sqrt{\rho V} \quad \text{micron} \tag{3}$$

$$E_m \cong 38 \times 10^3 \sqrt{\frac{V}{\rho}} \quad \frac{\text{volts}}{\text{cm}} \quad . \tag{4}$$

In (3) and (4) ρ is the numerical value of resistivity of the n^- silicon, measured in ohm-cm, and V is the numerical value of potential change across the junction, measured in volts.

We thus see that holes produced in the depletion region by bombardment ionization drift toward x_A and electrons toward x_D.   For $\rho \sim 8$ ohm-cm and $V \sim 8$ volts we obtain a depletion region about 4 microns thick with a maximum field of about 40,000 volts/cm.

Carrier Collection

Considering a volume V chosen as in Fig. 4, we integrate the time-static electron continuity equation

$$-\frac{1}{q} (\nabla \cdot \vec{j}_n) = g_n - r_n \tag{5}$$

where

$\vec{j}_n$ = electron current density

g_n = electron generation rate per unit volume

r_n = electron recombination rate per unit volume

q = magnitude of electronic charge

to obtain

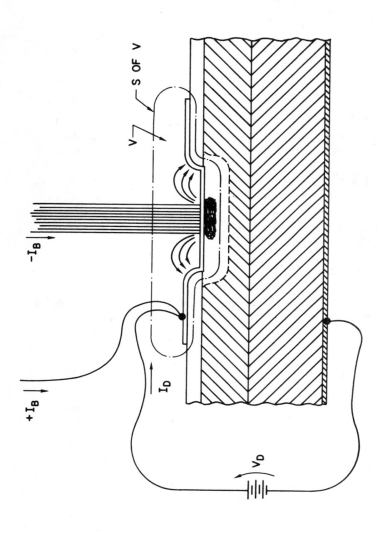

Figure 4. **Showing** the Volume V. It is assumed that Secondary Emission Current is Returned to the Top Contact or Neglected Entirely.

$$-\frac{1}{q} \oint_S \vec{j}_n \cdot \vec{ds} = \int_V (g_n - r_n) dV .   (6)$$

From continuity of total current, this becomes

$$-\frac{1}{q} I_D = \int_V (g_n - r_n) dV .   (7)$$

If carrier generation due to avalanche multiplication or thermal processes is negligible, and if recombination is also negligible, then

$$\frac{1}{q} |I_D| = \int_V g_n dV = \frac{1}{q} |I_B| N   (8)$$

so that we may obtained $N(\mathcal{e}_B)$ as

$$N(\mathcal{e}_B) = \left| \frac{I_D}{I_B} \right| .   (9)$$

$N(\mathcal{e}_B)$ is the average number of electron-hole pairs created in the silicon per bombarding electron of energy $\mathcal{e}_B$.

Generation and Multiplication

We now consider the validity of applying eqn. (9) to the present situation. As we shall see from the V-I characteristics presented later, reverse diode current originating from thermal generation in the depletion region is negligible compared to currents resulting from typical conditions of bombardment employed in this work.

In order to estimate the effect of avalanche multiplication of currents in the depletion region, we employ the first-order theory of this process based on the assumption of equal ionization coefficients for holes and electrons. From this we obtain

$$\frac{I}{I_0} = \frac{1}{1 - \int_{-x_A}^{x_D} \alpha(E[x]) \, dx} \tag{10}$$

where

　　I_0 = junction current in absence of avalanche
　　　　　multiplication
　　I　= junction current with avalance multiplication
　　$\alpha(E)$= probability of a carrier producing a secondary
　　　　　pair per centimeter.

For values typical of these experiments, $\rho \sim 8$ ohm-cm,
$V < 8$ volts, we see from eqn (4), that $E_m \lesssim 5 \times 10^4$
volts/cm. From the data collected by Moll [17] we find
for these conditions that, although $\alpha(E)$ is quite different
for holes and electrons, $\alpha(E_m) < 10$ for $E_m < 10^5$ volts/
cm, and hence

$$\int_{-x_A}^{x_D} \alpha(E) \, dx < \alpha(E_m) \, x_D < 2.5 \times 10^{-3} \quad ,$$

so that $I \cong I_0$, and avalanche multiplication is negligible.
This conclusion is supported by the negligible dependence
of bombardment-induced reverse diode current on reverse
voltage exhibited in Fig. 5.

Recombination

　　Estimation of recombination effects requires consideration of the processes involved in the separation of
bombardment-generated electron-hole pairs and the
transport of the resulting carriers. Unpublished experimental work with similar devices under 10-kV pulsed-
beam electron bombardment suggests that the time for
charge separation is less than 10^{-9} sec in electric fields
of 10^4 volts/cm or greater.

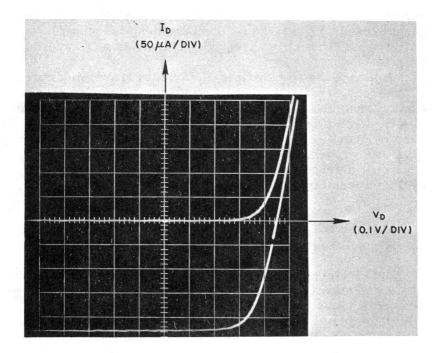

Figure 5.   Typical Diode V-I Characteristic for I_B = 0 and I_B = 0.23 μA. $\mathcal{E}_B$ = 6 keV

   After separation, the carriers traverse a region where the electric field is a function of distance and may have such magnitude that the mobility is not constant. Recombination affecting collection of bombardment-generated carriers created between x_A and x_R can occur only over this region, as electrons move toward x_D and holes toward x_A. Hence it is of interest to estimate the maximum time required for carriers to traverse the region of generation.

   It is adequate for this purpose to consider a situation where $x_D \sim 2x_R$, so that the minimum field for $0 \leq x \leq x_R$ is $E_m/2$. For fields of the order of 20,000 volts/cm, the data of Prior [18] show that carriers in silicon have drift velocities in excess of 3×10^6 cm/sec. Thus for the diodes employed here the transit time of carriers through $0 \leq x \leq x_R$ is less than 10^{-10} sec. We thus expect that recombination is negligble in this region; this conclusion is supported by the fact that bombardment-induced reverse diode current is essentially independent of reverse voltage.

Although the transit time of carriers traversing the p^+ recrystallized region is by no means so small, continuity considerations show that only carriers generated in this region may suffer recombination. If, at worst, all such carriers recombine, then we have in essence another 3 $\mu g/cm^2$ of dead-zone. As even this extreme situation would not markedly affect the results presented here, we neglect recombination in the p^+ layer.

EXPERIMENT

Experimental Apparatus

The electrical source employed for these measurements was a commercial gun designed for magnetic-deflection kinescope tubes. The gun was fitted with electrostatic deflection plates for convenience in the present application. Deflection potentials were derived from multi-turn potentiometers for accuracy in positioning the electron beam.

The gun was mounted above a massive aluminum heat sink in an oil-free bell-jar type vacuum system. Such a system was employed to eliminate concern over inaccuracies due to accumulated oil films on the diode surfaces. The diodes previously described were bonded with silver conductive paint to an aluminum sample holder, which was bolted to the heat sink beneath the electron gun.

The spot size of the electron beam was evaluated roughly from observations on a phosphor-coated focusing area immediately adjacent to the diode. It was concluded from direct observation at low beam currents and examination of melted regions in the phosphor after high-current bombardment that most of the energy of the beam was confined to an area about 1/10 that of the diode.

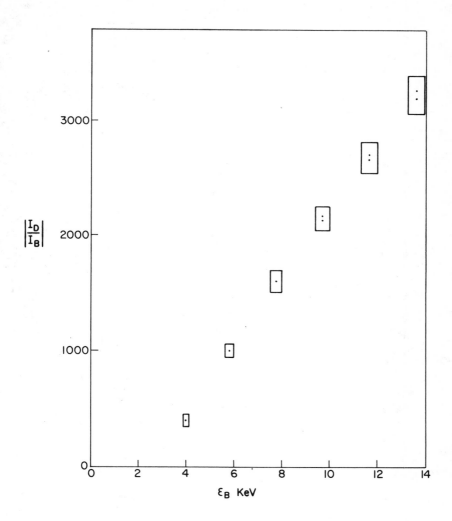

Figure 6.   Experimental **Data** for a Typical Diode.

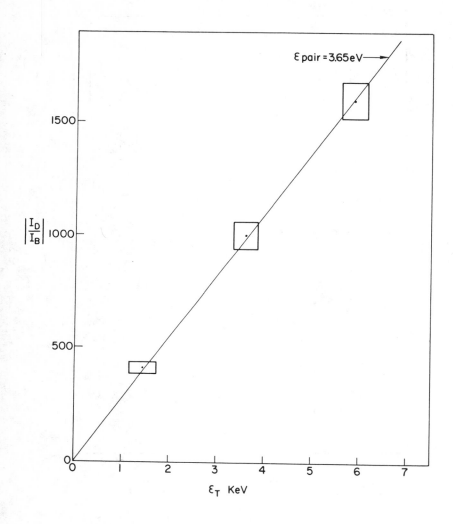

Figure 7(a). Typical Plot of $\left|\dfrac{I_D}{I_B}\right|$ vs. $\mathcal{E}_T$, Based on Dead-zone Corrections from Kanter's Data.

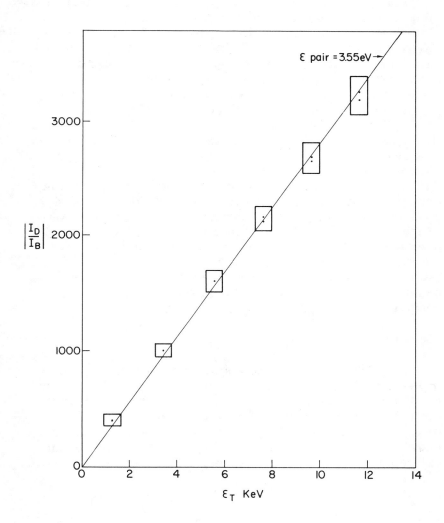

Figure 7(b). Typical Plot of $\left| \dfrac{I_D}{I_B} \right|$ vs. ε_T , Based on Dead-Zone Corrections from Grün's Data.

Experimental Procedure

Prior to measurements on a diode at a given bombardment energy, the beam was centered on the diode by employing the average of the deflecting plate potentials corresponding to the edges of the diode area. No significant
variation of beam-induced diode current was noted as the
beam was scanned across the diode, except at the edges.
Here a slight increase of diode current was seen, probably due to multiplication of injected carriers in the
higher fields at the diode edges.

With the beam centered on the diode, data were taken
at a given energy and beam current by photographing a
curve tracer display of the diode V-I characteristics
during bombardment. In this way it was insured that the
bombardment-induced diode current was independent of
diode reverse bias. The curve-tracer display was photographed again, on the same negative, immediately after
bombardment to observe possible alteration of diode
characteristics due to thermal heating or other effects.
Data were taken typically over more than a decade of
beam current; the beam currents used in these results
ranged from 0.01 μA to 30 μA.

Experimental Data

A typical measurement obtained in this way is shown
in Fig. 5. Data typical of those obtained for 3 diodes are
presented in Fig. 6. For a given bombardment energy,
the ratio of diode current to beam current was found to
be independent of beam current within experimental error,
showing that space-charge effects are not influencing the
collection efficiency of the diodes.

DETERMINATION OF $\mathcal{e}_{PAIR}$

We may now proceed to evaluate $\mathcal{e}_{pair}$ from eqns. (2) and (9) as

$$\mathcal{e}_{pair} = \frac{\mathcal{e}_T(\mathcal{e}_B)}{\left| \dfrac{I_D}{I_B}(\mathcal{e}_B) \right|}$$

or   (11)

$$\left| \frac{I_D}{I_B}(\mathcal{e}_B) \right| = \frac{\mathcal{e}_T(\mathcal{e}_B)}{\mathcal{e}_{pair}}$$

Relating $\mathcal{e}_T$ to $\mathcal{e}_B$ from earlier work, we may obtain $\mathcal{e}_{pair}$ as the reciprocal slope of a graph of $|I_D/I_B|$ vs $\mathcal{e}_T$. Figure 7 shows such graphs derived from the dead-zone corrections obtained earlier. $\mathcal{e}_{pair}$ is seen to be essentially independent of effective bombardment energy down to the order of 1 keV. Averaging the results from three similar diodes, dead-zone corrections based on Kanter's data give $\mathcal{e}_{pair}$ = 3.68 eV for $\mathcal{e}_T$ between 1.4 and 5.9 keV. From Grün's data, $\mathcal{e}_{pair}$ = 3.54 eV for $\mathcal{e}_T$ between 1.2 and 11.7 keV. Consideration of possible sources of error in these measurements shows that the maximum uncertainty in $\mathcal{e}_{pair}$ is ± 0.3 eV.

ACKNOWLEDGMENT

The authors wish to thank Profs. G. S. Kino and T. E. Everhart for their suggestions and comments concerning this work, and W. P. Kruger at Hewlett-Packard Company for providing the electron gun employed for these measurements.

This work was performed under support of Air Force Contract AF 33(657)-11144.

One of us (CBN) wishes to acknowledge fellowship support by the National Science Foundation during this work.

REFERENCES

1. I. R. E. Trans. Nucl. Sci. NS-8, 43 (1961).
2. J. Phys. Chem. Solids 8, 223-6 (1959).
3. IEEE Trans. Elec. Devices, ED-10:1, 8-12 (1963).
4. Solid State Electronics, 2:1, 44-45 (1961).
5. Bell System Tech. Journal, 39, pp. 205-234 (1960).
6. Trans. Faraday Soc., 23: pp. 152-3 (1927).
7. Phys. Rev. 95:2, p. 355 (1954).
8. J. Appl. Phys. 28:10, 1192 (1957).
9. Phys. Rev. 121:2, 466 (1961).
10. J. Appl. Phys. 30:9, 1428 (1959).
11. Phys. Rev. 121:3, 678 (1961).
12. Phys. Rev. 121:3, 682 (1961).
13. Z. Naturforsch 12A, 89-95 (1957).
14. Proc. Roy. Soc (London) A108, 187 (1925).
15. J. A. P. 30:9, 1430 (1959).
16. Phys. Rev. 126:2, 621 (1962).
17. Physics of Semiconductors, p. 222 (McGraw-Hill, 1964).
18. J. Phys. Chem. Sol. 12:2, 175 (1960).

The Spatial Distribution of Secondary
Electron Emission

R. F. W. Pease

Department of Electrical Engineering
University of California
Berkeley, California

INTRODUCTION

In scanning electron microscopy, a picture of the specimen surface is built up by scanning the surface with a fine electron beam and using the signal derived from the emitted electrons to build up an image in a cathode ray tube. The resolution obtained depends not only on the size of the primary beam, but also on the size of the area emitting electrons. The emitted electrons fall roughly into two classes: the reflected, or backscattered, electrons with energies comparable with the primary beam energy (generally about 15 kV), and the secondary electrons with typical energies of a few electron volts. Either or both of these classes of electrons may be used to form the image. Although some idea of the area emitting electrons can be obtained by examining micrographs of familiar specimens, the difficulty of preparing an ideal specimen and examining it under completely understood contrast conditions made quantitative measurements difficult.

A method of directly determining the area of emission of backscattered electrons was described by Pease [1] who used this area as a source for a reflection-point projection system. The results were chiefly of interest for scanning electron microscopy using backscattered electron collection.

For high resolution work, however, it is the area of
(low voltage) secondary electron emission which is the
more important in determining the limitation to microscope performance. [2]

This paper describes a method of determining this
area.

EXPERIMENTAL METHOD

The principle of the method is shown in Fig. 1. As
the electron beam is moved from left to right, scattered
electrons emerging through the thin insulating layer
underneath the top electrode create hole electron pairs
in the insulator and cause a current to flow which is recorded in the meter. This effect is frequently known as
electron beam-induced conductivity and has been described by Pensak [3], Ansbacher and Ehrenberg [4],
and others. The induced current, I_D, will continue to
rise as the area of scattered electrons is moved across
the electrode edge (position x_0) until this area is entirely
to the right of x_0. Thus, by measuring the distance
traveled by the beam to raise I_D to its maximum value, it
is possible to obtain an estimate of the area of scattered
electrons. This estimate will be in error due to the fact
that the lower energy electrons are the more productive
of induced current and the quantity measured is not

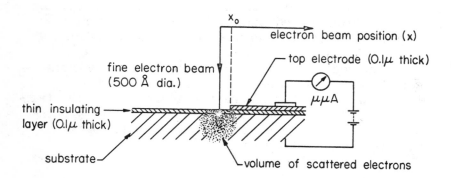

Figure 1. Schematic View of Experimental Arrangement.

distribution of scattered electrons but energy dissipation. Hence, for regions near the surface, a measure of the radial extent of secondary electron emission is obtained. [7] As a partial check, it was confirmed experimentally that the ratio of secondary electron current to I_D was constant over the range of primary beam energies used.

Experiments so far have been confined to heavily doped silicon substrates with a thermally grown SiO_2 insulating layer 0.10 or 0.15 μm thick. The top electrodes were evaporated aluminum about 0.1 μm thick. By making the top electrode sufficiently small (17 μm x 0.010 in.) it was found that the leakage current could be reduced to a value neglible compared with I_D.

The target assembly was viewed in the scanning electron microscope and a suitably sharp and straight portion of the aluminum electrode edge was selected. The scan generators were then switched off and the beam moved slowly across the edge; the distance moved was known from the magnification calibration of the microscope.

Initial experiments gave inconclusive results for two reasons:

1. I_D decreased with time, due possibly to trapped carriers setting up an opposing field; [5]

2. I_D varied with primary current density; it was even found possible to focus the primary electron beam by adjusting the final lens current for minimum I_D.

The first drawback was overcome by adjusting the bias across the insulator so that I_D remained constant; a value of 28 volts across 1500 Å SiO_2, or 22.5 volts across 1000 Å SiO_2, was generally found to be suitable, irrespective of polarity.

The second difficulty was avoided by using beam current of 10^{-11} amps or less. It was then checked experimentally that the induced current was proportional to the primary current and was independent of the primary current density.

EXPERIMENTAL RESULTS

Some results taken from a specimen with a layer of SiO_2 0.1 μm thick and an Al electrode about 0.1 μm thick are shown in Fig. 2. To get sufficient signal, it was found necessary to tilt the specimen by 45°; this is the usual configuration for scanning electron microscopy, but most scanning X-ray microanalyzers use a beam that is normal to the surface.

Figure 2(a) shows the results for a primary beam voltage of 25 kV and these can be compared with the results shown in Fig. 2(b) for the same specimen region but with a beam of 15 kV.

It was observed that the values of I_D were more repeatable when the beam struck regions not covered with

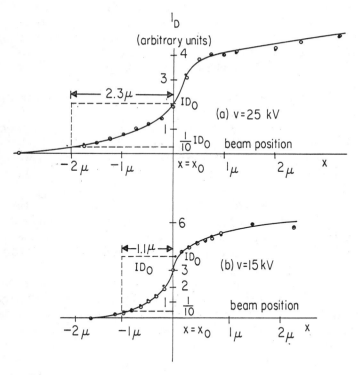

Figure 2.   Measurements of I_D as a Function of Beam Position.

the top electrode; this may have been due to unevenness in the Al film, but, as a result, values of I_D for beam positions to the left of the electrode edge (i. e. , $x < x_0$) were regarded as more significant. It can be seen that I_D has a measurable value for beam positions further from x_0 when $V = 25$ kV than when $V = 15$ kV. For $V = 15$ kV, $I_D = 0.1$ of its value at $x = x_0$ when $x_0 - x = 1.1 \mu m \pm 0.3 \mu m$. For $V = 25$ kV, the comparable value of $x_0 - x$ is $2.3 \mu m \pm 0.3 \mu m$. Results shown in Fig. 2 are for the most satisfactory specimen, i. e. , that with the thinnest SiO_2 and Al layers and with the straightest and the sharpest edges, but experiments on six other specimens all gave results which agreed with the above values within the stated accuracy of the experiment. Moreover, reversing the polarity of the bias, apart from reversing the direction of I_D, made no appreciable difference to the results obtained.

These results suggest that the area of emission of secondary electrons is considerably larger than the corresponding area of backscattered electron emission. [1] It is also interesting to note that in each case the radius of the emission area is about one third of the effective range of the primary electron as given by Holliday and Sternglass. [6]

The sources of error in measuring the beam travel are the finite size of the electron beam (0.05 μm dia.), the wobble of the electron beam due to 60 c. p. s. magnetic fields (0.1 μm peak to peak for $V = 15$ kV) and the uncertainty in the position of the electrode edge due to its roughness and thickness (0.2 μm). The accuracy of the values of I_D is ± 10 percent as estimated from the repeatability of its readings; errors may also be due to local variations in the thickness and composition of the SiO_2 film and the substrate and also due to the deposition of contamination by the electron beam.

Two possible sources of error are:

1. Carriers generated away from the electrode diffusing to the electrode region and contributing towards I_D, and

2. The drift field region extending to the left of the electrode edge and again causing carriers generated to the left of the electrode region to contribute to I_D.

However, had these errors been appreciable, the value of
I_D when $x = x_0$ would have been greater than one-half I_D
max. In fact, it was observed that the value of I_D for
$x = x_0$ was generally slightly less than one-half I_D max.

CONCLUSIONS AND FUTURE WORK

A method of determining the distribution of scattered
electrons at the surface of a flat target has been demonstrated. Since the method of detecting the scattered electrons depends on their energy in a manner similar to that
of secondary emission, it is felt that the method described
gives a more accurate measure of the distribution of
secondary electrons than of scattered electrons. Future
work will extend the range of beam energies and target
materials. It is also planned that a target be prepared
in which the substrate is a thin film (about 0.05 μm
thick); experiments on such a target would then give an
overall measure of the accuracy of the experiment since
backscattering from the substrate would be virtually
eliminated.

It should be possible to extend the method described
to determine the distribution of energy dissipation at any
given depth in the target. This could be done by depositing
a further thin layer of insulator on the target assembly
surface and then the required depth of substrate material.
Hence, it is hoped that a complete picture of the distribution of energy dissipation in the target can be built up.

ACKNOWLEDGMENT

The author is indebted to the staff of the Semiconductor Research Laboratory for the preparation of the
target assemblies and to Professors T. E. Everhart and
W. G. Oldham for their helpful comments. This work was
supported by U. S. Department of Air Force under contract
AF 33(615)-2306.

REFERENCES

1. R. F. W. Pease, J. Sic. Inst., 42, p. 158 (1965).
2. R. F. W. Pease and W. C. Mixon, J. Sci. Inst., 42, p. 81 (1965).
3. L. Pensak, Phys. Rev., 75, p. 472 (1949).
4. F. Ansbacher and W. Ehrenberg, Proc. Phys. Soc., 64A, p. 362 (1951).
5. K. G. McKay, Phys. Rev., 77, p. 816 (1949).
6. J. E. Holliday and E. J. Sternglass, J. Appl. Phys., 30, p. 1428 (1959).
7. H. Kanter, Phys. Rev., 121, p. 679 (1961).

Apparatus for Alternate Electron and Ion Treatment of Surfaces with a Micron Size Spot

H. Heil and B. W. Scott

Hughes Research Laboratories
Malibu, California

INTRODUCTION

The work reported in this paper was motivated by a desire to be able to remove material in dimensions in the micron range. This is not possible with an electron beam with a spot size in the micron range because the heat dissipation from a small spot requires impossibly high power densities. The process of sputtering by ions has no such limitations since it does not work by local heating and evaporation. In sputtering, direct transfer of the ion impact energy to one or more atoms causes their release from the solid surface.

An ion gun suitable for such an ion beam machining apparatus should not be affected by poor vacuum and its performance should not suffer by intermittent breaking of the vacuum. Surface ionization of cesium at the surface of the tungsten hairpin customarily used as the electron source in electron beam machines seems most promising. In addition, for an all electrostatic gun a simple reversal of the polarity of the applied voltages produces an ion beam identical to the electron beam, except that the currents are reduced by a factor of 500. A cesium dispenser which releases atoms from a chemical reaction upon heating may be used to provide the necessary alkali atoms at the hairpin and may be turned off before the vacuum is broken.

In order to obtain a spot of micron size, we operate the gun at nominally 1 kV, direct the collimated beam to an aperture of a size which can still be mechanically drilled (1 mil), and accelerate the beam onto the target to an energy equivalent to nominally 10 kV. Thereby the additional reduction of the beam to micron size is achieved.

In working with such small dimensions it is difficult to locate a certain position in a pattern. To this end, the apparatus may be switched to electron gun operation and a signal may be derived from the electron beam and displayed in scanning electron microscope [1] fashion. In our device, the target is moved and the beam is stationary. A precision microscope stage is used to move the target, and the stage movement is effected by a motor driving the two micrometers.

It is the main purpose of this paper to describe the apparatus in detail. It is built using a beam welder hairpin assembly, a cathode ray tube gun assembly, and a toolmaker type microscope stage with corresponding micrometers and electrical position sensors - all standard, readily available components. Experiments with the apparatus are described only briefly, the most significant finding was the surprising fact that best ion beam formation was found when the hairpin was heated high enough to cause simultaneous ion and electron emission.

DESCRIPTION OF THE APPARATUS

Our method of beam formation requires that the target be in a high electrical field. For ease of manipulation of the target and for ease of measuring small currents at the target, it is best to have the target at ground. Thus, it is necessary to have a gun power supply capable of operating at an elevated potential (20 kV max) of either polarity. The potentials needed in the supply are the heater, control grid G_1, grid G_2, the electrostatic lens, and the final voltage (1500 V maximum). The photograph in Fig. 1 shows (in the upper part) a version of such a supply constructed with batteries. Some voltage and current meters are seen, and to the left are the control knobs and the

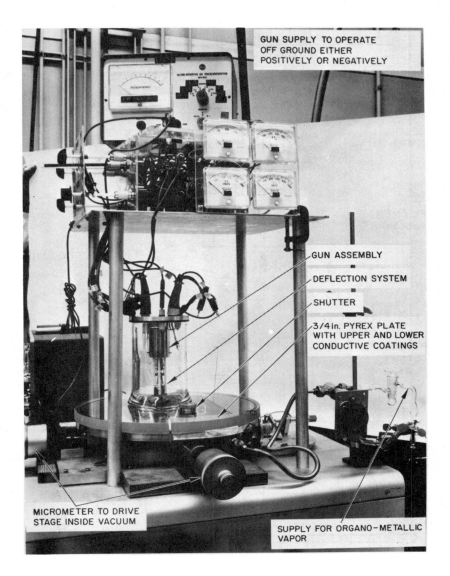

Figure 1.   Photograph of the Apparatus.   The Heavy Microscope Stage Assembly Seen at the Bottom is Sealed to the Top of the Pump Station with an O-ring.

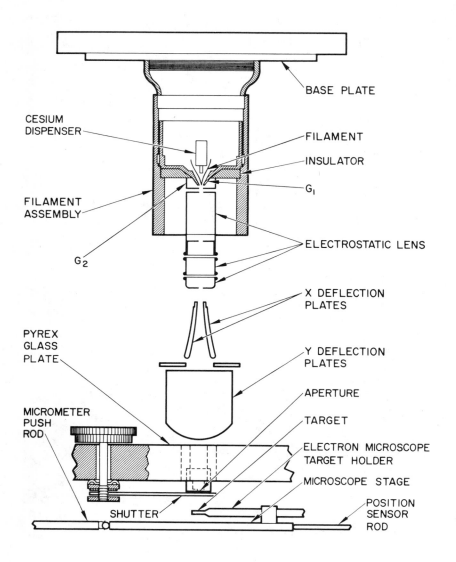

Figure 2.   View of the Elements Surrounding the Beam.

polarity switch. All potentials are derived from a string of potentiometers. A bundle of cables comes down to the metal plate which contains the vacuum feed throughs and provides the mechanical support for the gun assembly. This plate is at the potential of the control grid G_1. The pyrex glass plate bears two conductive coatings which are masked out where the aperture lens and shutter are mounted. Both coatings are at ground.

The hairpin emitter and gun assembly is depicted in Fig. 2. The hairpin-control grid assembly is of standard design, * allowing for alignment of the hairpin within the G_1 element. An insulator made of boron nitride and shaped as shown provides the base for the mount of the gun. It is a design standard for cathode ray tubes, and consists of a sequence of apertures held in position by glass beating. There are a G_2 aperture, two elements bearing the final voltage interrupted by the electrostatic focus element, and two pairs of deflection plates. It is the function of this assembly to form and focus a beam and deflect it onto the aperture shown at the bottom of the figure, an aperture from which the passing portion of the beam is post-accelerated and focused onto the target. The hairpin filament can be made to emit electrons thermionically or ions by contact ionization, depending on which polarity is chosen.

The cesium vapor dispenser is mounted between the leads to the filament, as shown in Fig. 2. Figure 3 shows an enlargement of the dispenser and gives design details.

A standard vacuum feedthrough** is modified to receive a tight cover on one side and an extension to the capillary tubing on the other side. The cover, made of Kovar is shown separately with its dimensions. Its opening is machined for a press fit to the corresponding Kovar ring, which is brazed to the nickel lip. A tungsten heater filament coated with alumina for insulation of the type used for cathode heaters is spot welded to the nickel tubing at one end and to the Kovar ring at the other end, in order

*Hamilton Standard Beam Welder, Hamilton Standard Division, Windsor Locks, Connecticut.
**Insulator bushing type D-312, U.S. Stoneware Corp., Anaheim, California.

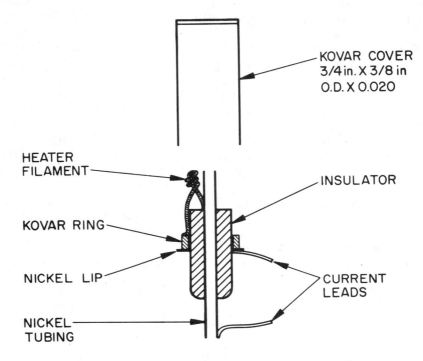

Figure 3.   Cesium Atom Dispenser Design.

that it may be heated by passing current through the current leads.   After the cover is filled with a mixture of
cesium chromate and silicon, * this side is closed tightly.
Instead of the cesium chromate-silicon mixture, we also
used a calcium-cesium chloride mixture, which is more
convenient because cesium release occurs at a lower temperature.   The open end receives an extension capillary of
heavier-walled copper, with which the stream of cesium
vapor may be directed to the filament tip.
   We feared initially that the release of cesium into the
vacuum system would have detrimental effects caused by

*Cesium-chromate-silicon powder mixed in the proper ratio was
obtained from A.D. MacKay, Inc. New York 38, New York.

photoemission, field emission, and electrical leakage. We therefore designed the dispenser so that the metal atoms would be directed onto the tip of the hairpin in order to utilize the atoms most efficiently and keep the total release low. However, as described below, in a filament operation where electron and ion emissions occur simultaneously, it appears that a substantially larger area of the hairpin surface delivers ions into the beam and a correspondingly lower arrival rate suffices. Thus, it is not necessary to design a nozzle which directs the neutral beam to the tip of the pin, and cesium release into the space between the pin and G_1 is sufficient. No ill effects were observed in the rest of the system after many hours of continuous operation of the ion beam.

The post focusing aperture which is positioned closely above the target is shown in an enlarged view in Fig. 4 (the dimensions are also given). A 4 mil hole tapered on the inside is drilled at the bottom of the main body. This hole represents the aperture lens when the potentials are applied. After drilling, a thin sheet of copper is braced over the tapered end of the hole, and a hole of about 1 mil diameter is drilled concentric to the lens hole. This represents the limiting aperture, and is well outside the electric field. These holes are drilled by spark erosion under oil. The part as shown is mounted with help of a screw and disc (not shown in Fig. 2) into a 3/4 in. hole drilled into the pyrex plate.

The target is mounted on an electron microscope target holder which is in turn mounted rigidly to a microscope stage*. The stage can be precisely positioned from outside the vacuum by means of the micrometer screws* which drive the pushrods shown at the bottom of Fig. 2. The position sensor rods, also shown in Fig. 2, drive the "Micro-Inch Comparator,"* an instrument which translates the position into an electrical signal. The smallest division on this instrument is 250 nm (2500 Å), while the smallest division of the micrometer drum is 2.5 μm. We

*Scherr-Tumico Company, St. James, Minnesota.

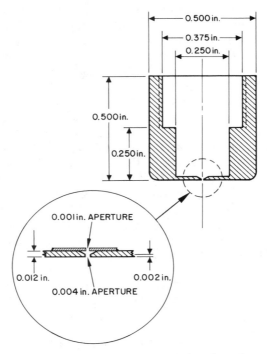

Figure 4.   Design of the Post-Focusing Aperture.

also built and used a constant speed drive at the rim of the
micrometer drum by means of a geared down dc motor
which moved the target at about 1 μm sec^{-1}.

The spacing between aperture and target is chosen
large enough to avoid pre-breakdown currents, approximately 1 mm.   The focus does not depend on this spacing;
a voltage ratio of 9 between target potential and aperture
potential is theoretically required, as derived in the ap-
pendix.   In practice, we found the minimum spot size at
a ratio closer to 8, which would indicate that the beam
was convergent above the aperture or that the gun system
was imaging the crossover to a point beyond the target.

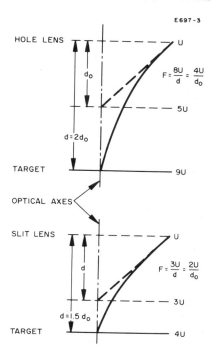

Figure 5. Schematic Drawing of Paraxial Rays for an Immersion Lens; Top, Round Hole; Bottom, Slit.

OBSERVATIONS AND TESTS

Some experiences with this apparatus concerning both the formation of the ion beam and the electron beam are discussed below.

Surface ionization requires operation of the filament above the critical temperature, which is around $1200°K$ for tungsten at the cesium pressures prevailing in this experiment. Above this temperature, the ion emission density is essentially equal to the neutral arrival rate. Electron emission densities for which these guns are designed range between 0.1 and 1 A cm^{-2}; at the upper limit, emission is limited by space charge. The comparable limits for ion current densities are smaller by a factor of 500 (the square root of the ratio of ion mass to electron mass). Thus we require a neutral arrival rate up to 10^{16} cm^{-2} sec^{-1}, a cesium pressure of 10^{-4} Torr, or an equivalent cesium reservoir temperature of $70°C$. [2] Tests with a 4 mil heated wire located 2 mm from the opening of the nozzle indicated that such arrival rates are easily obtained. In the design shown in Fig. 2, however, the atoms arrive at the rear surface of the tip of the pin and one would have to rely on cesium diffusion along the tungsten surface to provide sufficient neutrals for the indicated ion emission density. This diffusion is far too slow. The neutral flux returning from the inside surface of G_1 to the front surface of the tip was well below 1 mA cm^{-2}, and the resultant ion beams carried correspondingly low currents.

However, as the filament temperature was increased, also substantial electron emission became possible, and rather heavy electron currents were drawn to the positive control grid G_1 (1 mA). We obtained substantial currents in the ion beams in this mode of operation. The maximum ion currents passing the aperture would depend critically on the control grid voltage (+9. 5 V) and the filament temperature. We suspect that a plasma is emitted from a large area of the hairpin, that it fills most of the space between the hairpin and G_1, and that the ion beam formation takes place in a sheath spanning the orifice of G_1. Although this mode of operation forms the ion beam differently from the electron beam, the position of the final focus at the target may be assumed to be the same for ions and for electrons. The advantage of this method of ion beam formation rests with the fact that a very small cesium supply suffices. At 1000 V we typically measured several nanoamperes past the 1 mil post-focusing aperture. This indicates a current density close to the theoretical limit. [5] The ion beam size reduction resulting from post-focusing to the target has not yet been measured.

Beam size determinations were made with electrons. In an early experiment we placed a 750 per inch electroformed mesh at the target position and a collector below it. Both were moved with respect to the beam position by means of the constant speed drive described above.

The electrical output of the position sensor was used to drive the X-axis and the collector current to drive the Y-axis of an X-Y recorder. The beam size could be determined from the recorded curve. In a second experiment we followed J. M. Hlavin and R. A. Fotland. [3]   A collodion film as target was bombarded with the electron beam in the presence of a butyl tin trichloride atmosphere. The target was again moved by the constant speed drive to obtain a line. The image was amplified by zinc evaporation, and the line width was measured with a light microscope. Both experiments indicated spot sizes in the micron range. The impression was that spot size was limited by imperfect collimation rather than by aberrations of the aperture lens.

CONCLUSIONS

We would like to emphasize that the apparatus is still experimental and in need of much design work. However, the idea of using electron and ion emission alternately from the same source may easily be applied to the conventional electron optical arrangements of beam welders or scanning electron microscopes.

We are grateful to T. E. Everhart for suggesting the method of beam size determination by meshes. R. E. Pruss and E. R. Goodrich built and tested the apparatus.

REFERENCES

1. C. W. Oatley, W. C. Nixon, and R. F. W. Pease in Advances in Electronics and Electron Physics (Academic Press, New York, 1965), Vol. 21, p. 181.
2. J. M. Houston and H. F. Webster in Advances in Electronics and Electron Physics (Academic Press, New York, 1962), Vol. 17, p. 170, Fig. 25.
3. J. M. Hlavin and R. A. Fotland, First International Conference on Electron and Ion Beam Science and Technology, R. Bakish, Ed. (John Wiley & Sons, New York, 1965), p. 231
4. See, e. g. , K. R. Spangenberg, Vacuum Tubes (McGraw-Hill, New York, 1948), p. 354.
5. D. B. Langmuir Proc. IRE 25, 977 (1937).

APPENDIX

The voltage ratio to be used to post-accelerate the beam so that the lens focus coincides with the target is 9 for the round hole (and 4 for the slit) lens. Since the lens radius r is much smaller than the spacing d, all ray refraction takes place within a depth comparable to r and much smaller than d. The subsequent trajectories are parts of parabolae. If we disregard the post-acceleration effect, the focal length d_0 as a function of the potential at the aperture U (reference to cathode) and the field F is [4]

$$d_0 = \frac{4U}{F} .$$ (1)

This implies a field of $4U/d_0$.

Because of the parabolic trajectory, the focus occurs farther along the beam and the field F must be extended to the distance d as shown in Fig. 5. The degree of extension is calculated using the fact that (in paraxial approximation) the transit times for the straight ray going a distance d_0 and the parabolic ray going a distance d must be equal. With the velocity v related to the potential by $v_0^2 = (2e/m)U$, the transit time τ for the straight path is

$$\tau = d_0 / v_0 .$$ (2)

In the real case the electron experiences an acceleration

$$a = \frac{e}{m} \left(4 \quad \frac{U}{d_0} \right) = 2 \frac{v_0^2}{d_0} = 2 \frac{v_0}{\tau} .$$ (3)

Its velocity as a function of time t is

$$v = 2 \frac{v_0}{\tau} t + v_0 = (2t/\tau + 1) v_0$$ (4)

and it reaches a distance

$$d = \frac{v_0}{\tau} t^2 + v_0 t.$$ (5)

At the time $t = \tau$ and with the value of τ from (2), we find $d = 2d_0$ and the target potential equal to 9U.

For the slit lens,

$$d_0 = 2U/F \tag{1a}$$

$$a = v_0/\tau \tag{3a}$$

$$v = (t/\tau + 1)v_0 \tag{4a}$$

$$d = v_0 t^2/(2\tau) + v_0 t \tag{5a}$$

$d = 1.5\, d_0$ and the target potential equals 4U, as shown in the lower part of Fig. 5.

The Application of the Scanning Electron Microscope to Electronic Materials Problems

P. R. Thornton, I. G. A. Davies, K. A. Hughes,
N. F. B. Neve, D. A. Shaw, D. V. Sulway and R. C. Wayte

Department of Materials Science
U. C. N. W. Bangor, Caerns., U. K.

INTRODUCTION

In this paper we seek to illustrate the versatility of the scanning electron microscope (SEM) in the microelectronics field. The emphasis is placed upon the more "materials" aspects as this is the side of the topic that is the least well documented in the literature. We have adopted the approach of describing the application of the SEM to five problems of current interest which require the use of all the facilities inherent in the SEM. The problems selected are:

1. The detailed behavior of injection lasers. Here two possibly related problems are discussed. One is the cause of the "filamentary" behavior of the light output. The second is the self-inflicted damage which occurs when such lasers are run at very high currents.

2. The application of the SEM to "physics of failure" problems, particularly those related to localized breakdown, surface channels and "second breakdown" is discussed.

3. Studies of a PIN GaAs diode are described. These include breakdown studies and the observation and measurement of the intrinsic region width as a function of diffusion time. The spatial resolution of such measurements is illustrated. An additional interest is centered on the simultaneous observation of "voltage" [1] and "high field" [2, 3] contrast on micrographs of this diode.

4.   The detection of junction position in large area
field enhanced photoemitters. Here the problem is to relate the quantum efficiency, signal/noise and frequency
response etc. , to the relative position of the junction below
the surface and to detect the causes of surface leakage
brought about by the processing of these devices. So a
non-destructive and sensitive method of pn junction location is required.
5.   The application of the SEM to the study of surface
topography and crystal morphology in crystal growth problems is described, particularly to whiskers and to epitaxial
layers of materials of high electrical resistivity and which
therefore can be difficult to study.
     For the sake of clarity we now define our terminology.
We have used the SEM in three ways: (1) In the EMISSIVE
MODE using the emitted electrons to study surface detail;
(2) In the CONDUCTIVE MODE to obtain charge-collection
maps of diode structures and (3) in the LUMINESCENT
MODE in which the recombination radiation formed by the
beam induced plasma is used to obtain information. This
was done in our experiments by having a small Si photodiode close to the specimen to collect the beam induced
radiation. The photocurrent so created in the Si photo-
detector was then used to control the brightness of a CRT
being scanned in synchronism with the primary beam.
     Finally we would stress that it is the experimental
approach to these problems that we are emphasizing here
rather than the details of the problems themselves.

STUDIES OF INJECTION LASERS

     There is a general belief that material inhomogeneities
effect the performance of these devices. In particular it is
felt that the filamentary nature of the laser emission is related to inhomogeneity. In addition recent studies at
S. E. R. L. [4] and this laboratory, have suggested that
inhomogeneities may be a cause of the irreversible damage
sustained during high current running. In both problems
we need methods of relating the material in a given device
to the electrical and optical properties of that device. This
evaluation should also include inhomogeneities introduced by

manufacture, for example, during diffusion and during the
optical polishing of the surface.   We can illustrate the
value of the SEM in this context by considering the self-
damage problems.

Figure 1 shows line diagrams illustrating the geometry
of the following figures, while Fig. 2(a) is a low magnification emissive micrograph of the damaged regions viewed
"end on".   Figure 2(b) is the corresponding conductive
map and Fig. 2(c) is a higher magnification view of the
damage.   Such figures as these were used to establish the
general characteristics of the damaged regions: including
the microscopic details, the relationship with the emitting
filaments and to compare the damaged patterns on opposite
faces of the laser.   The conductive map shows the effect
of damage on the junction and reveals that the junction is

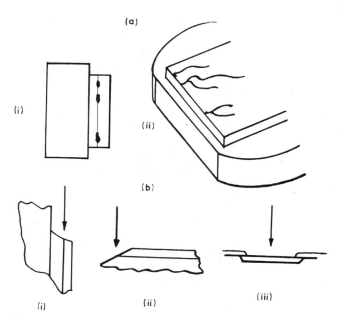

Figure 1.   Line Diagram of the Specimen Geometries Used in this
Work.   (a) Views of GaAs Lasers Shown in Figures 2 and 3, (i)
End on View (ii) Inclined View; (b) Illustrations of the Various
Junction Positions Relative to the Primary Beam Used in these
Studies.

forced further into the n-type layer in the damaged regions. In general, the distorted junction follows the contours of the damage region, although on occasions it extends further into the n-type layer than the damage does. The general impression gained is of debris left after some fast, catastrophic event.

Subsequent examination after etching gave sequences such as that shown in Fig. 3. Such studies showed that the damage structure on the surface is not indicative of what is happening in the bulk. The damage extended for ~400μ below the surface. It wandered throughout the crystal in a near random fashion. Damage regions which appeared to be separate on the surface joined together below the surface. There are completely internal regions of damage. Often these regions are associated with

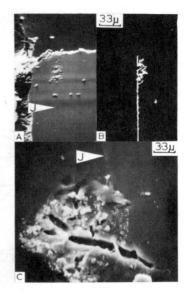

Figure 2. Self Inflicted Damage in GaAs Lasers; (a) Emissive Micrograph of Damage Regions Showing their Location Relative to the Junction, which is Marked J. (b) A Conductive Map Corresponding to (a) Illustrating the Distortion of the Junction which Occurs in the Damage Region. (c) Magnified view of a Damaged Region Illustrating the Once Molten Material, the Fissures at Right Angles to the Junction and the Fractures.

crystal mosaic. This crystal mosaic is observed in small amounts in these devices [5] (see Fig. 3(d)). Figure 4 shows the effect that a particularly gross region of the mosaic can have on the device property because of the enhanced diffusion of the zinc into the n-type starting material.

All that has gone before is concerned with bulk properties. We are also concerned with surface properties, here again the SEM makes a contribution. Figure 5 is a pair of conductive maps of a polished laser face viewed end on (position (i) of Fig. 1(b)) and they illustrate the versatility of the approach. Figure 5(a) was obtained using a low beam current ($\sim 10^{-12}$ amps) and a high gain on the amplifier and reveals the position of the junction and its general quality. Figure 5(b), on the other hand, was taken with a high beam current ($\sim 10^{-8}$) amps and low gain and low contrast on the recording system. Under these conditions the signals from the areas of the crystal remote to the junction become enhanced relative to the peak signal. This occurs by "optical coupling". That is to say, some of the recombination radiation created by the primary beam in the diode travels to the junction where it becomes absorbed and the carriers so created are collected by the depletion layer and so give rise to a conductive signal [6]. In this way a map of the whole surface can be obtained. This map reveals the presence of scratches, microcracks and other markings (see below) all of which are difficult to locate on emissive micrographs. A variant on this technique is shown in Fig. 6, which contains luminescent maps of a similar surface. It can be seen that the luminescent maps give much the same information as the conductive maps with a resolution ~ 1 to 2μ. It should be stressed that this luminescent technique does not need any contacts on the specimen or the presence of a pn junction. It should also be noted that all three modes can be run simultaneously as the presence of the photodiode has but a small detrimental effect on the emissive mode of operation.

It is fair to conclude that we now have techniques to study "materials" and "preparation" problems in GaAs devices with a versatility and resolution previously un-

obtainable and, more important, we can study the effect
of the defects on the electrical and optical properties of the
devices. This ability to relate the materials defects to
the device properties is further stressed in the next section.

STUDIES OF LOCALIZED BREAKDOWN

In this section we stress the ability of the SEM to
detect regions of avalanche breakdown. Here the SEM
detects current multiplication as the bias across a diode
is gradually increased just as a scanning light spot does.
We have reported elsewhere on the application of this technique to microplasmas [7] , edge breakdown and scratch

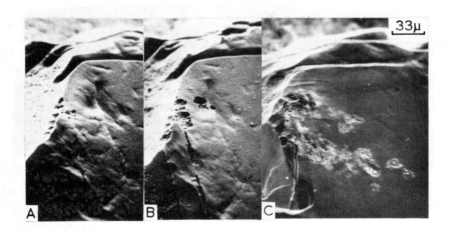

Figure 3. Systematic Study of a Damage Region in Which the
Region is Re-Examined After Successive Etches. The Extent of the
Damage, the Gradual Change in Direction and the Possible Associa-
tion with Crystal Mosaic (Marked M) are Points of Interest.

induced leakage paths [8] and to breakdown due to in-
clusions in Ge [9].   Here we illustrate the technique in
use on planar devices.   Figure 7 shows three illustrative
examples.   Figure 7(a) is a double exposure of a good
diode which breakdowns at the junction underneath the
SiO₂ .   The inner continuous circle is a conductivity map
of the diode taken with a few volts reverse bias.   The
outer "bursts" of signal are taken with a reverse bias of
240 volts on the diode and a reduced gain on the recording
system.   We associate these signals with avalanche
breakdown.   The inner edge of these bursts occur at the
edge of the depletion layer at the voltage at which they
occur.   This voltage approaches the predicted value for the
material from which this diode was made.   Figure 7(b)
shows a quadruple exposure of a poor diode which had
deteriorated by exposure to the atmosphere.   In this case
we obtain extensive charge collection under the silica.

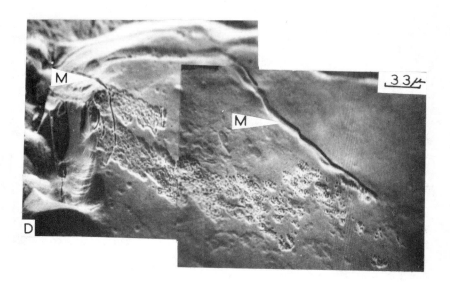

Figure 3 (d).

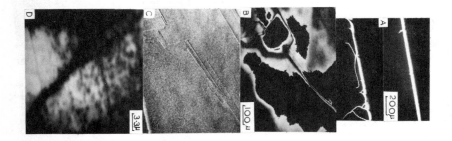

Figure 4. The Effect of Crystal Mosaic on Zinc Diffusion in GaAs.
(a) Two Conductive Maps of Bevelled Junctions taken with the
Primary Beam in Position (ii) of Figure 1b. The First Junction
was Grown in Material Free From Mosaic, the Second was not.
(b) Conductive Map of a Junction in Crystal with Mosaic taken
with Junction Parallel to Examined Surface-Position (iii) of Figure
1b; (c) Emissive Micrograph of the Area of (b) Taken after the
Specimen had been Selectively Etched to Reveal Subgrain Boundaries.
(d) High Magnification View of the Centre of the Twin Shown in the
Bottom Left-Hand Corner of (b).

We believe that this indicates the presence of an inversion layer under the silica. See below. The final example is given in Fig. 7(c). This again is a four-fold exposure. This time of a diode in which a mechanical or manufacturing defect led to breakdown at the silica edge. This is clearly shown in Figs. 7(d) to 7(i), which are magnified views of this fault. Figure 7(e) is a high magnification conductivity map of the fault region with zero bias on the diode, while Fig. 7(f) is a multiple exposure of the region showing the build up of the breakdown region at voltages ~ 50 volts. Figure 7(g) is included because it was taken with a vertical scan as opposed to the horizontal scan used in Fig. 7(f), and so illustrates the effect that the method of observation can have on the data. Figure 7(k) is a corresponding picture at 80 volts while Fig. 7(i) shows the "core" of the region at very high magnification. The emissive micrographs (see Fig. 7(d) at high magnifications showed the presence of scratches.

The possibilities inherent in this technique are apparent.

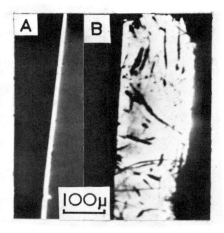

Figure 5. Conductive Maps of a Polished Face of a GaAs Laser (a) Taken at Low Beam Currents and High Gain and Contrast; Reveals the Junction Position and the Quality of the Junction (b) Taken at High Beam Currents and Low Gain so that "Optical Coupling" Leads to a Large Effective Diffusion Length and the Whole Surface can be Studied.

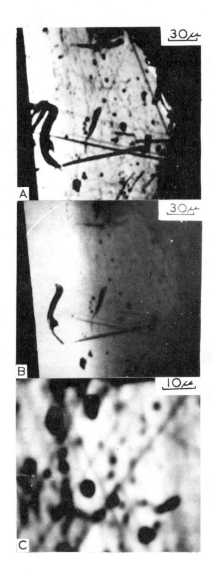

Figure 6. Luminescent Studies of a Laser Surface. (a) Luminescent Map at Low Magnifications. (b) Corresponding Conductive Map, (c) Magnified View of the Upper Centre Part of (a).

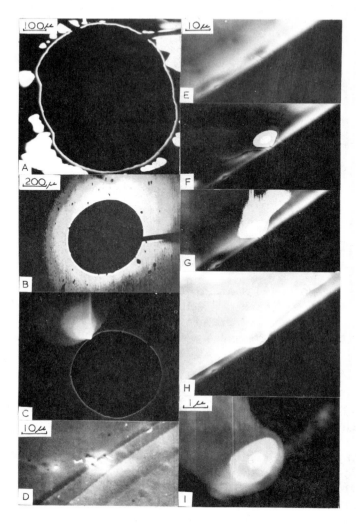

Figure 7. Avalanche Breakdown in Silicon Planar Diodes. (a) Double
Exposure of a Good Diode Showing Bulk Breakdown under the Silica.
(b) Multiple Exposure Showing the Presence of an Inversion Layer
under the Silica. (c) Multiple Exposure of a Diode which Breaks
Down at a Processing Fault; (d) – (i) Magnified Views of the Fault
in (c), Details as in Text.

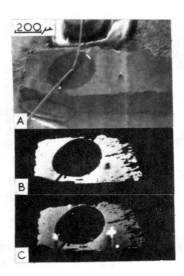

Figure 8. Studies of GaAs PIN Diodes. (a) An Emissive Micrograph of such a Structure taken at Volts Bias. (b) The Corresponding Conductivity Map Taken at Zero Volts Bias; (c) as (b) But with 30 Volts Bias, Showing Regions of Localised Breakdown.

STUDIES OF GaAs PIN DIODES

In Figs. 8(a) and (b) we have illustrated the geometry of the device by an emissive micrograph and the quality of the junction with a conductive micrograph while Fig. 8(c) shows the regions of localized breakdown. These devices were examined in two ways - on the shallow (2°) bevel and on the cleaved edge. The type of contrast observed on a bevel is shown in Fig. 9. This is of interest in that it represents the simultaneous occurrence of both voltage [1] and high field [2, 3] contrast. The interesting results were obtained by examining the cleaved edge. This edge was set perpendicular to the beam. This orientation precluded the observation of pn contrast, but with the conductive mode we were able to examine the PI junction, then by varying the diode bias we could locate the I N junction and determine the width of I region. This is illustrated in Figs. 10(a) to (e), while the line scans

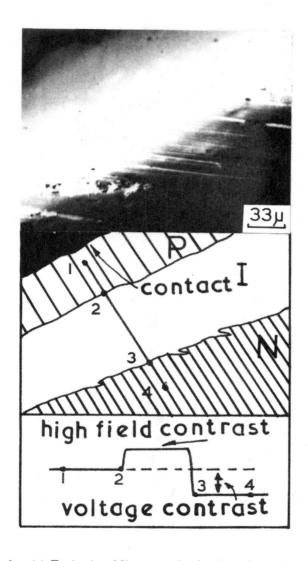

Figure 9.   (a) Emissive Micrograph of a Bevel at a Reverse Bias
of 14.5 Volts, Showing Both Voltage and High Field Contrast;
(b) Line Diagram to Clarify (a).

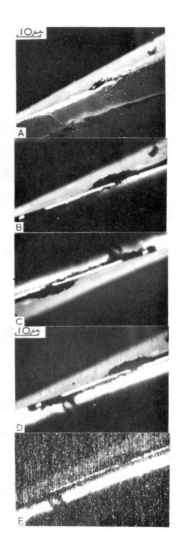

Figure 10. Studies of a Cleaved Edge on a PIN Diode. (a) Emissive Micrograph of Edge, (b) to (e) Corresponding Conductive Maps taken at Voltages of 0, 5, 10, and 30 Successively Showing the Direct Observation of the Near Intrinsic Region.

shown in Fig. 11 show the resolution the method is capable of with a little refinement on a well cleaved surface. Using this approach we were able to confirm a previous suspicion that these diodes contained an inadvertent deep diffusion and we were able to show that this deep diffusion obeyed the $\sqrt{t}$ relationship.

STUDIES OF FIELD ENHANCED PHOTOEMITTERS

The problem here is to locate the junction position relative to the surface. In particular we wish to differentiate between the three situations shown in Fig. 12. This is best done by the use of conductive maps. The expected variation of conductive signal with distance is also illustrated in Fig. 12, while Fig. 13 shows actual examples of all three cases. This figure also shows one of the limitations facing scanning electron microscopy at present i. e. beam induced contamination. Dimples such as those marked C had been studied at high magnification.

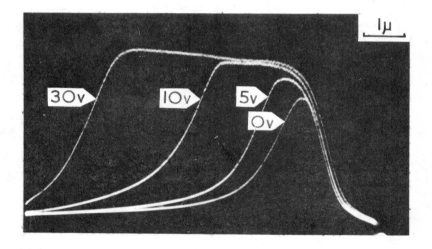

Figure 11. High Resolution Conductive Line Scans of a Cleaved Edge Similar to that Studied in Figure 10.

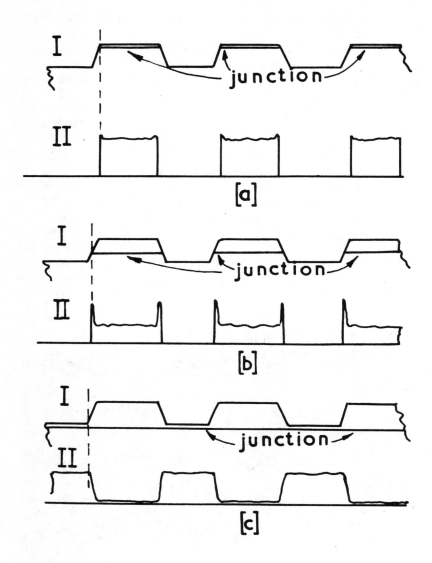

Figure 12. Schematic Drawings of Relative Junction Positions and the Expected Conductive Signal (a), (b) and (c). In Each Case Curve I Represents the Topography of the Device While Curve II Indicates the Predicted Signal.

The resultant increased rate of contamination resulted in a loss of contrast.

Figure 14 shows a further application, this time to the study of inversion layers. It is apparent that, in addition to the conductive signal from the bottom of dimples, we are observing substantial charge collection from the supposedly p-type region well clear of the square mesa. This additional signal arises because of an inversion layer brought about by the cesiation process used to lower the work function. This layer is patchy and its formation is inhibited in certain regions. We are interested in inhibiting this layer completely and in comparing the performance of other surface contaminants.

SURFACE STUDIES OF ELECTRONIC MATERIALS

This application is straight forward and has been included here as there are few examples in the literature of

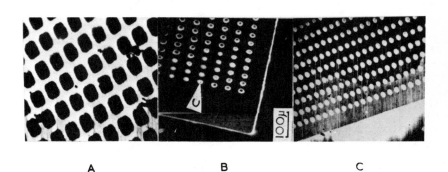

A   B   C

Figure 13. Conductive Maps of Field Enhanced Photoemitters. (a), (b) and (c) Correspond to the Cases Given in Figure 12(a), (b) and (c) Respectively. Dimples Spoilt by Beam Induced Contamination are Similar to those Marked with a C.

studies of electronic materials of high resistivity which are some times difficult to study. The example given here shows how indications of variations in resistivity become apparent in the SEM. Figure 15(a) contains a pair of micrographs taken of ZnS powder phosphors. The one on the left is a good phosphor, that on the right is a poor phosphor. An immediate difference is noticeable. Figure 15(b) shows the character of a boron film deposited on a Ta substrate, while the Ta substrate, after the removal of the film, is shown for comparison. Figure 15(c) is a silicon whisker grown by the VLS process. A resolution of 500Å is claimed for this micrograph. Figure 15(d) is a PbS film and shows a characteristic

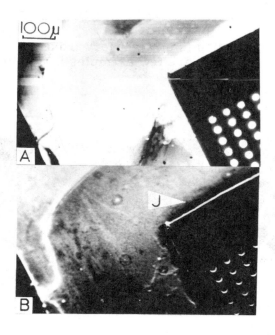

Figure 14. (a) Charge Collection from the p-Type Layer Remote from the Diffused Junction due to the Presence of an Inversion Layer (b) Corresponding Emissive Micrograph taken at a Reverse Bias of 8 Volts. The Junction is Marked with a J.

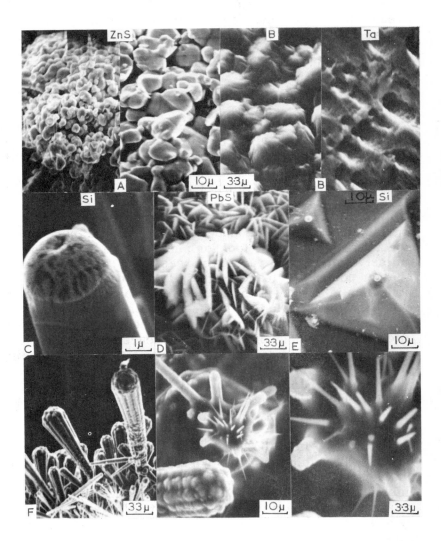

Figure 15. (a) Two Micrographs of Good and Poor ZnS Phosphor Powders; (b) Micrographs of Boron Film Deposited on Ta, the Substrate is Shown for Comparison. (c) Si Whisker at High Resolution (d) PbS Film Showing "Charge Up" of "Rosette". (e) Si Epitaxial Growth. (f) Boron Whisker Studies.

"rosette" which gives a far brighter signal than the background indicating "charge up" and a high resistivity. Figure 15(e) shows a silicon epitaxial growth, while Fig. 15(f) contains studies of boron whiskers which again show charge up effects.

SUMMARY OF PRESENT CAPABILITIES AND FUTURE EXTENSIONS

We have summarized in Table I the bulk of the facilities inherent in the SEM that we have been concerned with in recent months. Omitted from this table are the possibly important applications of resist exposure [10] and device preparation [11].

To this summary we would add our belief that, in the immediate future, the conductive mode will be more important as a diagnostic tool for junction studies than the emissive mode for a variety of reasons. These include greater contrast, cleaner signal, freedom to locate the structure in any position relative to the beam and the side benefits which are unique to the conductive mode such as avalanche detection, diffusion length measurements and microcircuitry diagnostics. In due course, once the necessary fundamental work has led to a full understanding of the voltage and high field contrasts, then the emissive mode could become as technically important.

It is perhaps of interest to state briefly the way in which we at Bangor are attempting to extend these techniques: -

a. Clean up of the vacuum system by the use of ion pumps will enable ambient studies to be done on materials and devices. By using the SEM for this work localized information can be obtained. Instead of obtaining the relationship between the total integrated leakage introduced by some surface treatment, the locations of the leakage paths can be examined and causes for their existence sought and changes in surface lifetimes can possibly be obtained (see below).

b. Once the problem of beam contamination is removed, the possibilities inherent in the SEM for quantitative measurement can be fully exploited. In addition

Table I. Summary of the Facilities Currently Available in the SEM

Facility	Comments
I. Conductive mode	Current continuity required - can be with at least 2kV bias on specimen if required and with diodes passing up to a few milliamps.
a. charge collection maps	resolution 2,000 to 2,500Å - high contrast useful at low magnification to detect surface faults which are not always easy to detect on the emissive mode without considerable search - microcircuitry diagnostics - non destructive examination of circuit behavior - direct measurement of amplification [13] - can be used with junction depths down to 9μ [14].
b. line scans at low beam currents	(i) Depletion layer movement to a resolution of $\sim 1\mu$ [12] and on occasions to $\sim 1/5~\mu$ (see Fig. 11).
c. charge collection maps with high voltages on diode	Current multiplication detected with spatial resolution $\sim 3,000$Å values of M as low as 1.05 can be detected. Breakdown by tunnelling can be distinguished from avalanche breakdown (unless the tunnelling is accompanied by current multiplication) - can be used to detect avalanche breakdown under SiO_2 layers.

Table I. (Continued)

Facility	Comments
II. Emissive Mode	
a. surface examination	Resolution: - variable, depending on specimen, often 400 to 500Å, occasionally ~250Å, lowest reported 120Å [15].
b. pn junction location	location ~ 1/2 μ , measurement 2 μ [16], contrast tends to decrease at high magnifications (x 10, 000) - contrast varies with orientation of specimen relative to primary beam.
c. high field contrast	Largely unexplored.
III. Luminescent mode	Does not require current continuity, can be used on bulk specimens [17] or damaged diodes. Resolution 1.5 to 2 μ. Limited, at present, to good emitters. High beam currents required therefore beam contamination can be troublesome. Can be run concurrently with other modes.

to bulk carrier diffusion lengths [6, 12] and depletion
layer movement [16, 12] current multiplication [18]
and enhanced diffusion rates are tractable by this approach.
In principle the SEM can be used to measure surface lifetimes by measurement of surface diffusion lengths.   This
can be done by reducing the mean depth at which the
primary electrons create electron-hole pairs by lowering
the primary beam voltage.   We are interested in developing this technique for application to physics of failure
studies including irradiation effects on microcircuitry.

    c.   Once a cold stage is developed (this presents no
major problem) the application of the SEM to electroluminescent devices should be of interest.   The origin of
the light emission and its spatial variation in injection
electroluminescent devices are subjects which could be
investigated.   This could be done by providing the bulk of
the carrier injection by passing a conduction current
through the device and by using the SEM beam to provide
additional "plasma".   The light created by the beam can
be detected and used to control the brightness of a CRT
being scanned in synchronism with the beam.   The beam
can be used chopped to "pick out" the beam induced signal.
This variant of the luminescent mode may allow the origin
of the emitted light to be determined to an accuracy better
than that set by the diffraction limit of the emitted light.
This accuracy results because the position of the origin
of a given light signal is determined by the electron optics
not by the path of the emitted light.

    d.   The use of storage and sampling techniques to
study the dynamic movement of junctions has not really
begun.   Using the conductive mode it should be possible to
observe the dynamic movement of junctions up to 1 M/C.

ACKNOWLEDGMENT

The authors gratefully acknowledge the technical help
received from the staff of the Services Electronics Research Laboratory, Baldock, particularly B. R. Holeman,
R. J. Sherwell and C. Gooch.   Dr. D. W. F. James and
his group of this Department have willingly provided
photographs prior to publication.   Mr. G. Antell of S. T. L. ,

Harlow provided the GaAs PIN diodes. Acknowledgment to Ministry of Defense (Navy Department) and the Science Research Council for financial assistance is gratefully made.

REFERENCES

1. C. W. Oatley and T. E. Everhart, Journ. of Electronics, 2, p. 568 (1957).
2. G. V. Spivak, G. V. Saparin, B. Massarani and M. V. Bekov, Proc. of 3rd European Reg. Conf. on Electron Microscopy, Prague (1964).
3. P. R. Thornton, M. J. Calpin and L. W. Drummond, Solid State Electron., 6, p. 532 (1963).
4. D. Cooper, C. Gooch and R. J. Sherwell. To be submitted to Quantum Electronics.
5. D. A. Shaw, K. A. Hughes, N. F. B. Neve, D. V. Sulway, P. R. Thornton and C. Gooch. To be published in Solid State Electron. April (1966).
6. D. B. Wittry and D. F. Kyser, Journ. Appl. Phys., 36, p. 1387 (1965).
7. N. F. B. Neve, K. A. Hughes and P. R. Thornton, Journ. Appl. Phys., 37, to be published (1965).
8. I. G. Davies, K. A. Hughes, D. V. Sulway and P. R. Thornton, Solid State Electron., 9, p. 275 (1966).
9. D. V. Sulway, I. G. Davies, K. A. Hughes, P. R. Thornton and B. R. Holeman. To be published in Microelectronics and Reliability.
10. A. N. Broers. Microelectron and Reliability, 4, p. 103 (1965).
11. O. C. Wells, T. E. Everhart and R. K. Malta, presented at the autumn meeting, Electrochemical Society, New York, October (1963).
12. P. R. Thornton, K. A. Hughes, D. V. Sulway and R. C. Wayte. Accepted by Microelectronics and Reliability.
13. K. A. Hughes et al. Unpublished results.
14. Unpublished observations on epitaxial GaAs.
15. R. F. W. Pease and W. C. Nixon, Journ. Sci. Instrum., 42, p. 81 (1965).

16. N. C. MacDonald and T. E. Everhart, Appl. Phys. Letters, 7, p. 267 (1965).
17. D. B. Wittry and D. F. Kyser, Journ. Appl. Phys., 35, p. 2439 (1964).
18. N. F. B. Neve, M. Sc. Thesis, U. C. N. W. (1966).

A Comparison of Information Signals and Displays Using the Scanning Electron Microscope

C. J. Varker

Westinghouse Molecular Electronics Division
Elkridge, Maryland

and

T. E. Everhart, A. J. Gonzales

University of California
Berkeley, California

INTRODUCTION

The scanning elelectron microscope [1] has been demonstrated to be useful in examining semiconductor integrated circuits [2, 3]. This paper describes a high-resolution contrast display mode for surface detail, the electron-beam induced target current (EBITC) mode, and compares it to the more common secondary electron and electron beam induced current (EBIC) modes of display. This EBITC mode is similar in some respect to the contrast mechanisms discussed previously [4-6] but the high resolution properties have not previously been pointed out. This display mode may prove especially useful for thin film deposition studies, or any studies where the sample is thin, and can be placed on a semiconductor substrate containing a planar p-n junction. Semiconductor integrated circuits offer many such samples, and, therefore a p-n-p integrated transistor has been chosen as the sample from which a comparison is drawn utilizing these modes of information display.

1003

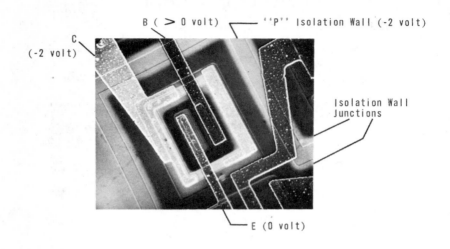

Figure 1. Secondary Electron Display of PNP Transistor
Revealing Voltage Contrast   M=230x.

Fig. 1 - Secondary Electron Display of PNP Transistor
      Revealing Voltage Contrast   M = 230x

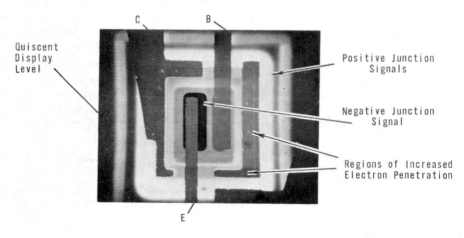

Figure 2. Electron Beam Induced Current Display of Same
Transistor   M = 330x.

SECONDARY ELECTRON DISPLAY MODE [1]

The transistor previously described, is shown in the secondary electron micrograph of Fig. 1. The surface and voltage topography of the device are displayed simultaneously in this mode which utilizes the low energy secondary electrons emitted at the target surface for the information signal. Typical micrographs normally reveal the topographic details in terms of enhanced or suppressed electron emission at surface irregularities. This effect is illustrated in Fig. 1, at the surface and edges of the aluminum interconnects, which are typically rough in texture, and along the oxide steps as shown at the isolation wall oxide cut.

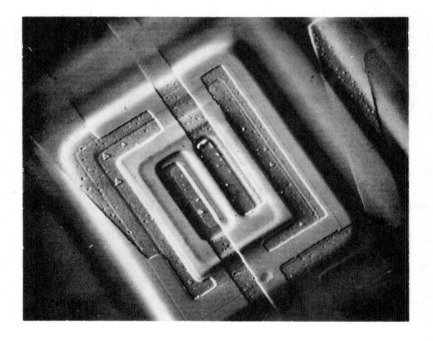

Figure 3. Electron Bean Induced Target Current Display (Emitter-Capacitor Coupled to Ground)   M = 250x.

The large area contrast, which results from an externally applied bias, displays the voltage topography of the device. In Fig. 1, the P-collector region and isolation wall are biased at -2 volts with respect to ground and appear lighter than the intervening N-region. Generally, with ground potential corresponding to the grey level of the display CRT, negative biased regions appear lighter than the surrounding areas, whereas positive regions appear darker. On the other hand, it is evident that the emitter appears lighter than the N-region, between the P-collector tub and the isolation wall, even though both areas are at ground potential. This results from the difference in the oxide thickness between the N-emitter and N-tub region which is approximately 2000Å and 8000Å, respectively. A similar effect is evident between the P+ region of the collector contact ring and the P-collector tub, with oxide thicknesses corresponding to 2000Å and 6000Å, respectively. For the correct location of the regions described, see Fig. 5. This contrast mechanism can be useful for differentiating between oxide layers of different thicknesses over equipotential regions, and it must be taken into consideration when analyzing voltage contrast micrographs.

The voltage contrast display is particularly useful for analyzing the functional characteristics of the circuit in normal and overstressed voltage conditions, and for locating regions of excessive dissipation or substrate leakage. In addition, the voltage contrast display can be used to locate vertical PN-junctions under reverse biased conditions. This aspect is revealed at the isolation wall in this figure by the change in contrast on either side of the oxide cut.

ELECTRON BEAM INDUCED CURRENT (EBIC) DISPLAY MODE [2]

In contrast with the electron emission display, the electron beam induced current mode displays the junction current which results from the electron-hole pair generation in the semiconductor by the primary electron beam. Figure 2 displays the transistor in the EBIC mode with

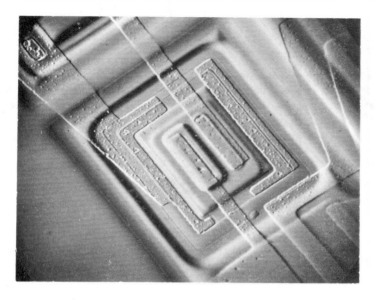

Figure 4.   Electron Beam Induced Target Current Display
(Isolation Wall-Capacitor Coupled to Ground)   M = 230x.

Note: The Change in Perspective Between Figure 3 & 4.

the collector and emitter terminals connected to the signal and signal ground respectively. The quiescent level
of the display tube is shown at the left hand edge of the
micrograph for reference. Relative to this grey level,
the white and black regions correspond respectively to
positive and negative going junction signals. The junctions
corresponding to the isolation wall, P diffused tub, and
emitter region (see schematic Fig. 5) are revealed in the
EBIC display because the emitter and N-tub region are
electrically shorted together. Collector current induced
at the two PN junctions associated with the collector is
in one direction, producing a positive output. Whereas,
collector current induced when the beam strikes the
emitter base PN junction is in the opposite direction,
producing a negative output.

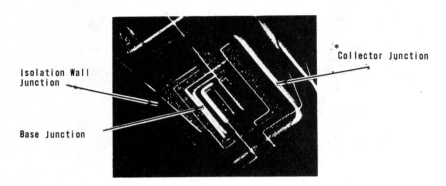

Region of Greatest Surface Detail Shown Above Overlies Planar
Junction of P Diffused Tub
Shown Schematically Below

Figure 5. Electron Beam Induced Target Current Micrograph
and Structural Schematic Revealing the Information Displayed
in the EBITC Mode.

In the EBIC mode, the regions of increased or decreased electron penetration and energy dissipation in the semiconductor surface are displayed directly in terms of induced junction currents as shown in Fig. 2. However, the information is presented in a shadowgraphic display somewhat analogous to an optical transmission light microscope image. Here the PN-junction acts as a substage illumination for the surface films viewed from the direction of the primary beam.

For example, consider a uniformly diffused planar PN-junction at some predetermined depth. The EBIC display of the area above this junction will reveal a uniformly illuminated region resulting from the junction currents induced by the primary electron beam. If one subsequently deposits a thin film on the silicon surface, the electron beam will undergo microscopic changes in transmission through the surface layer resulting from the structural discontinuities in the deposited film. The EBIC display will reveal these microscopic changes as intensity variations within the boundary of the surface film as shown in the interconnects of Fig. 2. Now, this is somewhat analogous in perspective to a transmission light micrograph (or "shadowgraph") display of a metal film on a glass substrate utilizing an optical substrate illuminator, if the polarity of the junction signal is chosen to produce a positive junction signal for increased transmission.

ELECTRON BEAM INDUCED TARGET CURRENT (EMITC) DISPLAY MODE

A more effective display of this video information can be presented by modifying slightly the input circuit configuration to the video amplifier from Fig. 14(c) to Fig. 14(d) as shown in Fig. 14. The schematic illustrates the display circuit configurations and their respective equivalent circuits for both modes of scan. It is evident that two distinct types of information are displayed. In the EBIC mode, the magnitude of the junction signal is recorded, whereas, in the EBITC mode it is the time derivative of this signal.

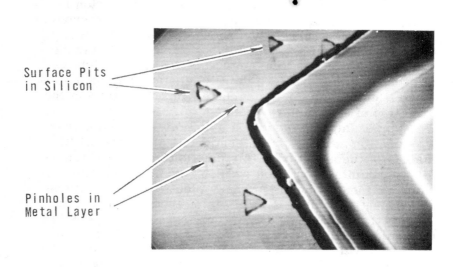

Surface Pits
in Silicon

Pinholes in
Metal Layer

Figure 6. Electron Beam Induced Target Current Display Revealing
the Loss of Topographical Detail in the Collector Contact Region
Resulting from Reduced Electron Penetration Beam Voltage = 10 kv
M = 1450x.

    The effect is clearly revealed in Fig. 3, in which the
emitter is capacitively coupled to ground. If one compares Fig. 3 with Fig. 2, the differentiated nature of the
EBITC display becomes apparent at the leading and trailing edges of surface layers and artifacts. It is worthwhile
to point out, that in all subsequent EBITC micrographs the
direction of scan is from left to right. The confusing contrasts in some regions results from the complexity of the
diffused transistor structure and not the display mode itself. In Fig. 3 traversing the target from left to right the
beam crosses eight vertical junctions, and generates
junction currents in a three layer planar diffused structure
at the emitter (refer to the structural schematic at the
bottom of Fig. 5). As a result, the display appears con-

Surface Pit

Pinholes in
Metal Layer

Asperities on
Aluminum
Surface

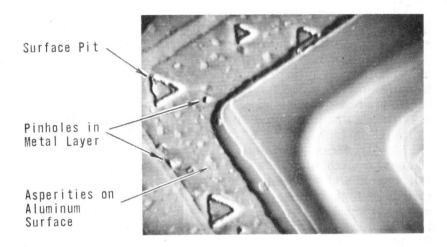

Figure 7. Electron Beam Induced Target Current Display of
Same Region with Increased Electron Penetration Beam Voltage =
12 kv   M = 1700x.

fusing at first glance, nevertheless, the information yield
is considerable and the displays are relatively easy to
interpret when both the scan conditions and the input circuit configuration are known.

To illustrate this point, consider Figs. 2 and 3 in
which the perspective has changed from a transmission
"shadowgraph" to a high contrast topograph (so called
because of the three dimensional appearance). This
change in perspective results from the differentiating effect obtained in this display mode. In Fig. 3, if an interpretation is made in terms of surface relief, the apparent
source of illumination for the interconnects is located to
the right, whereas, in Fig. 4 with the polarity of the input
signal reversed, the apparent source of illumination shifts

to the left. This interpretation although convenient for
single junction displays, can lead to an incorrect analysis
in complex structures with multilayer junctions.

The correct interpretation is in terms of electron
penetration and energy dissipation. If the direction of
scan and the direction of positive current flow for the
planar junction collecting the beam induced carriers are
known, a direct interpretation of this display can be obtained. In regions overlying a planar diffused junction
increasing or decreasing electron penetration and energy
dissipation are displayed directly on the micrograph as
white or dark bands at the leading and trailing edge of
surface artifacts. This effect is clearly evident at the
triangular etch pits and surface asperities displayed in
this region and will be discussed in subsequent micrographs at higher magnifications. In Fig. 3, at the P-
collector tub junction, an increase in the junction current
results in a white band at the leading edge of the junction.
Therefore, within a region overlying the collector-tub
junction, for example in the interconnect at the left hand
side of the micrograph, the white bands correspond to increasing junction current, whereas, black bands are related to decreasing junction current.

In Fig. 3 and Fig. 4, as pointed out previously, a
change in perspective has occurred as a result of the
reversed polarity of the video signal. Now if one inter-
prets the display in terms of transmission Fig. 3 reveals
a decreasing penetration of the electron beam at the leading edge of the aluminum interconnect. Since the collector
tub junction produces a positive going signal.   On the
other hand, Fig. 4 also reveals a decreasing penetration
at the leading edge, displayed in white, since the junction
now produces a negative going signal.

In addition, the EBITC display reveals the approximate
positions of vertical PN-junctions in unbiased conditions
as may be seen by comparing Figs. 2 to 5. The micrographs revealed in these figures were obtained with an
18 kV electron beam at 8×10^{-11} amperes of beam current. The capacitance utilized for signal enhancement is
~ 200PF at a scan time of 64 ms/line. The grey area at
the lower left hand corner of these micrographs corresponds to the quiescent level of the display CRT. It should

be pointed out that this mode of display will also incorporate leakage paths in the integrated circuit which are beyond the control of the investigator resulting from the transient nature of the video signal.

The information density in Fig. 3 and 4 is much too great to display in a single large area scan. The subsequent displays will reveal the information content in a smaller selected region of the transistor. This area overlies the planar junction of the P diffused collector region and results in a less ambiguous display, as shown in Fig. 6, and will illustrate the underlying mechanism for this display mode.

The prominent features in the display are the regions of increased electron penetration at the surface pits and at the pinholes in the metal layer. The dark band border-

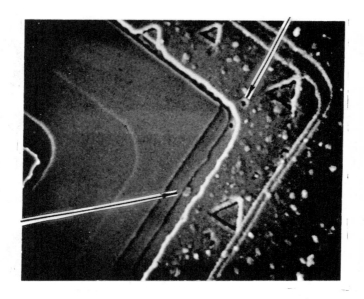

Figure 8. Secondary Electron Display of Selected Area of PNP
Transistor Beam Voltage = 10 kv   M = 1500x
Bright Regions – Enhanced Emission
Dark Regions – Inhibited Emission.

ing the metal layer is an exposed area of the silicon and, as a result, the electrons pentrate most deeply in this region. The dark region, corresponds to increased currents at the P-collector tub junction which is planar to the surface in this display and located at a depth of ~ 8 microns. Since the junction was diffused prior to the formation of surface pits and before the interconnect metallization, the magnitude of the junction current during the scan displays the relative penetration and energy dissipation of electrons at the surface layers.

In Fig. 6 the electron beam at 10 kV has not penetrated sufficiently deep to generate the junction signals required for the video display in the metallized region. At 12 kV (Fig. 7 the beam penetrates more deeply and

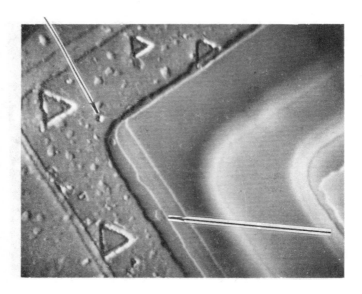

Figure 9. Electron Beam Induced Target Current Display of Same Area.
Beam Voltage = 15 kv   M = 1600x
Bright Regions - Decreasing Electron Transmission
Dark Regions - Increasing Electron Transmission
Degree of Surface Detail Comparable in Both Displays.

begins to reveal the surface structure of the aluminum interconnect. It is apparent at this point, that if during device manufacture an EBITC display of the silicon surface were obtained prior to the metal deposition step, one could separate the information relating to both the metal layer and the silicon surface independently.

A COMPARISON BETWEEN THE SECONDARY ELECTRON DISPLAY AND THE ELECTRON BEAM INDUCED TARGET CURRENT DISPLAY

In Figs. 8 and 9, a comparison is drawn between the secondary electron mode of display and the electron beam induced target current mode. From these micrographs,

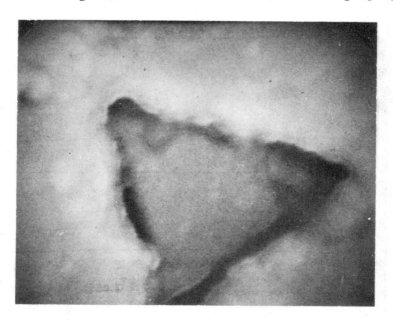

Figure 10. Secondary Electron Display Revealing and Isolated Triangular Etch Pit
Beam Voltage = 18 kv   M = 12,000x
(The Loss of Detail Results From Surface Contamination During Electron Bombardment).

it is evident that both modes present a high degree of surface detail.   The information obtained from both modes
relates to the surface topography, however, in the secondary electron mode the mechanism is surface emission
whereas, in the electron beam induced target current
mode the mechanism is electron transmission.

The complementary nature of the information contained in these displays is revealed in Figs. 8 and 9.
The secondary electron display in Fig. 8 reveals small
dark spots on each side of the bright band corresponding
to the edge of the aluminum layer.   If these artifacts
represent an abrupt surface depression, or hole, a reduced secondary electron signal is expected at this artifact.   The EBITC display in Fig. 9 reveals these spots

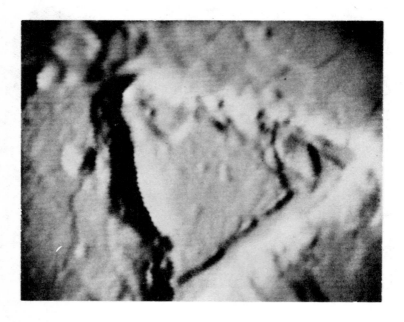

Figure 11. Electron Beam Induced Target Current Display of
the Same Pit
Beam Voltage = 18 kv   M = 12,000x.

as regions of increased electron penetration (the junction signal in this display has a negative polarity). This result confirms the structure of the artifact as a surface depression. Likewise, the suspected oxide patch revealed in the secondary electron display in the exposed silicon region, below the center of the micrograph, is revealed as a region of reduced penetration in the EBITC display. In this manner, the continuity of surface film can be determined unambiguously when deposited on uniformly diffused planar substrates.

Figures 10 and 11 compare the resolution capability of the secondary electron and electron beam induced display modes. The micrographs display an isolated pit at 12000 x. Unfortunately, the secondary electron display was limited by surface contamination, whereas, in the EBITC display the resolution is not affected by the presence of the polymerized layer. From the EBITC micrograph shown in Fig. 11 a surface topograph can be sketched directly from the contrast changes. Tracing from left to right in the direction of scan, the left hand edge of the triangle represents a steeply inclined channel represented by the black and white bands. The area enclosed by the triangle appears level with the surrounding surface since the edge is represented by a dual contrast change. At the right hand side, the channel is less steeply inclined and contains a relatively flat bottom as shown by the intervening grey level. This interpretation is consistent with the junction signal polarity. Other prominent details can be interpreted similarly, for example, the conical shape mound at the left and the fissure below as indicated in Fig. 12.

Figure 12 clearly displays 0.1μ resolution, and shows that the EBITC mode is a high resolution display mode, even though the electrons penetrating into the semiconductor beneath the surface are scattered through distances of over a micron at the voltages used here. The reason resolution of structure at the surface is not impaired is connected with the scattering and energy-loss mechanisms of the penetrating primary beam. The number of primary electrons scattered increases exponentially with penetration distance near the surface, where the beam has lost little energy.   An electron has to be scattered transversely before it reduces the resolution of the microscope. Therefore, in this mode, one expects high resolution of detail on the surface, lower resolution of detail slightly beneath the surface, and still lower resolution of detail far below the surface.   Resolution of imperfections below the electron penetration depth will be limited by electron scattering and carrier diffusion in the semiconductor.[6, 7]

The simulated display shown below in Fig. 13 duplicates very well the details shown in Fig. 12 and therefore, it appears reasonable to assume that the simplified equivalent circuits shown in Fig. 14, approximate the display condition reported here.

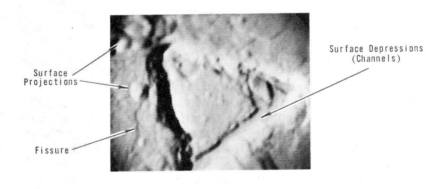

Figure 12.   Electron Beam Induced Target Current (EBITC) Display from Previous Figure Direction of Scan.

It is also worthwhile to mention that the equivalent capacitance associated with the PN junctions and signal leads is sufficient to obtain EBITC displays at higher scan rates. Similar displays have been obtained on transistor structures and integrated circuits utilizing scan rates of 16 ms/line without the use of external capacitance.

However, in Fig. 14(d) the expression for the input signal in the EBITC mode, schematic 11, reveals the dependence of the input signal amplitude on both the circuit time constant and the signal rate. From this expression it becomes apparent that for short time constants, the rate of scan must be increased proportionately to maintain the input signal level. For example, at 16 ms/line the nominal amplifier gains were $3 - 6 \times 10^5$ without utilizing external capacitance, whereas, in the capacitor enhanced displays, a gain of 5×10^4 was compatible with a scan rate of 64 ms/line.

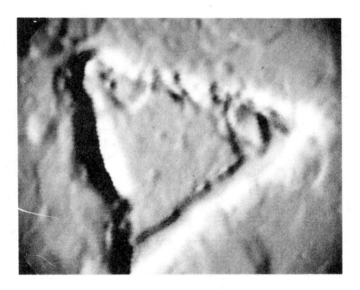

Figure 13. Differentiated Electron Beam Induced Current Display (EBIC) Simulates Exactly the EBITC Display Shown Above
Beam Voltage = 18 kv   M = 12,000x
Scan Time = 64 ms/Line,   Rc = 10^{-4} Sec.

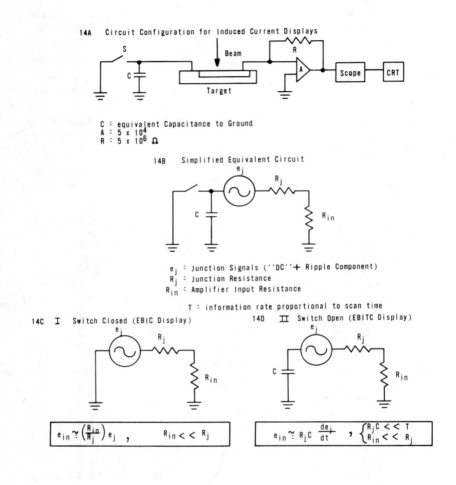

Figure 14. Simplified Equivalent Circuits for Electron Beam
Induced Current Displays.

CONCLUSION

A comparison has been drawn between the secondary electron mode and the electron beam induced target current mode of information display utilizing the scanning electron microscope. The former mode reveals the surface topography of the target as a secondary electron current display in which the contrast results from enhanced or suppressed emission at microasperities on the target surface. The latter mode reveals the topography as an induced junction current display in which the magnitude of the induced current is related to the penetration of electrons through the surface layers of the target.

A direct comparison between these modes reveals that although both are capable of producing high resolution micrographs ($< 0.1\mu$), the resolution obtained utilizing the EBITC mode is not affected by surface charging effects, or by the growth of surface polymers during electron bombardment.

The secondary electron mode can be used to reveal the location of vertical PN junctions under reverse biased conditions, whereas, the electron beam induced target current mode reveals the location of these junctions without external bias.

It has been verified experimentally that the EBITC mode results from the differentiator action of the input circuit and as a result converts the more conventional EBIC display to a high contrast topograph in which the contrast patterns reveal the regions of increasing or decreasing electron penetration and energy dissipation at the surface when referenced to a uniformly diffused planar PN junction.

ACKNOWLEDGMENT

The authors wish to acknowledge helpful discussions with colleagues, both in Baltimore and in Berkeley. The work reported here was sponsored in part by both the Avionics Laboratory, Research and Technology Division and the Manufacturing Technology Division at Wright-Patterson A. F. Base under contracts AF 33(615)-2306 and AF 33(615)-1378 respectively. The micrographs shown were obtained using the Berkeley SEM-1 which was constructed with support in part from the Air Force Avionics Laboratory, Wright-Patterson A. F. Base under contract AF 33(615)-1045, in part from Joint Services Electronic Program under grant No. AF-AFOSR-139-65 and in part by the University of California.

REFERENCES

1. C. W. Oatley, W. C. Nixon, and R. F. W. Pease, "Advances in Electronics and Electron Physics", Ed. by L. Martin, Academic Press (1965).
2. T. E. Everhart, O. C. Wells, R. K. Matta, "Evaluation of Passivated Integrated Circuits using the Scanning Electron Microscope", J. Electrochem. Soc., Vol. No. 3, No. 8, August (1964).
3. T. E. Everhart, O. C. Wells, R. K. Matta, "A Novel Method of Semiconductor Device Measurements", Proc. IEEE, 1642, December 1964.
4. J. J. Lander, H. Schreiber, Jr., T. M. Buck, "Microscopy of Internal Crystal Imperfections in Si P-N Junction Diodes by Use of Electron Beams", Appd. Phys. Letters 3, 206 (1963).
5. C. C. Nealey, C. W. Laskso, P. J. Hagon, "Planar Silicon Device Analyses with the Electron Probe Microanalyser", Electron Microprobe Symposium, Washington, D. C., October 12, 1964.
6. J. J. Lander, H. Schreiber, T. M. Buck, and J. R Mathews, "Microscopy of Internal Crystal Imperfections in Silicon p-n Junction Diodes by use of Electron Beams", Appl. Phys. Lett., Vol. 3, pp. 206-207, December 1963. W. Czaja and G. H. Wheatley "Simultaneous Observation of Diffusion Induced Dislocation Slip Pattern in Silicon with Electron Beam Scanning and Optical Means", J. Appl. Phys, Vol. 35, pp. 2782-2783, September 1964.
7. D. B. Wittry and D. F. Kyser, "Cathodoluminescence p-n Junctions in GaAs", J. Appl. Phys. Vol. 36, pp. 1387-1389, April 1965.

ION BEAMS IN
MICRO ELECTRONICS

Ion Beams in Micro Electronics

The first paper in this section is of considerable broader scope that the section itself, and it could have been included equally well in several other sections of this volume. By locating it in this section it renders an excellent introduction to the papers here. These deal with specific uses of ion beams for modification of conductive properties of solid state materials and devices and some related to this subject matter work. I am particularly excited about the prospect of ion beams as carrier implantation devices and the new vista in solid state devices manufacture that they open. Perhaps the days of diffusion treatment to effect the same are counted. The other equally exciting area is that utilizing ion beams as a tool for micromachining.

(**Editor**)

High Voltage Beams and Their Place In Industry

A. J. Gale

Ion Physics Corporation
Burlington, Massachusetts

Today, I am going to take a liberty with the title of
my talk and broaden its concept somewhat. I am going
to discuss charged particle beams - beams of ions, as
well as beams of electrons - as industrial tools. I
happen to believe that the use of energy beams - lasers,
X-rays, as well as charged particle beams - will turn
out to be one of the most important advances in industry
in the next decade and that the charged particle beams
will dominate the others. Therefore, in order to provide
what I believe to be a comprehensive picture, I will sometimes consider low as well as high energy beams.

Since I am going to discuss the industrial tools aspect of high voltage charged particle beams, I will spend
a few minutes relating this new tool in the spectrum of
tools that have become progressively available to man.

One of the attributes of man that supposedly differ-
entiates him from the other animals is his use of tools.
This is not strictly true for some primates also use
crude tools and even some varieties of birds, the
Galapagos Finch, for example use twigs to lever larvae
out of tree bark. Perhaps, "bird-brain" is not as derog-
atory a term as we sometimes intend. However, man
certainly has developed sophisticated tools.

Now, I am going to define tools in the narrowest
sense - means whereby materials are modified. Perhaps
the word fabrication covers it best. This excludes such
items as inspection tools and abstract concepts like

mathematical tools. Both of these, of course, have important places in industry, but they lie in the category of instrumentation, not fabrication.

Let me illustrate this point. When man first picked up a stick to club a small animal or knock down fruit - let's hope it wasn't to beat his wife - he used a crude tool. When he used this stick as a lever, perhaps to split off a branch to build a shelter, he started a line of industrial tools. Much later in time he suspended the stick, found that it oscillated regularly and enabled time to be measured. In this he was building an instrument. This very naive example is used to illustrate that the same device may be used in both fabrication tools and instruments. In the case of the stick its use in fabrication undoubtedly preceded instrumentation. In the use of particle beams the reverse order applies.

Until the most recent centuries, tools have been extensions of man's physical senses overlayed by his own understanding. His manual dexterity has led to the mechanical tools of great diversity. His recognition of fire and heat led to the promotion of chemical reactions. If I may stretch the allusion somewhat the sense of sight and its understanding stem into such things as photo engraving and the photo machining of fluorescent light fixtures. Sound leads us to ultrasonic cleaning and machining. In both these cases optics and sound led to instruments long before they led to fabrication tools.

One-hundred thirty-five years ago the basic understanding for a new industrial tool appeared when Faraday made his great discovery of the relationship between electricity and magnetism. We tend to think of the results of this invention as giving a convenient means of distributing energy. In this sense, electricity is only a substitute for local prime movers. But it also did something entirely new. It made electrolysis available as an industrial tool and spawned, for example, the aluminum industry.

It is in this sense that I want to regard the new tool - charged particle beams. Just as electricity enabled an entirely new way of handling materials to be developed - namely, electrolysis - so also do particle beams. To this end, therefore, I will not consider electron beam welding, machining and melting - each of these applications of electron beams are more sophisticated ways of doing what to some extent is also accomplished by other means.

Charged particle beams date perhaps from J. J. Thomson's elucidation of the nature of the electron just less than 70 years ago. At the same time Perrin had made some observations on Kanal-rays and their nature was positively identified (again by J. J. Thomson) in 1911. Of course, the discovery of the electron eventually produced the vast electron tube industry as we know it today. But forgive me if I discount it in the present context, because this industry relates almost exclusively to instrumentation, whether for measurement for which the electron microscope is the most sophisticated example, or for entertainment.

The use of the electron beam as a tool dates back as some of you heard earlier to Pirani in 1907, and this has given rise to a family of tools for melting, machining, and welding, that will be more competently discussed by other people at this symposium.

Now I turn to those users of the electron beam in industries where its properties other than as a concentrated form of energy are required. The dominant property to consider is its ability to ionize material in depth, not merely at the surface.

The end effect of ionization in materials systems is dependent, of course, on the system and on the dose applied.

The first use I will point to is the ability of ionizing radiation to promote chemical synthesis. In this it acts so to speak as a catalyst without a catalyst and, under the right circumstances, avoids the contamination or rejuvenation requirement that chemical catalysts incur. Now industrial research into the use of ionizing radiation as a catalyst has been going on for at least fifteen years, but has generally foundered on the grounds of economics. In fact, radiation has mostly been used by the research chemist to determine what chemical synthesis can be made to go so that he can then seek chemical catalysts to achieve economic production. This, of course, is an unsatisfactory state of affairs for the equipment manufacturer. However, one chemical synthesis is being carried on commercially by the Dow Chemical Co. This is the production of ethyl bromide from ethylene and hydrogen bromide -

$$C_2H_4 \ + HBr \ \overset{e}{\rightarrow} \ C_2H_5 Br$$

The yield of this reaction is a few grams per joule of absorbed radiation so that the production requirement of 500 tons per year on a continuous basis can be met by an input power of about 10 watts. It would be nice to point to this as an industrial use of high energy electron beams, but at this production level a competitive product - Cobalt 60 - manufactured by nuclear reactor

Figure 1. 300 Kev Shelf-Shielded Tube, Scanner and Conveyor Facility for Irradiation of Panels (High Voltage Engineering Corporation).

owners - can be employed much more economically.
However, it does indicate that as production requirements for radiation synthesized chemicals increase, this
role for high energy electron beams may be found.

This second use for ionizing radiation lies in its
ability to cross-link polymers. Here the high energy
electron beam is working in much more secure territory
because most, but not all, the applications are for
relatively thin coatings or films and thin-walled tubings.
The first examples lie in the field of the curing of coatings - paints and polyester and epoxy varnishes. These
applications require about 40 joules of absorbed radiation
per gram of coating (4 megarads) but since these coatings
are generally less than 1/4 milliameter thick, a 20

Figure 2. Dynamitron Facility for Irradiation of Plastic Tubing
(Radiation Dynamics, Inc.).

milliampere machine can treat surfaces at the rate of one square foot per second or half a million 8 x 4 foot panels per year on a two-shift basis.

Figure 1 shows a typical set-up. This machine manufactured by High Voltage Engineering Corporation, is a self-shielded unit powered by a 300 Kv ICT (Insulated Core Transformer). The tube current is 20 ma and the electron beam is scanned over a 48-inch long "window" of titanium beneath which the boards are conveyed. The window is air-cooled and the volatile products and ozone ducted away. Such an equipment can be placed in existing production lines. This process is also useful in the hardening of impregnated soft wood veneers. In this case, 1 mm of penetration is needed requiring beam energies up to 1 Mev. For this higher energy a concrete vault is more economic than local shielding.

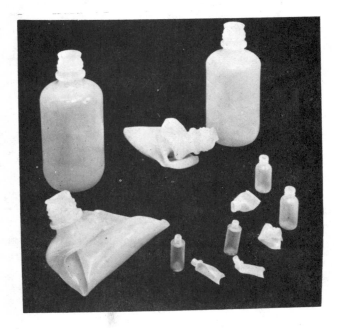

Figure 3. Irradiated Polyethylene Bottles and Controls After Heating. Unirradiated Controls have Collapsed. (High Voltage Engineering Corporation).

Polyethylene is the best example of a polymer that is cross-linked by radiation. Sufficient radiation will turn essentially all the individual chains in a sheet of polyethylene into one gigantic molecule. The result is that the material acquires extreme memory, can be mechanically deformed and, on heat treatment, will return exactly to the form it had at irradiation. Similar properties are exhibited by neoprenes. Heat shrinkable films and tubings are largely made by this method. At this time of writing, there are at least 36 machines in the United States and also a few overseas used for this process. Heat shrinkable films are used in food and other packaging. Tubes are used in wire and harness assemblies. The dose required is about 200 joules per gram of

Figure 4. Arrangement for Surface Pasteurization of Beef Quarters Using Two 300 Kev Electron Irradiators. Beef Quarter Rotates During Passage Between the Beams. (High Voltage Engineering Corporation).

material (20 megarads).   Films require electron energies on the order of 500 Kev and tubes up to 2 Mev.

The cross-linking of polyethylene not only improves memory, but also introduces other desirable properties. The temperature range of wire insulation is increased, the impact strength and toughness of plastic bags is improved, and stress-cracking of cable hardnesses largely elimi-nated.   It is expected that plastic forms will in due course be stabilized by this technique.

The third thing that ionizing radiation accomplishes is the degradation of material.   Now this may seem a strange property to desire in an industrial process, but the synthetic fibers in use today are so dye-resistant and so given to electrostatic charging that some treatment is needed to make them useful in fabrics.   On the other hand, the natural fibers, cotton and wool, needed strengthening by combination with synthetics to give crease and shrink resistant properties.   Slight degradation of the synthetics by radiation renders them hydrophilic rather than hydro-phobic, permits them to take up dyes and some moisture

Figure 5.   Arrangement for Surface Irradiation of Oranges (High Voltage Engineering Corporation).

from the atmosphere to reduce electrical charging.
Radiation also opens up the interesting field of graft
polymerization, enabling the individual natural fibers to
be coated with a skin of synthetic. Quite soon the motto
65%-35% we see in the makers' tags in our shirts, suits,
and dresses, may well apply to the individual fibers,
rather than the threads they are spun into.

The dose required for this process lies between 10
and 40 joules per gram and this is attractive economically.
Energy requirements are between 300 and 500 Kev.

The fourth thing that ionizing radiation can do is
kill - kill microorganisms, such as spores, and macro-
organisms, such as weevils. This kill dose ranges from
20, 000 rads - 18 metric tons per kilowatt-hour - to knock
out the weevils in wheat to 2. 5 megarads - about 150
kilograms per hour to sterilize surgical supplies.

Unfortunately, for the electron beam enthusiast,
many of the products for which sterilization is required
are bulky and, therefore, more economically treated by
the gamma radiation from Cobalt 60. There is, for

Figure 6. Implantation Equipment for Solar Cell Production
(Ion Physics Corporation).

example, a Megarad installation near Melbourne, Australia, that treats bales of goat hair used in carpet manufacturing to rid it of anthrax. A 4 Mev electron machine is fully engaged sterilizing surgical products in Great Britain and three facilities in this country contract sterilize similar products. There are two or three other electron beam projects that are close to fruition.

One deals with the surface pasteurization of beef requiring a dose of 1/10 megarad at 500 Kev. It is expected that such treatment will greatly reduce the spoilage in intercontinental trans-shipment of chilled sides. Standard machines can each process 500 heads of cattle per hour. Somewhat allied to this process, but at the higher dose of 250,000 rads, is the preservation of citrus fruit - particularly oranges - by the elimination of surface molds.

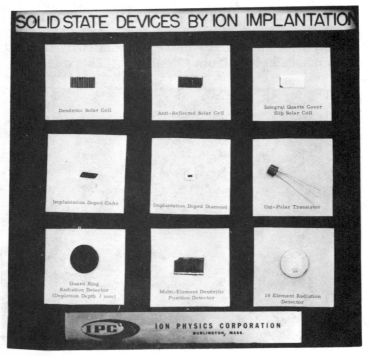

Figure 7. Semiconductor Devices Produced by Ion Implantation. The Center Panel Contains an Implanted Diamond. (Ion Physics Corporation).

Finally, there is the deinfestation of grain, where treatment rates on the order of 200 metric tons an hour or more are required at the storage site, and the use of large quantities of radioactive Cobalt 60 becomes uneconomically hazardous. The problems of population explosion and depleting United States reserves makes this humanitarian application increasingly attractive, provided always that the distribution problems can be solved.

These then are the four uses of ionizing radiation - make (or synthesize), upgrade, degrade, and kill - a somewhat surprising spectrum.

But there is still one more use, in a production tool sense, for the ubiquitous electron. Above about 250 kev, it has enough energy to displace atoms in a silicon crystal lattice. This is strictly billiard ball mechanics. The lattice binding energy is 15 ev, the silicon atom is about 33,000 times as heavy as the relativistic mass of a 250 Kev electron, and so lattice displacement takes place above this threshold value. These point defects reduce the minority carrier lifetime in the crystal with the results that semiconductor diodes can operate in nanoseconds, rather than microseconds. Such fast switching diodes are used extensively in data processing equipment.

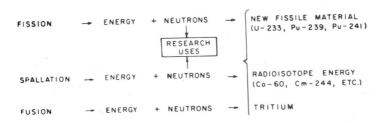

Figure 8. Three Possible Methods for the "Economic" Production of Neutrons. Fission Reactors Exist, Fusion is Still Much in the Research Stage, Spallation, Proposed by AECL's Chalk River Laboratories, May be Said to be in the Design Feasibility Stage. (Atomic Energy of Canada, Ltd.).

At this time there is a total of 38 electron beam
machines used for electron processing, of which 3 are
used for semiconductor diodes.   The total installed
capacity is about 350 Kw.

The use of electron beams to degrade, in a desirable
sense, semiconductor diodes leads us naturally into the
use of ion beams to make semiconductor devices and their
applications in some other areas.

A method of producing transistors by ion bombardment
was disclosed in patents issued to Ohl in June 1956 and
Schockley in April 1957.   The author also proposed the
technique of implanting dopant ions into silicon in April
1954, when difficulty was being experienced in diffusing
into this material.   Several attempts to convert semiconductor materials by ion bombardment were subsequently made, but at the low energies involved, it is not
clear whether true junctions were being formed or simply
the surface states being modified.   As far as the author
is aware, the first useful device - a modest efficiency
silicon photovoltaic cell was made at Ion Physics Corpora-

Figure 9.   The ING Project Proposal to Use Separated Orbit
Cyclotrons (Atomic Energy of Canada, Ltd.).

tion in 1961. A boron beam with energy spectrum up to
1. 5 Mev was used giving a junction depth of 2. 2 microns.
Subsequently, solar cell development proceeded largely
under Air Force support to the point where implantation
fabricated cells have superior efficiency and radiation
resistance to those produced by diffusion techniques. The
process, being easily controlled, gives high yield and
high uniformity. It is, therefore, economically competitive.

Now ions are introduced into crystal lattices by two
different methods. The first is true implantation in
which the ion travels a given relatively fixed distance,
dependent on the stopping power of the material, the ion
species, and its energy just as the alpha rays from radium
travel a given fixed distance in air. In the second, more
accurately known as channeling, relatively low energy
ions can migrate or straggle along crystal axes when the
substrate is correctly aligned with the ion beam. The
distance these ions channel is dependent on crystal perfection, as well as other parameters. Unfortunately,

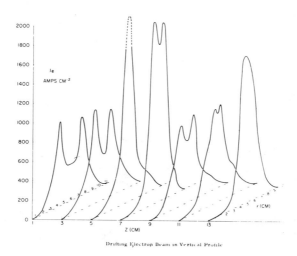

Figure 10. The Cross-Section of Current Density of a Self-
Pinched Electron Beam (Ion Physics Corporation).

channeling means something entirely different to the semiconductor device engineer with the result that the term
implantation has been incorrectly used to cover both processes.

The advantage of channeling is that it can produce
much greater junction depths and at lower beam energies
than implantation. However, it does not permit profile
control to the same extent, and that, I believe, will be the
most important parameter in the fabrication of the complex
semiconductor devices. The higher energies used in implantation permit doping through an oxide or other passiv-
ating layer so that many of the wet chemistry steps associated with semiconductor device production can be eliminated.

For the development quantities of solar cells and other
large area devices, a 400 Kev Van de Graaff accelerator
with beam analysis and spot scanning is used. Implantation equipment for solar cell production at the rate of
5000 2 x 1 cm cells per week is shown in Fig. 6.

Figure 11. A Large Tandem Van de Graaff Ion Accelerator.
Multiple Electron Stripping Permits Production of Uranium Ions
Exceeding 200 Mev. (High Voltage Engineering Corporation).

Now the value of implantation rests not only in its
ability to produce existing devices, but also in its ability
to put any ion into any material.   An example is shown
in Fig. 7 in which a natural diamond has been implanted
with boron to produce a diode.   Polycrystalline materials
for which diffusion takes place along grain boundaries, as
well as into the bulk of material, are also amenable to
implantation.   Finally, the precise control of junction
depth that implantation affords means that higher frequency - faster switching - devices can be built.   Also,
that as semiconductor materials technology develops,
higher packing and power densities can be used.

Today we are at the birth of implantation - of ion
beams as a true industrial tool.   Production quantities of
solar cells will be rolling off the line in the next few weeks.

Allied with implantation is another use for ion beams -
that is to deposit material by the energetic sputtering
process.   Rare gas ions at about 30 Kev energy are used
to bombard targets of various elements and some compounds - notably fused silica.   The sputtered target mate-

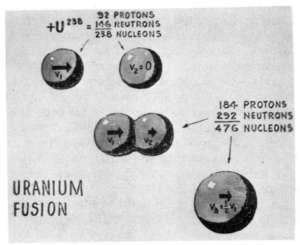

Figure 12.   Uranium Fusion Concept. High Energies Overcome the
Coulomb Forces and May Permit the Formation of New Transuranic
Elements. (High Voltage Engineering Corporation).

rial leaves with a cosine distribution about the normal to
the target surface, and keys into the substrate surface
toward which it is directed. We use it to deposit pas-
sivating layers on semiconductor device surfaces and
have used it to put carbon coatings on mylar films.

So far I have dealt with production or near-production,
as it is today. All the production tools I have shown you
relate to processes that are out of the laboratory and on
the floor. I cannot conclude without some near-term predictions and some longer-term speculations.

First, implantation. This ion beam technique is already proving its efficacy in large area devices, such as
solar cells, radiation detectors, and so forth. Can it be
applied to the intricacies of integrated circuits and high
resolution devices? The answer lies in another question.
Can equipment be developed that will permit economic
production - circuit production rates measured in millions per month? Right now implantation equipment is in
a stage akin to the early radio tube. We must leapfrog to
the electron microscope. Such economic studies as I
have undertaken tend to say that it can be done with the
advantage that greater freedom in circuit design will
accrue to the integrated circuit engineer.

Second, the electron beam as an ionizing radiation tool
is penetrating a number of industries. After a number of
false starts, solid economic ground for its use has now
been found. During nearly twenty years equipment manufacturers and potential users have learned the economic
and technical pitfalls. It is now evident that electron
beams and isotope radiation each have their relevant fields
and it is unthinkable that the millions of dollars of food
spoilage existing in the world today will not yield to the
two in harmony. In the field of thin materials - textiles,
films for packaging, shrinkable tube - the electron beam
on strictly economic grounds will dominate.

Now, for a more speculative look into the future. What
charged particle beam projects now in the laboratory or
in the planning stage may eventually emerge as industrial
tools? I will select three possible examples.

First, there is the ING (Intense Neutron Generator)
project under active study at the Atomic Energy of Canada

Ltd.'s Chalk River laboratories. Through spallation reactions 1 Gev proton beams produce neutrons with a lower
expenditure of energy than occurs in nuclear reactors.
For research purposes this means that still higher neutron
fluxes can be attained than the temperature limitations of
fission reactors permit. But, there is also the further
implication that if such an accelerator is powered by a
nuclear reactor the complex can produce more fissile
material than it burns. The engineering problems are
formidable - the beam power alone is 65 megawatts - but
they are engineering problems - not the research uncertainty that still exists in controlled fusion.

Second, we have the intense power densities obtainable in self-pinched electron streams. The accompanying
Fig. 10 shows the profile of a 4 Mev 17, 000 ampere electron beam as it moves from the electron window through a
gas at low pressure (10^{-1} torr). The power density at the
first node is about 10^{11} watts cm^{-2} . Machines are being
developed that can raise even this intense power level by
an order of magnitude and at the same time deliver several
hundred kilojoules per pulse.

Third, is the possibility of accelerating very heavy
ions to energies approach 1 Gev. By stripping these heavy
ions of most of their electron shells, relatively modest
potentials - such as are obtainable in the larger tandem
Van de Graaffs - can be used. When the heavy ion has
sufficient energy to overcome the coulomb barriers of a
heavy target, atom nuclear reactions take place that can
include the formation of transuranic elements. An exciting
possibility exists that isotopes containing 126 protons and
184 neutrons - an element about 30 per cent heavier than
uranium - may be sufficiently stable for separation and
identification.

Thus three charged particle machines now in evolution
may respectively lead us to new methods of producing
energy, new magnitudes of applied power density and perhaps to new materials. The research programs of the next
decade will unravel these possibilities.

It is not possible to refer effectively to all the literature in the fields I have broadly covered. However,
material I have used has been supplied not only by Ion

Physics Corporation and High Voltage Engineering Corporation - the companies with which I am associated - but
also by the Atomic Energy of Canada, Ltd. , Radiation
Dynamics Inc. , and the X-ray Division of the General
Electric Co. It is my pleasure to acknowledge this contribution.

Characteristics of Sheet Resistors Prepared by Ion Implantation of Alkalies

L. A. Garasi, S. Kaye, D. B. Medved and G. P. Rolik

Electro Optical Systems, Inc.
Pasadena, California

INTRODUCTION

The fabrication of microcircuitry employing ion implantation can be carried out with varying approaches, each requiring different degrees of sophistication. There appear to be roughly three distinct procedures that can be employed to produce microcircuit configurations. These are:

1. Microbeam Writing. The use of a microbeam to implant desired ion species, with controlled changes in conductivity type and resistivity, would represent the ultimate application of the ion implantation process. Deflection of such beams by application of electric or magnetic fields opens up a possibility of designing digitally programmed ion beam writing machines for the fabrication of microcircuits in an all-maskless technology.

2. Metal Masking with Demagnified Beams. A metal mask containing apertures for ion beams in the desired pattern can be fabricated with dimensions scaled order of magnitude greater than the desired array resolution. Demagnification of large area ion beams incident on such a mask can then produce desired results.

3. Use of Macrobeam with Oxide-Mask Targets. The use of large area, uniform macrobeams to implant selected paets of a silicon slice represents an immediate application of ion implantation doping. This technique is particularly appealing since most problems on target processing have already been extensively investigated as

1045

part of the highly developed diffusion technology. The clear advantage to be gained by the use of an ion beam in this manner lies in the properties of the implanted layers, which may be considerably different than those made by diffusion. Active elements may already be present in the targets prepared whether by diffusion or by previous implantations. The following key problems need to be defined in establishing this technique as a reliable production process:

a. Doping effects of incident ions on the oxide should be known and minimized.

b. Sputtering of the oxide layer should be kept within necessary tolerances. Knowledge of the oxide sputtering as a function of beam species, energy, and target temperature is essential.

c. Charge effects due to implanted ions need to be controlled in order to avoid undesirable formation of inversion layers and channels at the oxide-silicon interface.

d. Degradation of device performance by exposure to the ion beam should be avoided. It is assumed that active devices prepared by standard diffusion technology may be part of the slice and radiation damage effects on their electronic characteristics can result from improper beam exposure conditions.

APPARATUS

A typical pure tungsten surface ionization source used to generate cesium or potassium ions is schematically illustrated in Fig. 1. The ionizer assembly consists of the ionizer, manifold, feed tube, metal bellows, and terminating flange. The ionizer is composed of porous tungsten buttons, 3/16 inch in diameter, brazed into the refractory metal manifold in a hexagonal array. The buttons have a density of approximately 80 percent that of solid tungsten and have a vast number of interconnected pores or channels to allow the cesium or potassium metal vapor to diffuse through to the front surface. The manifold is designed to give a uniform distribution of vapor at the rear of the buttons, supplied at a pressure of a few torr from a reservoir connected to the manifold by the

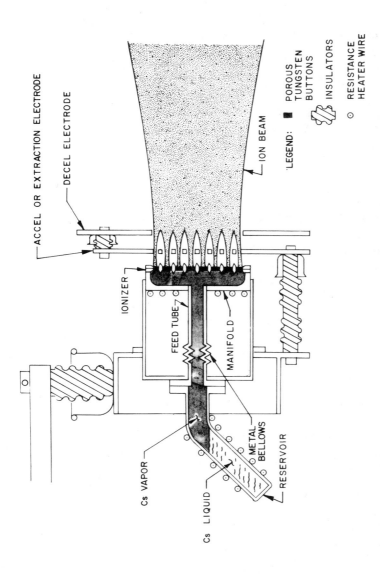

Figure 1.   Schematic for Typical Pure Tungsten Surface Ionization.

feed tube. The reservoir is constructed of thin-walled stainless steel tubing, which provides fast response to any changes in the reservoir power. This is advantageous since the reservoir temperature governs the cesium or potassium vapor supply rate (i. e. , the vapor pressure). Special care is exercised to ensure a monotonically increasing temperature gradient from the reservoir to the ionizer to prevent condensation of vapor in the feed tube.

The ions formed on the ionizer surface are extracted using an accelerate-decelerate electrode configuration designed for high perveance. Cesium and potassium ion currents ranging from a few mA to greater than 125 mA have been routinely extracted from sources used in implantation runs. The 81-button ion source used in large-area implantations, shown in Fig. 2, is a modified version of the EOS cesium ion engine that has operated continuously for 2600 hours and has been successfully tested in space. The principal modification, for purposes of ion implantation, is to the ionizer assembly mounting structure permitting source operation at voltages up to 20 kV. With sources of this type, up to ten 1-inch diameter slices, each containing several hundred devices, can be processed in typical exposure times of 5 - 15 minutes.

RESISTORS

P-n Junction isolated, high-value resistors can be formed by ion implantation, with easier control than with diffusion. The highest sheet resistance obtainable by diffusion is approximately 400 ohms sq^{-1}. Sheet resistance on the order of 1000 - 5000 ohms sq^{-1}, however, can be obtained rather reproducibly by ion doping with potassium. The range of sheet resistance can be extended from 10 kΩ per square up to megohms per square by employing cesium implantation.

The details of the sheet resistor construction are shown in the sequence from Figs. 3 through 5. The procedure employed was to polish and etch a 20 ohm-cm p-type silicon slice, which was then thermally oxidized to form a 1 μ-thick oxide layer. Windows were cut into the oxide by the usual photoresist and etching techniques.

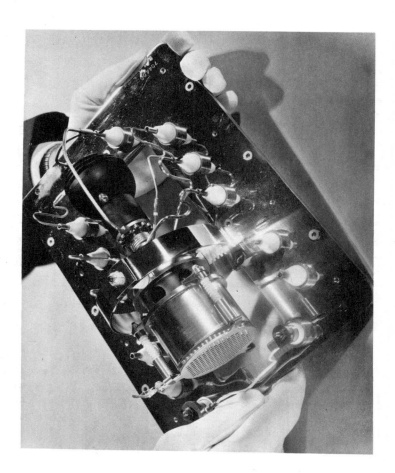

Figure 2.   Cesium Surface Ionization.

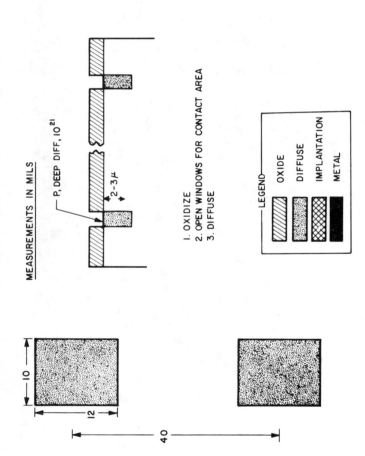

Figure 3.   Pre-Implantation Processing of Sheet Resistors.

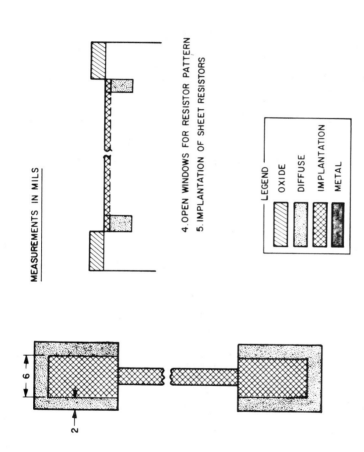

Figure 4.   Implantation of Sheet Resistors.

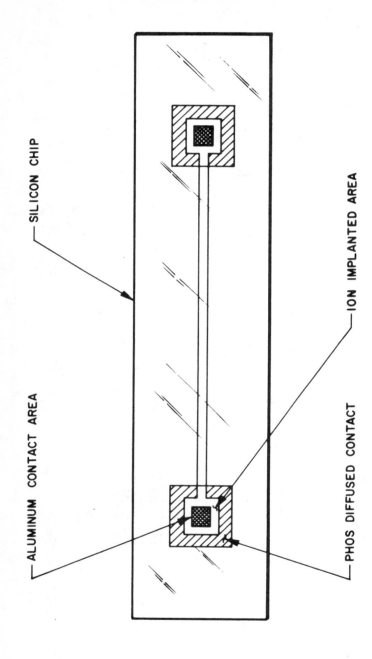

Figure 5. Top View of Ion Implanted Resistor Configuration.

Phosphorus was then diffused to the appropriate windows to a depth of approximately $2\,\mu$ to form contact pads. In a subsequent photoresist and etching process, the additional windows corresponding to the resistor array were opened, and the n-type resistor layer was then formed by potassium ion implantation at 5 keV. The implantation was followed by evaporation of an aluminum layer which was masked and etched to form the metal contacts. Final electrical contact was made by 1-mil gold wire compression bonded to this aluminum layer. Figure 6 shows a photograph of the section of the slice after exposure to the implantation process. It turned out that resistor numbers 32, 36, 40, and 48 were in the direct path of the beam, whereas others were somewhat shadowed by a mechanical mask. Figure 7 shows the reverse bias isolation characteristics. Figures 8 and 9 are temperature coefficient studies. The distribution of resistance values of those units in the direct beam showed a scatter of about 5 percent. The temperature coefficient for these resistance units is extremely interesting, since it turned out to be an order of magnitude lower than those associated with the best diffused types. There was some hysteresis exhibited in the temperature coefficient behavior which has been ascribed to possible changes in the metal silicon-contact resistance or associated surface effects. In this preliminary work, no provisions have been made to protect the sheet resistors from ambient conditions.

CIRCUITS

The use of ion implantation techniques are being explored in conjunction with standard techniques for the fabrication of a Darlington amplifier. This circuit was designed to take advantage of the high value, low temperature coefficient resistors that can be made by potassium implantation and utilizes a pair of diffused transistors with implanted resistors. This circuit will demonstrate the feasibility of using ion implantation for at least a portion of the fabrication procedures required.

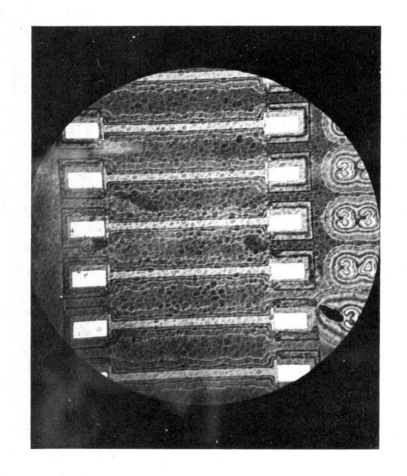

Figure 6. Photomicrograph of K-Implanted Resistors with Aluminum Contracts.

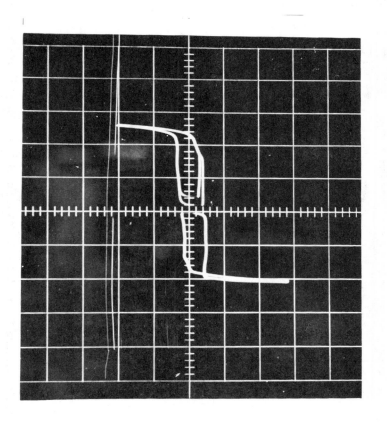

Figure 7.   P-n Junction Isolation Between Two Adjacent Resistors.

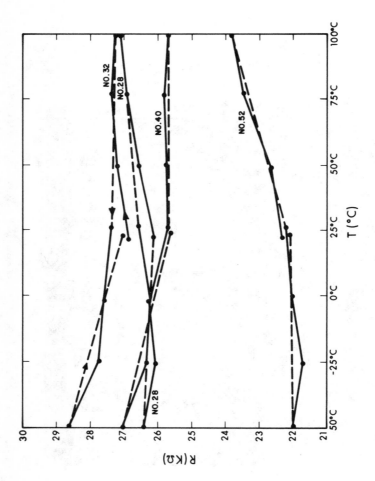

Figure 8.   Resistance Characteristics as a Function of Temperature for Ion-Implanted Resistors.

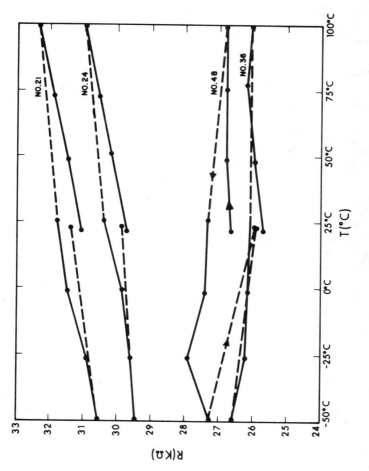

Figure 9.   Resistance Characteristics as a Function of Temperature for Ion–Implanted Resistors.

The requirement for the circuit is such that input resistors of 1 megohm are desired. The use of conventional diffusion techniques which yield sheet resistances in the order of 500 ohms per square would necessitate a resistor chain 2000 squares long. However, since with ion implantation, sheet resistances of 5000 ohms per square are easily attained, the resistor chain need only be 200 squares long.

The second requirement that the resistors be in the ratio 10^2:10:1 is easily solved by the geometrical shape of the oxide mask windows which are etched prior to the implantation. Since in a large area ion beam the individual resistors of any one circuit are in close proximity to each other, identical sheet resistances are assured. The maintenance of beam uniformity also ensures reproducibility of results over many slices.

Such a device finds immediate use in microcircuits. One stage of this type would replace several stages of conventional impedance matching stages. It would also allow the use of high-impedance devices along with low-impedance devices which is now prohibitive because of the number of matching stages required. Experimental results will be reported separately in another publication.

Ion Bombardment Effects in Semiconductors

I. Liberman

Westinghouse Research Laboratories
Pittsburgh, Pennsylvania

INTRODUCTION

Some of the original work on ion bombardment of crystals was done by Stark [1] and Baum [2]. Stark bombarded flat crystals of NaCl, KCl, CaF_2, etc., of 1 mm thickness. After some time he observed .03 mm high bulges on the back side of the crystals which he concluded were due to the impact of the bombarding ions. Baum bombarded one side of a .05 mm copper foil with either hydrogen or nitrogen ions. The other side of the foil was a portion of a wall of an evacuated chamber. After bombardment for 20 minutes with 3 KeV ions, he observed a rise of pressure to about 1 mm in the previously evacuated chamber. He concluded that the pressure rise was due to gas transported into the chamber by the bombarding ions passing through the copper foil. He thus showed that low velocity ions can penetrate through significant thicknesses of solids.

In the late 1940's renewed interest in ion bombardment resulted from the development of accelerators and high purity crystals. Radiation from high velocity ions as well as neutrons were used to produce surface states in crystals. The altered surface states are due to either doping or damage. Doping can occur in two ways. The bombarding ions can become embedded in the crystal, or particularly with neutron bombardment, transmutations can occur. For example, Si^{30} can be transmutted to Si^{31} which then

decays to p^{31} [3]. Lattice damage can result in either
vacancies and/or interstitials. It was found that with
high energy particles the dominating effect was lattice
damage [4]. The majority of research performed used
high velocity particles (50 keV to 5 MeV) and was on
single crystals of silicon or germanium. Ohl [22], for
example, studied the rectification characteristics of ion
bombarded silicon. A good review of recent work in this
field is found in an article by Kay [5].

This paper describes the effect of intermediate
velocity ions (10-20 KeV). The majority of the work described is concerned with the bombardment doping of
single crystal MnO. The crystals were grown by the
flame-fusion process and were brought from the Fiju
Titanium Industry Co., Osaka, Japan. In addition, some
work was performed with single crystal Si and Ge for
comparison with other research on ion bombardment. The
only limitation of the choice of dopant ion is that it be
available as part of a gaseous compound or vapor at the
pressure required for operation of the discharge. Thus
gases such as H_2, He, A, O_2, N_2, CO_2, and CO were
used as well as volatile liquids such as CCl_4 and $SiCl_4$.

EXPERIMENTAL APPARATUS

Ion Gun

The crystals used were bombarded by positive ions
originating from a positive ray tube (kanalstralenrohre).
A great deal of research has deen done on positive ray
tubes in order to study the effects of the resulting ions on
targets as well as to study this type of discharge. Consequently, positive ray tubes have been constructed with
large variations in geometry [6]. The geometry used for
this study (Fig. 1) was obtained from Hailer [7]. This
gun is designed for optimum efficiency when used with
hydrogen gas. Utilizing mass spectroscopy, Hailer determined the properties of the ion beam for conditions not
unlike those present in this investigation. Thirty percent
of the ions generated were protons. The majority of these
protons had energies between 35% to 70% of the applied
voltage. The rest of the beam was composed of H_2 + ions

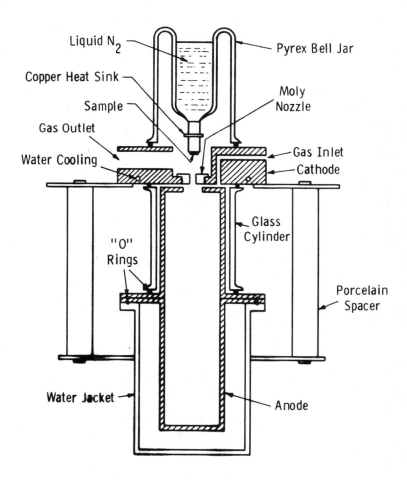

Figure 1.   Positive Ray Tube.

I. LIBERMAN

although traces of H_3^+ ions were also observed. The H_2^+ and H_3^+ ions had most of their energy concentrated at 70% of the applied voltage.

The gun design contains many noteworthy characteristics. The anode is a closed cylinder with a small opening in the end facing the cathode. This small opening is aligned with the nozzle hole through the cathode (see Fig. 1). Thus, the positive ions generated inside the anode cylinder are focused by the field configuration so that they pass through the nozzle rather than striking the cathode. This not only leads to high efficiency, but also prevents rapid erosion of the cathode and contamination of the beam. The face of the anode is about 1 mm from the cathode. At typical operating pressures this distance is much less than the mean free path between collisions so that unwanted discharges cannot occur. The gas enters the tube below the cathode and leaves above it in order to create a pressure gradient. The required pressure gradient limits the diameter of the nozzle. The pressure below the nozzle is of the order of 0.1 torr. Under these conditions the tube can deliver a 3 mA ion current at about 15 keV energy, or up to 45 watts of power can be delivered to the target. The ion current was measured by attaching a Faraday cage to the sample holder. During the actual bombardment, the Faraday cage was removed due to geometry problems and transient instabilities in the discharge. The sample was kept about 50 volts negative with respect to the cathode to preclude buildup of positive charge.

The large amount of power produced by the ion beam concentrated in a small area (.05 cm²) required cooling of the thin sample to prevent its disintegration. The crystals were circular discs about 1 cm in diameter and .1-.2 mm thick. The back of the crystals were held against a lapped aluminum block by means of pressure contacts. The alumunim block was kept at liquid nitrogen temperature. Assuming good thermal contact between the crystal and the aluminum block, the temperature of the exposed surface can be estimated. The temperature across a pillbox of area A and thickness t is given by

$$\Delta T = \frac{1}{k} \cdot \frac{P}{A} \cdot t \qquad (1)$$

where k is the thermal conductivity and $P = E \cdot I$ is the
incident power. Using a conservatively small value of
$k = .025$ cal sec^{-1} $^{\circ}$C^{-1} cm^{-1} and using typical values
of $t = .025$ cm, $A = .05$ cm^2, $E = 15$ kV and $I = 2$ mA
one finds that $\Delta T = 150^{\circ}$C. Therefore, if one face is at
liquid nitrogen temperature, the bombardment face will be
below room temperature due to thermal conduction.
However, it is possible that the first few hundred ang-
stroms of target in absorbing the kinetic energy of the
ions, become much hotter than the calculation indicates,
and heat balance is obtained by radiation of the surface.
It can be stated with certainty that the cooled bombarded
samples never become visibly hot. Strict attention was
given to the preparation of the crystals to obtain good
thermal contact. A diamond saw was used to cut the
crystals in any desired orientation as determined by
Laue x-ray photographs. These crystals had a final
polish with 1 micron diamond and the lapping apparatus
insured that the surfaces were flat.

Electrical Measurements

The primary electrical measurements made were
those of conductivity and Seebeck coefficient. Both were
measured as a function of temperature. The temperature
could be continually regulated between -196°C to + 250°C.
The measurements were carried out in a dark, shielded
container and in a dry inert atmosphere. Either two terminal or four terminal resistive measurements could be
made. It was found in almost all cases that two terminal
measurements would suffice since the crystals were of
high resistance, and both high and low work function
materials (platinum, gold, silver, and indium) were used
as the metal contacts. Platinum contacts were used pre-
dominantly and were sputtered on. The sample was then
clamped to two aluminum blocks spaced about 1 mm apart.
For thermoelectric measurements, a temperature
difference between the two ends of the crystal was achievd

by embedding a small resistor in one of the aluminum supports. The temperature difference was kept between 6°C and 10°C. The temperature difference produced a thermoelectric effect of millivolts as measured by a Leeds and Northrop K-2 potentiometer.

Since the resistance is a function of geometry, the desired property of the material is its resistivity. However, the geometry inherent in the bombardment process makes accurate measurements of resistivity virtually impossible. First, the bombardment penetrates the surface no more than 10's of microns. Thus, any resistance measurement involves the thin layer of bombarded material in parallel with the bulk. Second, even if these two parallel circuits could be separated, the distribution of the resistance of the bombarded layer is very heterogeneous. Therefore, in an analogy with resistivities of thin layers, all resistivities and conductivities taken from resistance measurements are expressed in ohms per square. The metallic electrical contacts are not placed on the ends of the sample but directly on the surface.

The samples were in the shape of rectangular parallelipipeds of thickness .13 mm and surface area 1.5 mm by 8 mm. The circular bombardment pattern covered the entire sample width and the electrodes covered the entire surface except for a gap about 1 mm over the bombarded area.

EXPERIMENTAL RESULTS

Germanium

Figures 2 and 3 shows the effect of bombardment on the resistivity and the Seebeck coefficient of Ge as a function of temperature.

As the germanium used was fairly pure (40 ohm-cm), it remained intrinsic as low as 0°C and had a higher resistivity than any of the other samples. The decrease in the resistivity of the bombarded samples can be attributed to either doping of the crystal with the bombarding ions, interstitially or substitutionally, to the creation of vacancies, or to a combination of all these effects. From the

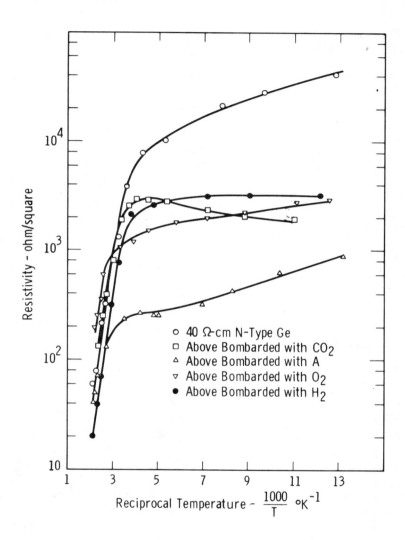

Figure 2. Resistivity vs. Reciprocal Temperature of 40 ohm-cm Germanium.

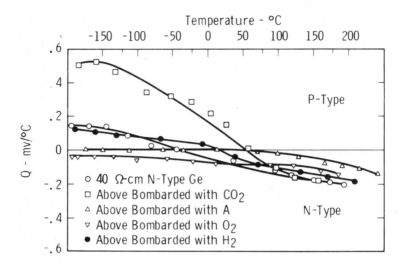

Figure 3. Seebeck Coefficient vs. Temperature of 40 ohm-cm Germanium.

Seebeck effect a clear insight into the consequences of bombardment is obtained.

At the higher temperatures (above 50°C), where intrinsic conductivity dominates, all samples remain n-type since there are approximately an equal number of holes and electrons, the latter having a greater mobility. However, at lower temperatures either n- or p-type conductivity can be obtained, depending upon the ions used for bombardment. It has been shown [4] that at high bombardment energies lattice destruction is the primary effect of the bombardment regardless of the type of ion used. In germanium this leads to greater p-type conductity [8]. However, since oxygen bombardment results in n-type behavior, it is proposed that bombardment with ions of medium energy can produce a significant amount of doping.

It is also seen (Fig. 3) that bombardment with argon has the same effect as high energy bombardment. That is, since argon cannot dope germanium substitutionally its principal effect is lattice destruction. In the intrinsic range the argon bombarded germanium behaves less n-type and becomes slightly p-type in the low temperature range. Bombardment with CO_2 gas results in positive ions of C, CO, CO_2, O, and O_2 [9]. This bombardment produced positive Seebeck coefficients far greater than bombardment with other gases. Therefore, the crystal was appreciably doped. Since oxygen ions yielded negative Seebeck coefficients, it is concluded that the large See-beck effect was due to a multiple doping of carbon acceptors and oxygen donors, as well as some vacancy acceptors.

Bombardment of Silicon

1000 ohm-cm silicon and 41 ohm-cm p-type silicon were bombarded with a number of gases. Figures 4 and 5 summarize the results of the bombardment of 1000 ohm-cm silicon. The high resistivity of the unbombarded silicon made accurate measurements over the tempera-ture range studies difficult to obtain with the existing apparatus.

After bombardment the resistivity is lowered as ex-pected. Studies of ion bombardment of silicon at high energies show that due to damage an equal number of donors and acceptors result [10]. Bombardment with argon bears out this statement because it results in a marked decrease in resistivity without creating an ap-preciable thermal voltage. Apparently, hydrogen bom-bardment has a similar effect on silicon. The Seebeck effect shows that with the other available gases only n-type doping could be achieved. At high temperatures all re-sistivity curves become identical indicating that the low average concentration of donors added by bombardment are exhausted. The conductivity is then controlled by the original defects in the silicon corresponding to a doping level about .29 eV below the conduction band.

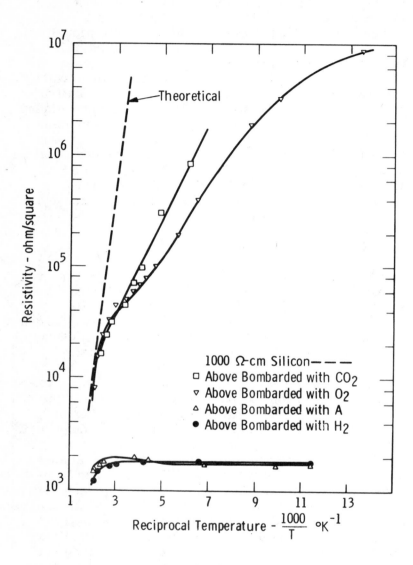

Figure 4. Resistivity vs. Reciprocal Temperature of 1000 ohm-cm Silicon.

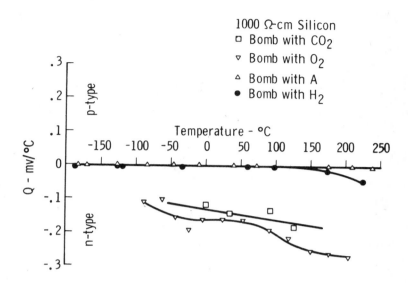

Figure 5.   Seebeck Coefficient vs. Temperature of 1000 ohm-cm Silicon.

When p-type instead of "intrinsic" silicon is used for bombardment the resulting thermoelectric voltages are entirely different (Figs. 6 and 7).   In this case either positive or negative Seebeck coefficients may be achieved and in fact, these thermal voltages can be quite large. When multiple donor and acceptor levels are present, the Seebeck coefficient is difficult to interpret.   Under certain conditions it is possible to obtain a negative Seebeck co-efficient despite a predominant p-type conductivity [11]. Due to the large and opposing effects resulting from the ion bombardment of silicon it is clear that the dominating effect of moderate velocity ions is that of doping.

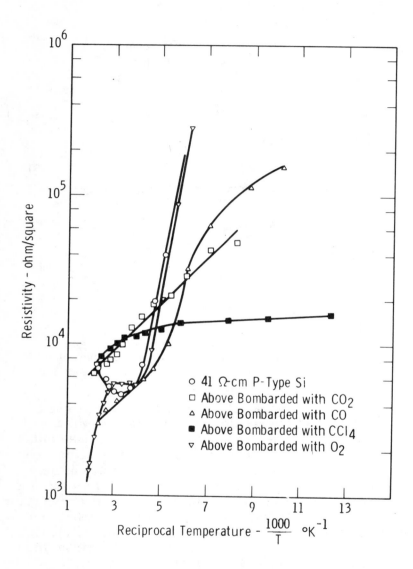

Figure 6. Resistivity vs. Reciprocal Temperature of 41 ohm-cm
p-Type Silicon.

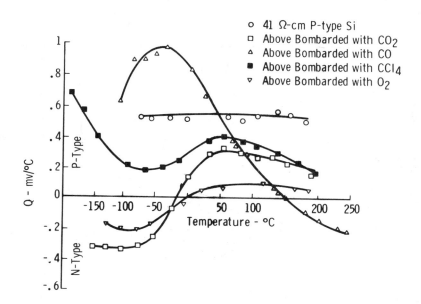

Figure 7. Seebeck Coefficient vs. Temperature of 41 ohm–cm
p–Type Silicon.

Bombardment of MnO

MnO is a face centered cubic crystal with a lattice
spacing of 4. 438A [12].   Using 12 mil samples, transmission measurements (not corrected for reflection),
show that the transmission gradually increases from . 7
microns to a peak between 9 to 12 microns and then cuts
off abruptly at 14 microns (Fig. 8).   No transmission in
the visible was observed for these samples although the
crystal does appear green when thin.   Within the trans-

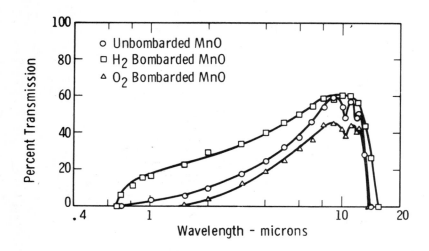

Figure 8. Optical Transmission of 12 mil MnO.

mission peak there are two small absorption dips at 10. 2
microns and 11. 8 microns. Ion bombardment does not
affect the position of the peak, but in the case of nitrogen,
helium, and hydrogen tends to broaden it and remove the
dips, while oxygen bombardment narrows the peak. Carbon dioxide has little effect. Measurements were taken
with the Beckman IR 5 and DK 2 spectrophotometers, and
covered the range from 16 micron to . 2 micron. As the
bombarded area was small, only a portion of the beam
could be utilized thus reducing both the accuracy and precision of the instruments.

More sensitive measurements of optical density
taken with the Cary 14 spectrophotometer explain the weak
green transmission. From Fig. 9 it is seen that for a
4 mil unbombarded sample the transmission at 4300 A and

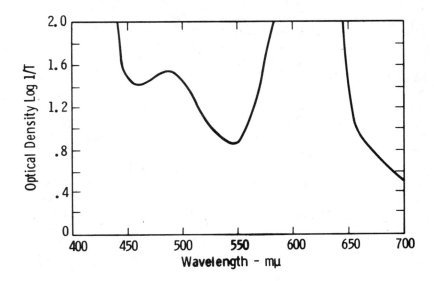

Figure 9.   Optical Density of 4 mil Unbombarded MnO.

6000 A is less than 1%.   However, at 5440 A it is about
14%.   Thus measurements with 12 mil samples would not
show the small transmission at 5450 A.

Helium and hydrogen bombardment created color
centers in the MnO.   Helium bombardment resulted in a
deep red crystal, while hydrogen bombardment turned
the MnO a light green.   The deep red color is found by
means of the following experimental observations, to be
associated with a partial reduction of the MnO.

1.   The unbombarded thin green crystals showed
localized spots of red indicating some deviation from
stoichiometry.

2.   Heating MnO crystals in 10^{-3} torr of hydrogen at
800°C turns them a deep brownish red.

3.   Bombardment with hydrogen ions in which the kinetic energy of bombardment is allowed to heat the crystals (instead of being absorbed by the liquid nitrogen sink as is usually done) also turns the crystal deep red.

The conclusion is that the deep red color is produced when oxygen ions are removed from the lattice.   Because of their larger ionic radius, oxygen ions are removed more easily than manganese ions.   The higher the temperature of the lattice, the greater the probability of dissociation.   Therefore, at high temperature hydrogen bombardment gives the same result as does helium at low temperature.

It is believed that the light green color resulting from hydrogen bombardment at low crystal temperature is due to hydrogen penetrating into the lattice without causing appreciable reduction.   It was found that the light green crystals are photoconducting.

A modified Beckman DU 2400 spectrophotometer was used to measure the photoconductive response (Fig. 10). The spectral intensity was kept constant by regulating the slit width to give constant voltage readings on a thermocouple.   The major peak of photoconductivity occurs at 425 m μ while a smaller peak is present at about 620 mμ.   Due to the photoconducting behavior of hydrogen bombarded MnO, a detailed study of this material as well as information about ion bombardment was obtained as will be shown.

X-ray Studies

The orientation of the MnO was determined from Laue photographs.   Slices of about .25 mm thickness and 1 cm^2 were cut and polished parallel to the [100], or [110], or [111] planes of the crystal.   The faces were within 2° of these planes.   After hydrogen bombardment, no appreciable difference in the photoconductivity connected with orientation could be observed.   Since significant differences in photoconductivity were observed for similarly oriented crystals under "identical" bombardment conditions, the conclusion drawn is that orientation effects are negligible compared to the other effects present in the bombardment process.

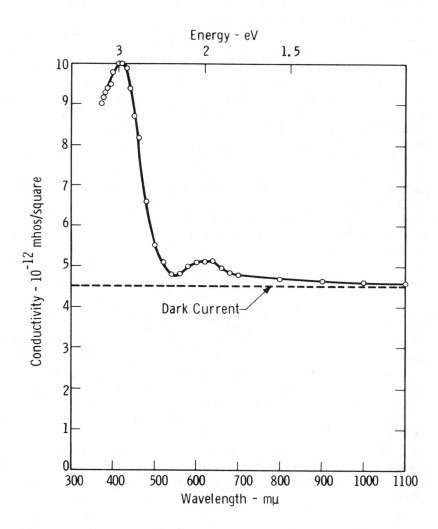

Figure 10. Photoconductivity vs. Wavelength for Hydrogen
Bombarded MnO.

Polished unbombarded samples etched in H_3PO_4
resulted in x-ray diffraction half width, β of $.06° \pm .002°$
for first order reflection. This value was independent of
orientations and equalled that obtained by cleaving the
crystal along the [110] plane. Thus, it appears that due
to tilts and strains within the crystal, $\beta = .06°$ is an indication of the perfection of the crystal used. The receiving
slit width of the diffractometer was nominally $.02°$.
Polished but unetched crystals had larger half widths due
to surface smearing. Bombardment of these crystals
reduced β to $.06°$. Only under extremely heavy bombardment did β increase to $.08°$. Thus, the bombardment
tends to etch the surface and does not appear to alter the
lattice structure. It might then be assumed that the induced photoconductivity is due to point defects within the
lattice rather than caused by gross lattice dislocations.
Electron diffraction of $.1$ to $.15$ MeV bombarded silicon
also yield the same conclusions since the Kikuchi line
pattern was unaltered [13].

Depth of Penetration

The photoconductive behavior of the bombarded material lends itself to a study of the depth of penetration of
bombarding ions. The technique used, was to measure the
photoconductivity after successive removals of the surface
in small increments. Surface removal by mechanical
lapping was a poor technique. It was difficult to obtain
small as well as uniform increments since the bombarded
surface was depressed after bombardment. Therefore,
two other techniques were tried, and they yielded similar
results. The first was etching the surface with H_3PO_4
and the other was sandblasting. The increments of removal were approximately 1 micron steps and were measured by weight analysis. The results indicate that log
(σ_p/σ_d) decreases to 10% of its initial value after removal of about 20 microns of the surface; where σ_p is the
photoconductivity and σ_d is the dark conductivity (Fig. 11).
Furthermore, at these depths there is still a distinct dif-

ference in the green transparency of the bombarded and non-bombarded material. After removing about 50 microns of the surface, the transparency between the bombarded and non-bombarded surface becomes roughly equivalent.

The depth of penetration of bombarding ions and neutrons in a crystalline lattice has been a source of interest for a number of years. Both theoretical and experimental techniques, as well as a combination of both of these, have been attempted. Deduction of ion ranges from sputtering yields have been made but are not applicable for light ions [14]. It has also been shown [13] by using optical fringes, that the depth of penetration of light ions in silicon increases almost linearly with energy. At 450 keV the penetration extends to only about 5 microns. However, the amount of ionic charge imparted to the silicon was only .043 C/cm^2. Piercy et al [23] concluded that deep penetration of ions can occur in aluminum if they travel down channels between the rows of close-packed atoms. Neilsen [15] derived a model based on the assumption that the bombarding ions behave as neutral atoms and make elastic collisions with the lattice nuclei. His results, while not applicable for light ions, give values far less than those observed in this study.

None of the above theoretical or experimental approaches to penetration depth consider the density of ion bombardment, or the total number of coulombs as a significant factor. However, according to Brebec et al [16] this factor can be very significant. They used a hollow cathode discharge, containing rare gases, to show that in certain geometrically favorable sections of the hollow cathode, the depth of ion penetration is a strong function of duration of discharge. Using radioactive tracers, they found that the penetration was linear over a 4 hour period and reached a depth of 35 microns. After 13 hours the penetration was 60 microns.

These authors concluded that large penetration depths are not possible without the mechanism of redeposition. That is, the base material is loosened and then covers

the bombarding ions.   This appears to be the most plausible
explanation for obtaining the large depths of penetration
in hydrogen bombarded MnO.

Electro-Optical Properties

Band Gap Determination

The energy band gap was determined from a plot of
photoconductivity versus wavelength for the hydrogen
bombarded MnO (Fig. 10).   The peak occurred at 425 m μ
corresponding to an energy transition of 2. 5 eV.   Presumably this represents the same band gap of the unbombarded MnO, since the bombardment produces only
local doping and does not distort the lattice appreciably.
An additional small peak was observed at 620 mμ corresponding to 2 eV.   A possible explanation for this peak will
be given later.   An attempt was made to observe visible
photoluminescence by means of ultraviolet radiation from
a mercury lamp (λ = 3650 A), but none was observed.

Fermi Level Location

The conductivity was measured as a function of temperature for unbombarded and hydrogen bombarded MnO.
The temperature range used was -40 to 60°C.   The conductivity changed between 3 to 4 orders of magnitude over
the temperature range and well fitted the equation

$$\sigma = A \exp \left(\frac{-eV_f}{kT} \right) \tag{2}$$

The bombarded conductivity was less than the intrinsic
conductivity over this temperature range.   The values of
the constants were: For non-bombarded MnO A = 17. 4
mho/square, V_f = . 692 volts; for hydrogen bombarded
MnO A = 6. 33 x 10^{-4} mho/square, V_f = . 523 volts.   The
Fermi levels are taken with respect to the conduction band
since in all cases the conductivity was n-type, as determined by thermoelectric measurements.

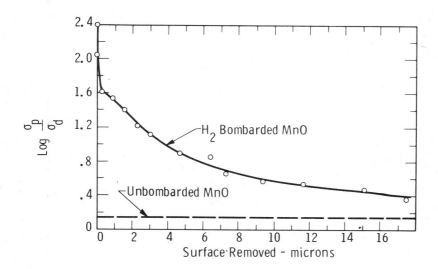

Figure 11. Photoconductivity vs. Depth of Penetration for Hydrogen Bombarded MnO.

The relation between conductivity and light intensity is as shown in Fig. 12. A tungsten lamp with the infrared filtered out was used, although similar results were obtained with a mercury lamp. The intensity was varied by placing neutral density filters between the lamp and sample. From the equation of the linear portion of the curve ($\Delta\sigma \ \alpha F^{1\cdot 2}$), it is seen that increasing intensity sensitizes the crystal (Fig. 12). That is, the lifetime of the photo-excited electrons increases with increasing intensity.

D. C. Dielectric Constant

The relative dielectric constant ϵ_r was obtained from capacity measurements. Because of the small sample

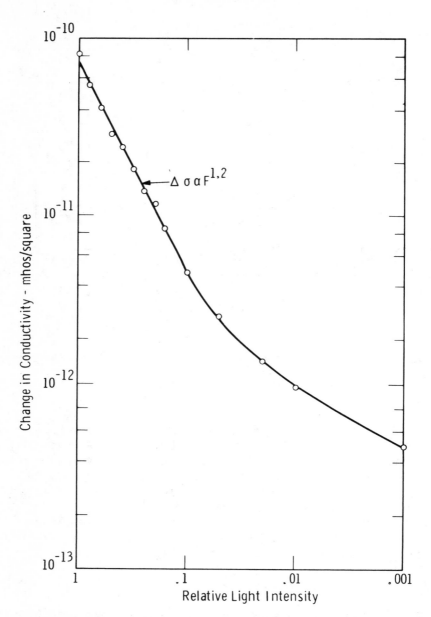

Figure 12.   Photoconductivity vs.   Light Intensity of Hydrogen Bombarded MnO.

size, the capacities measured were quite small and near the limits of the apparatus used. The result was that $\epsilon_r = 7.5 \pm 1.5$.

Photoresponse Time

Due to high resistance and unavoidable stray capacity, primarily as a result of shielding, RC time constants greater than the response time were present during measurements. Meaningful results were obtained by comparing the response time of a vacuum phototube with that of the photoconductor under the same conditions. The difference in response time is attributed to the photoconductor. The results indicate the response time to be faster than .25 msec.

THEORY OF PHOTOCONDUCTIVITY IN H_2 BOMBARDED MnO

A simple model can be hypothesized which would explain and unify the experimental evidence. Although the Fermi level was raised from about .69 eV from the conduction band to .52 eV after bombardment, the conductivity decreased. This, coupled with the fact that the material became photoconducting, indicates that the hydrogen behaved as hole traps rather than donors. This being the case, we can estimate the maximum energy of these traps (interstitial neutral hydrogen atoms and molecules) from the valence band. One way of filling a trap with a hole would be to ionize the hydrogen atom to H^+. In vacuum this requires about 13.5 eV. In a solid this figure is reduced, as a good approximation, by a factor of ϵ_r^{-2} [17]. Using the value $\epsilon_r = 7.5$ found experimentally, the equivalent ionization potential becomes .24 eV. The ionization of hydrogen in this manner, while possible, is not likely for a number of reasons. First, when ionized, an extra positive charge due to the hydrogen nucleus would exist locally. This would tend to have a large electron capture cross section [18], and thus the hydrogen atoms would tend to act more like recombination centers than hole traps. Also, it is known that when hydrogen reacts with anions to form molecules or ions, ionization rarely

occurs. That is, when hydrogen reacts with chlorine
to form HCl, or with oxygen to form (OH)⁻ or H₂ O, the
bonding is strongly covalent. In the case under consideration, a hole created in optical excitation would wander
around until it nears a hydrogen atom. Then the hydrogen
atom could covalently neutralize the hole. For the sake
of clarity, we can imagine the photon exciting one of the
electrons of the doubly ionized oxygen atoms in the MnO
lattice. The hole created would then move in the direction of the applied field. Neighboring O^{--} ions would
sequentially give up an electron to the hole. This process
continues until an O^- ion reaches an H atom where they
combine as in an (OH)⁻. That is, $[H] + [\cdot \ddot{O} :]^- =$
$[H \cdot \ddot{O} :]^-$, and the hole is trapped. In addition, there
are hydrogen molecules placed in the lattice which are
capable of trapping two holes. In an analogy with H₂ O
we have $[H:H] + [\cdot \ddot{O} :] = [H : \ddot{O} : H]$, and the two
holes implied by the uncharged oxygen are trapped.

Since (OH)⁻ and H₂ O compounds are stable in molecular form, it is likely that in a crystalline lattice they
should be more stable than interstitial H^+ or H_2^+ or
H_2^{++}. If this is the case, the filled trap will not have a
large capture cross section for electrons. This allows the
photoexcited electrons to spend a relatively long period
in the conduction band, giving rise to appreciable photoconductivity. A similar situation has been observed with
hydrogen diffusion into single crystal ZnO [19]. In this
system hydrogen behaves as a donor. The authors concluded that the most likely nature of the centers are
hydroxl groups formed from the hydrogen and oxygen ions.

To summarize, the basic model of hydrogen bombarded
MnO consists of an optical band gap of 2. 9 eV with hole
traps resulting from hydrogen atoms and from hydrogen
molecules. Holes created thermally or by radiation are
trapped by the neutral hydrogen atoms and molecules and
thus prevent rapid recombination of the free electrons.
Although strong absorption occurred at 6200 Å, little
photoconductivity resulted. It is known, that when transition metals are placed within a lattice, the crystal fields
split the 3d levels of the metal ion. Absorption within the
3d orbitals results in excited 3d electrons which are

EFFECTS IN SEMICONDUCTORS   1083

localized and cannot contribute to the conduction process. However, if these excited 3d levels are within a few KT of the conduction band, some condition electrons can be created thermally. The weak photoconductivity associated with the 6200 A absorption band (2 eV) is thus proposed to be due to optically excited 3d electrons gaining sufficient thermal energy to become conduction electrons.

It should be pointed out that the optical band gap (2. 9 eV) can be considerably greater than the thermal band gap (2 eV) as would be expected from the Franck-Condon principle [20]. To a first approximation, the optical band gap is inversely proportional to k_o , the optical relative dielectric constant; while the thermal transition is inversely proportional to k, the D. C. relative dielectric constant. Since k_o = 4. 3 [21] and k = 7. 5 from experimental measurements, it is possible for the thermal band gap to be only 60% of the optical band gap, or 1. 7 eV. Therefore, it is not surprising to observe a thermal band gap of about 2 eV.

SUMMARY

In contrast to results obtained by high energy bombardment, medium energy, high current ion bombardment changes the electrical and optical properties of crystal by doping rather than by damage. This was concluded by observing that bombardment with different gases made germanium either n or p-type and made intrinsic silicon n-type. Hydrogen bombarded MnO produced photoconductivity at 425 mμ and 620 mμ . Photoconductivity was not observed by bombarding MnO with other gases or by heating MnO in hydrogen. The bombardment penetrated over 25μ into the crystal and created color centers. The photoconductivity was found to be due to electrons having large free lifetimes. The photoexcited electrons are kept from recombining with the holes because of hole trapping. The holes combine with the interstitial hydrogen atoms forming localized $(OH)^-$ radicals, or with interstitial hydrogen molecules forming localized H_2O molecules. It was therefore shown that ion bombardment can alter crystal properties in a unique manner not possible by convenventional means. Furthermore, the doping is not limited to the surface of the solid, but extends many thousands of lattice spacings into the crystal.

ACKNOWLEDGMENT

The author is greatly indebted to Dr. Rudolph Frerichs, Northwestern University, Evanston, Illinois, for suggesting the topic and for giving guidance throughout the duration of the research.

This work was carried out in the Electrical Engineering Dept., Northwestern University, Technological Institute. The work was supported by the Wright Air Development Center, Air Research and Development Command, Contract Number AF 33(616)-6194.

REFERENCES

1. J. Stark and G. Wendt, Ann. Physik, $\underline{38}$, 941 (1912).
2. T. Baum, Z. Physik, $\underline{40}$, 686 (1927).
3. J. Crawford and J. Cleland, "Transmutation Doping and Recoil Effects in Semiconductors Exposed to Thermal Neutrons" (to be published).
4. U. Gianola, J. Appl., $\underline{28}$, 868 (1957).
5. E. Kay, Advances in Electronics and Electron Physics (Academic Press, New York, 1962), Edited by L. Marton, Vol. 17.
6. M. von Ardenne, Tabellen Der Elektronenphysik, Ionenphysik and Ubermikroskopie (Veb Deutscher Verlag der Wissenshaften, Berlin, 1956). Vol. I, p. 531.
7. C. Hailer, Wiss. Veroff. Siemans-Werken, $\underline{17}$, 321 (1938).
8. J. Crawford and J. Cleland, Progress in Semiconductors (Heywood and Co., London, 1957), Edited by Gibson, Aigrain and Burgess, Vol. 2, p. 67.
9. F. Aston, Handbuch der Experimental Physik (Leipzig, 1927), Edited by Wien and Harms, Vol. 14, p. 623.
10. T. Longo and D. Kleitman, Phys. Rev., $\underline{100}$, 1260 (1955).
11. A. D. Pearson, J. Electrochem. Soc., p. $\underline{111}$, 753 (1964).

12. Nouveau Traite de Chemie Minerale (Masson Inc.,
    Paris, 1960), Edited by P. Pascal, Vol. 16, p. 747.
13. W. Primak, Y. Dayal and E. Edwards, J. Appl.
    Phys., 34, 827 (1963).
14. M. Robinson, Appl. Phys. Letters, 1, 49 (1962).
15. K. Nielson, Electrically Electromagnetically Enriched
    Isotopes and Mass Spectroscopy (Academic Press
    Inc., New York, 1956), Edited by Smith, p. 68.
16. G. Brebec, et al., Le Bombardment Ionique
    (Bellevue, 1962), No. 113, p. 155.
17. N. Mott and R. Gurney, Electronic Processes in
    Ionic Crystals, Clarendon Press, Oxford, 1948), p. 82.
18. R. Bube, Photoconductivity of Solids (Wiley, New
    York, 1960), p. 61.
19. D. Thomas and J. Lander, J. Chem. Phys., 25,
    1136 (1956).
20. A. Dekker, Solid State Physics (Prentice-Hall Inc.,
    New Jersey, 1957).
21. Handbook of Chemistry and Physics (Chemical Rubber
    Pub. Co., Cleveland).
22. R. S. Ohl, Bell System Tech. J., 31, 104 (1952).
23. G. R. Piercy et al, Can. J. Phys., 42, 1116 (1964).

Implanted Profiles of Substitutional Doping Ions in Silicon

K. E. Manchester

Research and Development Laboratories
Sprague Electric Company
North Adams, Massachusetts

The use of ion implantation as a doping technique for device production requires precise knowledge of the concentration distribution or profile which can be introduced. Initially of interest is the shape of the injected profile.

Jens Lindhard, at the University of Aarhus, has advanced a theory which can be applied to calculate implanted distributions based on energy of the ion and nuclear charge and mass of both ion and target [1] . One such calculated distribution is seen in Fig. 1 for a 40 keV phosphorus ion in a silicon target. This sharply peaked distribution is what one would expect for random placement of atoms in the substrate.

When the substrate consists of an ordered array of atoms such as we find in the single crystal materials, it becomes evident that the directional properties of these ordered arrangements can influence the distance which an ion can travel in a target material before losing its energy and stopping. This substrate effect on penetration was predicted by Robinson and Oen in 1963 [2] and subsequently verified experimentally by Davies and co-workers at Chalk River [3] and also our work at the Sprague Electric Company laboratories.[4] At present, the theory has not been advanced to a point that will allow the calculation of a directional or "channeling" influence of the substrate on the final distribution. The channeling property of substrates must be determined experimentally.

Impurity ion distribution in silicon may be determined in a number of ways. We have applied three techniques to ion implanted silicon in which the following properties are measured which are related to concentration:

1. Variation of junction depth with substrate resistivity at constant beam conditions.

2. Variation of sheet conductance with depth.

3. Variation of activity of implanted radioactive isotope with depth.

The first two methods give distributions related to the electrically active impurity concentration, while the last method measures a distribution related to total impurity concentration.

The implantation technique is not an equilibrium process and it has been shown that electrical properties of the implanted substrates are influenced by "damage".[5] To correlate sheet resistance to impurity concentration, it is necessary to assume carrier mobilities are the same as in thermally diffused samples. This requires knowledge of the "damage" factor. Our initial studies to investigate this damage factor have been presented at an earlier meeting in terms of variation of sheet resistance with both temperature and time, as well as variations of I-V characteristics of the junctions. Results of these studies indicate that a 600°C ten-minute anneal cycle results in a stable substrate configuration. During this anneal cycle, the junction can be observed to move deeper into the substrate with the position stabilizing when the sheet resistance reaches a constant value. An indication of the magnitude of junction movement is shown in Table I.

It is important to know whether this is a damage enhanced impurity atom diffusion or a change in the ratio of electrically active to inactive atoms. The radiotracer experiments in which we implant P^{32} and determine the distribution within the substrate have shown no atom movement during the annealing cycle. Figure 2 is a plot of the activity distribution in depth for an implanted silicon substrate which has not been annealed. Also included are data points for an annealed sample which had been implanted under identical conditions.

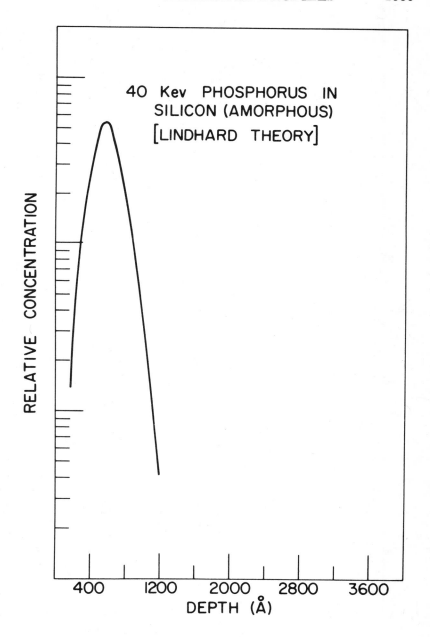

Figure 1.

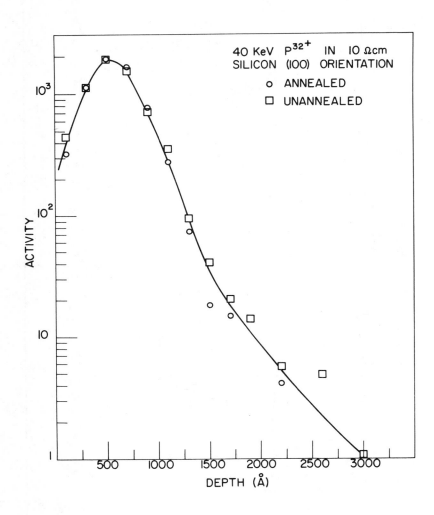

Figure 2.

Table I. Effect of Anneal Process on Junction Position

Sample[+]	Initial Depth (Å)	Depth After Anneal (Å)[++]
x-2-1	9, 250	11, 400
x-3-1	11, 850	13, 025
x-9-1	3, 780	5, 690
x-10-1	7, 260	9, 740
x-4-2	5, 210	8, 760
x-5-2	5, 340	8, 730
x-8-2	4, 540	6, 750
x-9-2	none	2, 610

[+]Substrate resistivity varied in the range 1000--0.004
ohm-cm (p-type) and P^+ or P^{++} implanted with varying
energies and total dose.
[++]Anneal temperatures = 600 °C; anneal time = 10 minutes.

The distribution shown in Fig. 2 represents the general shape of the total implanted ion profile. The predicted
Lindhard peak is evident and in agreement with the calculated depth. The width and shape of these experimentally
determined distributions vary from theory as function of
previous implant history. As an example, in Fig. 3 two
distributions are seen which show the initial and final contributions to the total profile of the first and last 10^8
ions/cm^2 of a total of 5 x 10^{14} ions/cm^2. Notice how the
final contribution to the profile approaches Lindhard's
calculated curve. This indicates that point concentrations
are not linearly additive with the total number of implanted
ions.

The radiotracer distributions have been implanted
with orders of magnitude fewer P^{32} ions than are necessary for device application. The total number of implanted
ions was increased with P^{31} ions to a level which allowed
determination of the distributions of electrically active
atoms by differential sheet conductance measurements.

Two different techniques have been mentioned for the
determination of the electrical profiles. Figure 4 is a distribution constructed by angle lapping and delineating samples which encompassed a wide range of resistivities and

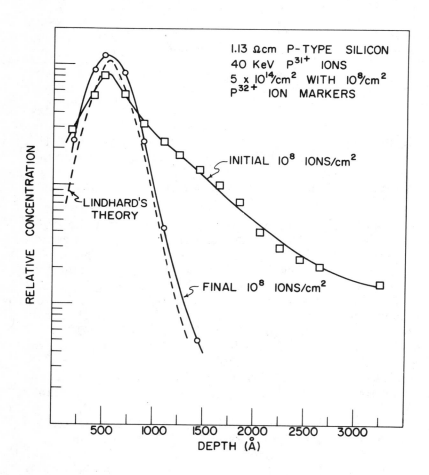

Figure 3.

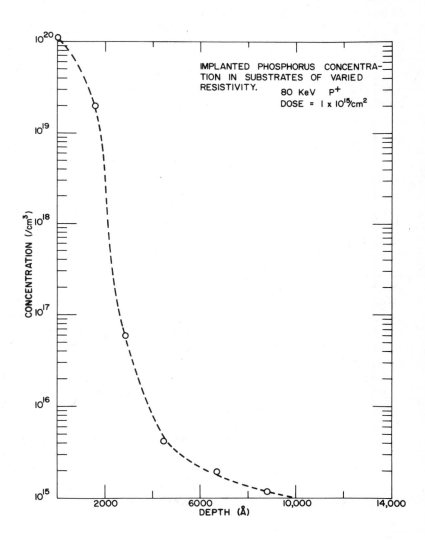

Figure 4.

which were implanted with phosphorus ions at constant beam conditions. Each sample provided a concentration-depth point from resistivity and junction depth. Note that this curve does not appear to have the Lindhard peak. The presence of a peak is not ruled out; however, since the spread of sample resistivities was wide enough to contain the peak. This profile is interesting in that it does show a useful range of concentrations. The technique is not accurate because of the material variable and also the error in determining junction depth by the delineation method.

Two distributions resulting from careful application of a differential sheet conductance technique are shown in Figs. 5 and 6. In these distributions a direct plot of the conductance measurements without smoothing the curve produced the two peaks which occur at the Lindhard depth for 40 keV ions. Disagreement is observed with the radiotracer profiles in that a high surface concentration is found. In Fig. 7 a tracer distribution has been nor-malized to the electrically active distribution and the general curve shapes are similar with the exception of the surface region. It is suggested that the two curves should be normalized at the surface since a maximum of 20% of the total ions are not accounted for electrically. Table II illustrates the material balance in terms of electrically active ions. Two independent methods have been employed to determine this balance. In the one case, an oxidation drive-in method was used (this may measure the total implanted phosphorus) and in the other case a graphical integration was performed on the distributions obtained by the differential conductance method. The agreement observed in Table II affords more evidence that the damage introduced by the implantation process has, for the most part, been eliminated since the values of point concentra-tions are highly dependent on carrier mobility.

To summarize, it has been shown by the combined use of radiotracers and electrical measurements to deter-mine implanted distributions that:

a. Implanted ion movement (diffusion) does not take place under the anneal conditions necessary to stabilize the electrical and structural properties and the junction

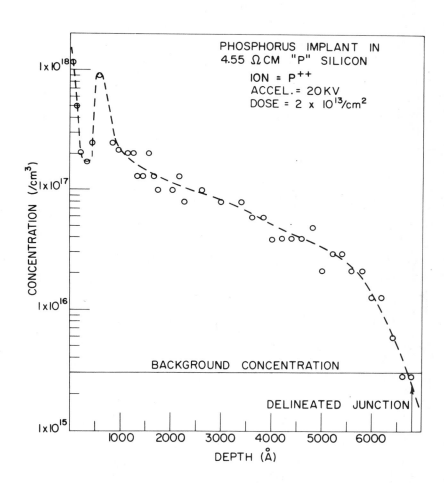

PHOSPHORUS IMPLANT IN
4.55 Ω CM "P" SILICON

ION = P^{++}
ACCEL.= 20 KV
DOSE = 2 x 10^{13}/cm^2

BACKGROUND CONCENTRATION

DELINEATED JUNCTION

CONCENTRATION (/cm^3)

DEPTH (Å)

Figure 5.

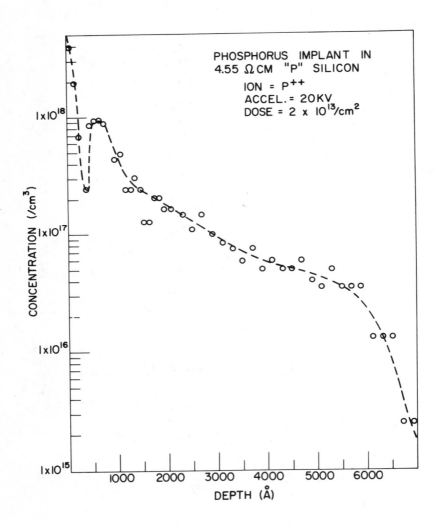

Figure 6.

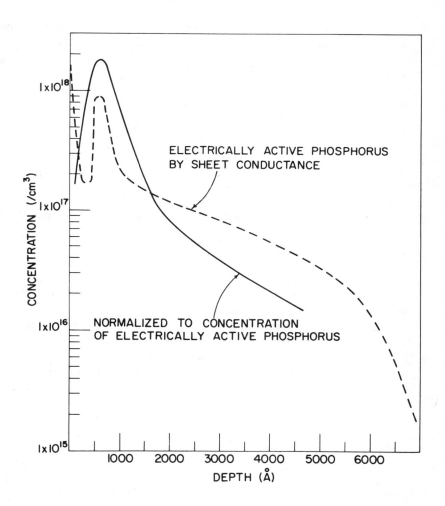

Figure 7.

Table II. Correlation Between Total Number of Ions
Striking Substrate and Electrically Active Atoms Found

Species	Ion Energy (keV)	Ions Striking Substrate (ions/cm²)	Ions Found Substitution-ally in Substrate (ions/cm²)	
P^+	26.8	5.0×10^{14}	3.1×10^{14}	(a)
P^+	26.8	1.0×10^{14}	0.84×10^{14}	(a)
P^{++}	40	2.0×10^{13}	1.7×10^{13}	(a)
P^{++}	33	1.0×10^{14}	0.80×10^{14}	(a)
P^{++}	66	1.0×10^{14}	0.91×10^{14}	(b)
P^+	40	1.0×10^{14}	1.6×10^{14}	(a)
P^+	80	1.0×10^{15}	0.95×10^{15}	(b)

(a) Oxidation drive-in technique
(b) Profile integration

movement results from the variation in the active-inactive
ratio (which may be the substitutional-interstitial ratio).

b. For room temperature implantations the channeling
properties of the silicon lattice in the open directions drop
off with increasing ion dose possibly because of the increased number of interstitials in the channel; however,
this reduction in channeling does not prevent the implantation of usable distributions.

c. A discrepancy between total implanted ion distribution and electrically active ion distribution exists at the
surface and must be resolved, and

d. The implantation process conducted with ions having
energies less than 100 keV followed by a gentle anneal is a
very efficient process with approximately 80% of the ions
striking the substrate accounted for in substitutional positions.

ACKNOWLEDGMENT

The author is grateful to Dr. Karl M. Busen for valuable discussions concerning electrical techniques for profile determination and also for supplying diffused samples for checking our methods. I also extend my thanks to Mr. Ernest LaFlamme for his invaluable assistance in making the experimental measurements.

REFERENCES

1. Lindhard, J., Scharff, H. M., and Schitt, H. E., Kgl. Danski. Vedenskab. Selskab. Mat.-Fys. Medd., 33, No. 14 (1963).
2. Robinson, M. T., and Oen, O. S., Appl. Phys. Letters, 2, 30 (1963). Robinson, M. T., and Oen, O. S., Phys. Rev., 132, 2385 (1963).
3. Davies, J. A., Pierce, G. R., Brown, F., and McCargo, M., Phys. Rev. Letters, 10, 399 (1963).
4. Manchester, K. E., and Sibley, C. B., Bull. Am. Phys. Soc., 10, No. 1, 123 (1965).
5. Manchester, K. E., and Sibley, C. B., Trans. AIME, 236, 379 (1966).

Junction Formation in Germanium by Sb$^+$ Ion Bombardment

L. N. Large

Services Electronics Laboratory
Baldock, United Kingdom

INTRODUCTION

A number of workers have shown that silicon can be chemically doped using ion implantation. Considerable work has been done on this material using channelled alkali ions at relatively low energies (5 - 10 keV). The work of King [1] has shown that solar cells can be made by doping silicon with ion beams of boron and phosphorus at much higher energies (50 keV - 1 MeV) deliberately orienting the crystal so that channelling cannot occur. Although considerable radiation damage is produced during the bombardment, he has shown that it is possible to obtain good junctions after annealing at ~ 600°C. At relatively low temperatures such as this the impurity profile of implanted ions is moved very little by diffusion and the profile is therefore capable of a high degree of control by variation of the incoming ion energy.

The need to produce a very shallow but uniform p-n junction on germanium led us to investigate ion implantation as a means of obtaining such junctions. We have used a very divergent beam to avoid channelling. By so doing it would also be possible to produce junction depths considerably less than reported here.

EXPERIMENTAL PROCEDURES

The shallow junctions were produced by implanting antimony ions at energies up to 100 keV into 8 Ωcm p-type germanium and converting the surface layer to n-type. The germanium was mounted on an electrode which was negatively pulsed co-incidentally with the ion source so that ions were accelerated across a gap on to the crystal surface. The beam of ions was highly divergent and was capable of doping a crystal of diameter ~ 1.3 cm. The pulse length used was 3.5 μsecs. Owing to the fact that the germanium was mounted in a high electric field it was not possible to suppress secondary electrons from the surface so that the pulse currents to the germanium surface are not known accurately. The germanium was kept at room temperature during the bombardment and it is known that the pulse heating was such that the surface temperature rise during the pulse was less than 50°C.

IMPURITY PROFILE

The impurity profile of electrically active ions has been measured by four point probe measurements of the surface conductivity of the doped layer. This was done after various bombardments but the annealing schedule was essentially the same for each, namely 16 hours at 450°C, in a background pressure of 10^{-8} mm Hg. The resistivity of a very thin slice of a conducting medium on a non-conducting substrate is given by

$$\rho = \frac{V}{I}\, 2\pi s \left/ \frac{2s}{w}\, \ln 2.\right.$$

$$= \frac{V}{I}\, \pi w \left/ \ln 2 \right.$$

where   V = voltage across inner probes
      I = current through outer probes
   s/w = ratio of spacing of probes to thickness of layer.

Assuming that the p-n junction is reverse biased by one of the probes so that the current flow is essentially through the n^+ layer the above formula can be used since the probe spacing used was $0 \cdot 025''$ and the junction depth $\sim 10^{-5}$ cm. The resistivity of an incremental layer removed from the surface of the thin conducting n^+ region can then be shown to be given by

$$\bar{\rho} = \frac{\pi}{\ln 2} \left. \Delta t \middle/ \frac{I_1}{V_1} - \frac{I_2}{V_2} \right.$$

where Δt = thickness of layer removed

I_1 and V_1 are the current and voltage readings before the layer is removed and I_2 and V_2 similar readings after the layer is removed.

Prior to bombardment and annealing the germanium surface was micro-polished and lightly etched to remove the polishing damage whilst retaining the essentially flat surface. After bombardment and using a slow etch, successive thin layers of germanium were removed and probe measurements were performed before and after each of these etches. The thickness of germanium removed was initially determined by micro-balance weighings but it was later possible to use a standard etch rate figure found by experience to be applicable to these particular layers which had been radiation damaged during the ion doping but later annealed to remove most damage. The method has been used by previous workers some of whom have been content to take standard etch rates for single-crystal germanium and apply these to surfaces some of which have not been annealed. This is a source of considerable error which can be minimized by micro-balance determination of the amounts etched off. The main sources of error in the experiments above were as follows:

a. The probe voltage measured for the same position on a slice were found to vary in practice by around $\pm 5\%$ after taking many readings. A possible reason for this is differing contact conditions for the light pressures that were necessary to avoid punching through to the junction.

b. The slope resistance of the reverse biased junctions used was sufficiently low at the probe voltages used to allow some current to flow across the junction into the

bulk material. The bulk component of current could be
as much as 25% in certain cases. The errors introduced
in this way were usually small however compared with
those in the former case. Variations in probe voltages
could introduce errors as much as a factor of 2. 5 either
way from the stated value in the final incremental resistivity of an etched layer. Errors in the determination
of layer thickness etched off were estimated at ± 100 Å.

   c. Non-uniform etching of the surface, minimized
by using a very flat surface and masking off all edges
during etching.

   The results obtained are shown in Fig. 1.

   In each case the bombardment was carried out at a
single energy. In the case of curve 1 this was 95 keV
and for 2 and 3 it was 100 keV. The total charge introduced can be estimated only if the secondary emission
co-efficient γ for Sb$^+$ ions incident on a clean germanium
surface is known as a function of energy. Indications are
that γ would be in the region of 5 under the conditions of
the experiment described. Using this figure, the total
charge introduced for curves 1, 2 and 3 is 2.1×10^{-5},
1.6×10^{-5} and 3.1×10^{-5} coulombs/cm^2. Because of
uncertainties in γ however these figures are only accurate
to within a factor of ~ 2.

   In each profile measured it was found that there was
no apparent conduction near the surface. The conductivity
was high in a buried layer as shown in Fig. 1 then decreased as the junction was approached. The transition
between the high conductivity doped layer and the p-type
bulk occurred over a finite distance indicated by the dotted
portion of the curves. The junction depths can be said to
be somewhere in these regions.

   The reason for the discrepancy in the depth of the
highly conducting layer from the surface between curves
1 and 2 and curve 3 is not definitely known. When dealing
with such shallow junctions however the effects of surface
contamination may be considerable. The bombardment
and annealing procedures were essentially the same for
each sample. The main difference is that sample 1 was
annealed in a vacuum furnace capable of background
pressures ~ 10^{-5} mm during the bake whereas a much

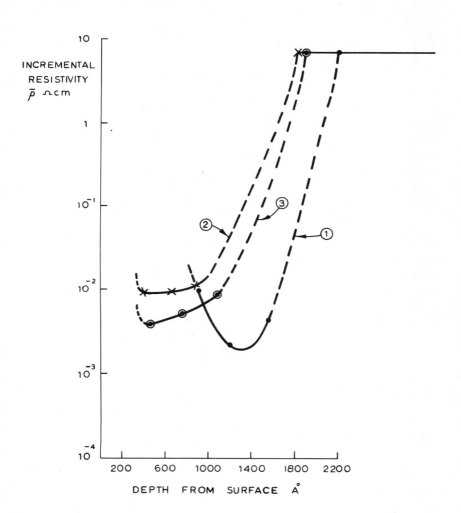

Figure 1. Impurity profile of electrically active ions.

cleaner furnace (~ 10^{-8} mm) was used for the other two
specimens. A thicker contaminating layer may have been
produced on the surface of sample 1 giving rise to an
apparently greater penetration of the ions when the surface was gradually etched off.

DIODE CHARACTERISTICS

The rectifying characteristics of a number of junctions
have been measured by first etching a mesa to expose a
fresh edge to the n^+ layer and then using a clean up etch
to minimize the effects of surface contamination. This
procedure was adopted for junctions which had undergone
various annealing schedules and the characteristics were
displayed using a single point contact on the highly doped
n^+ layer and a pressure contact to the p-type bulk.
Figure 2 (a) - (d) shows the effect of different annealing
schedules. In each case the diodes have undergone a 16
hour anneal in high vacuum, but the temperature was increased from 100°C to 300°C, 450°C and 600°C. It is
clear that after a 450°C anneal satisfactory diode characteristics are reproduced, and the following data was
therefore measured after this annealing schedule.

Figure 3 shows some forward biased current-
voltage characteristics of typical mesa diodes when
measured using four probes so that the voltage and current are measured on different point contacts but in close
proximity. This prevents the voltage drop occurring at
the probe contact appearing as voltage drop across the
junction. The results show that over a limited range of
forward bias (several kT/q) the current voltage dependence
is given approximately by $J = J_0 \exp(^{qV}/_{nkT})$ where J is
the current density and V the applied voltage. Typical
values of n range between 0.8 and 1.2 as expected since
the ideal theory of a p-n junction accounts for the electrical
characteristics of a germanium junction quite well.

The reverse characteristics were measured in air
and were always dominated by surface contamination.
Soon after a clean up etch, however, the best diodes gave
reverse currents of the order of 0.1 mA at 25 volts using
an area of 1 sq mm. The reverse current did not appear
to saturate and the turn-over was not sharp due to heating

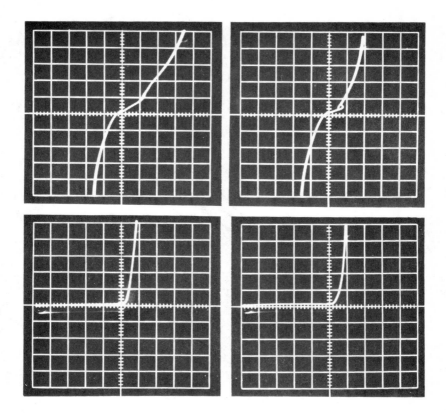

Figure 2. Effect of annealing on diode characteristics.
(a) Top left, 100°C; (b) Top right, 300°C; (c) Bottom left,
450°C; (d) Bottom right, 600°C.
Scale abscissa. 5 volts/division
        ordinate. 5 mA/division.

effects.   The best diodes were similar to those made by
diffusion when measured under the same conditions.

ELECTRON DIFFRACTION STUDIES

In these experiments a single wafer of 5 Ω cm germanium was cut along the (111) plane then micro-polished

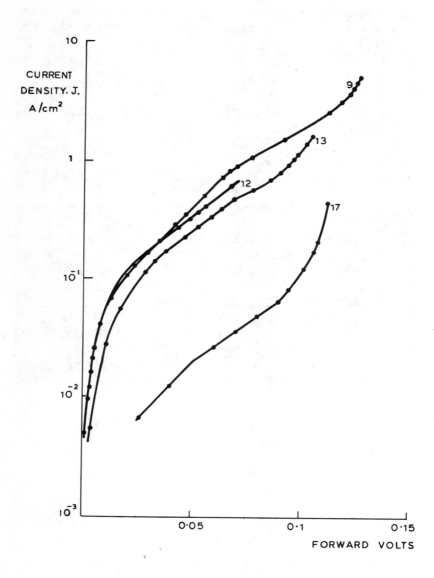

Figure 3.   Forward biased current–voltage characteristics
of small area junctions.

and lightly etched to remove polish damage. The wafer
was then bombarded by Sb^+ ions at energies between
25 keV and 100 keV to give an approximately uniform
distribution of ions of ~ 10^{19}/cc to a depth of ~ 1000 Å.
The wafer was then cut into chips and these were subjected
to various annealing schedules. A 75 keV electron beam
was used at glancing angle of incident to investigate the
structure of the surface of these wafers as a function of
annealing temperature. The annealing time was kept constant at 16 hours. Figures 4 (a) - (e) are the diffraction
patterns obtained. These prints have lost some of the detail evident on the original plates. In particular the
Kikuchi lines which were clearly seen on some plates
have been lost in the reproduction process.

Figure 4 (a) is the pattern obtained from a (111) surface of similar 5 Ωcm p-type germanium which has been
etched but not bombarded or annealed. The spot pattern
characteristic of a single crystal is clear together with
Kikuchi lines indicative of well ordered crystal planes.
The elongation of the spots can be caused by a number of
factors one of which may be the uneven crystal surface
obtained after etching.

Figure 4 (b) is the first of the bombarded crystal
patterns; this has been annealed for 16 hours at 100°C.
The ring pattern obtained is due to randomly oriented
single crystals which have not coalesced to form a large
single crystal. It is clear however, that even at this low
temperature partial annealing has occurred. It is possible
that contamination on the surface could give rise to a ring
pattern but the coincidence of the only spots obtained with
the rings shows that the ring pattern is mainly due to
polycrystalline germanium. After a 300°C anneal the
pattern shown in Fig. 4 (c) was obtained. At this temperature further annealing has occurred and the single-
crystal spot pattern is stronger. There is still a strong
ring pattern indicative of polycrystalline material.

Figure 4 (d) is the pattern obtained after annealing at
450°C. From this pattern two important points emerge.
The first is that the crystal has twinned during the annealing. The positions of the satellite spots superimposed
on the original single-crystal pattern indicate that the

Figure 4. Electron diffraction examination of effect of annealing temperature. (a) No bombardment or anneal; (b) 100°C
anneal.

Figure 4.   (Continued) (c) 300°C anneal; (d) 450°C anneal.

Figure 4.   (Continued) (e) 600°C anneal.

crystal has twinned about a single <111> axis only.   The
second is that faint Kikuchi lines are obtained showing
that much larger areas of the material are now coherent
single crystals.

Finally, Fig. 4 (e) is the pattern obtained after annealing at 600°C.   The major difference between this
pattern and the previous one is that the Kikuchi lines are
stronger.

These investigations show that the major part of the
radiation damage is annealed out at 450°C but cannot
show a direct comparison of the number of faults per cc,
such as dislocations, before and after the bombardment
and annealing.

DISCUSSION

The results show that using a divergent beam of antimony ions at 100 keV, junctions can be made provided that the sample is subsequently annealed at 450°C. This temperature is low enough to prevent gross movement of the impurity ions by diffusion and results in high sheet conductivity in the implanted region. It is of interest to compare the observed range of 100 keV Sb^+ ions with the Bohr-Nielsen theory assuming elastic collision processes are dominant in the energy loss mechanism for the incident ion. The theory predicts a mean range of approximately 400 Å with a range straggling of approximately 350 Å. The observed impurity profiles (samples 2 and 3) suggest that the maximum concentration of electrically active ions is between 400 Å and 700 Å below the surface. Sample 1 shows considerable discrepancy, the reason for which is not definitely known but surface contamination may account partly for this. The results reported by Cussins [2] using similar ions and similar bombarding energy suggest that after bombardment germanium is dominantly p-type, independent of its initial state, and it is inferred that Cussins did not observe chemical doping effects, only damage production. The necessity for adequate annealing demonstrated by our electron diffraction studies and diode characteristics presumably accounts for this absence of interstitial doping in his work. Immediately after bombardment the damage is probably so great that amorphous clusters are formed [3], and their presence swamps any doping effects. The electron diffraction photographs show that the ordered single-crystal nature of the original material can be recovered by annealing. The method is not sensitive enough however, to give quantitative information as to dislocation density, stacking fault density, etc. The presence of twinned material also suggests that examination of the bombarded layers by electron microscopy would be desirable.

In general the results are in agreement with those of King [1] who has demonstrated the manufacture of good silicon diodes by bombarding with boron and phosphorus beams, but achieved without the use of channelling to increase junction depth and reduce damage.

This technique should be capable of greater control of junction depth than with diffusion and much easier control than when channelled ions are used since channelling in open structure materials is considerably influenced by blocking effects induced by damage. The degree of control is also greater when light ions are used, such as boron and phosphorus since for energies around 100 keV the velocity of these ions is sufficient to excite and ionize the target atoms. When the dominant process for energy loss is excitation and ionization the energy loss at each collision is very small and a large number of collisions can be made, before the ion comes to rest. This results in a much smaller range straggling as a percentage of mean ion range than for heavy ions such as those used in the work reported in this paper.

Ion bombardment should be much less affected by bulk properties of material so that when uniform shallow junctions are required, effects such as precipitations at dislocations should be avoided. The characteristic low temperature nature of the process also has potential advantages including the relatively small degradation of bulk lifetime and mobility.

ACKNOWLEDGMENT

The author would like to thank Mr. H. Gill and Miss M. Dann for experimental assistance and Mr. B. H. Holeman for his co-operation and useful technical discussions. Also the Plessey Co. Ltd., Caswell for their work on the electron diffraction examination of surfaces.

This paper is published by permission of the Ministry of Defense.

REFERENCES

1. W. King. Technical documentary Report No.
   APL TDR 64-113, U. S. Contract No. AF33(615)-1097.
2. W. D. Cussins. Proc. Phys. Soc. 68, 213 (1955).
3. J. A. Parsons. Phil. Mag. , 12, 1159, 1965.

Some Fundamental and Device Aspects of Sodium Ion Injection in Silicon

R. P. Ruth

Autonetics Division
North American Aviation, Inc.
Anaheim, California

Sodium ions in the energy range below 20 keV have been used to produce junction structures in single-crystal p-type silicon throughout a wide resistivity range. [1] This paper describes some of the fundamental characteristics of the alkali-metal ion-doping process as applied to silicon and some of the results obtained from applying the technique to fabrication of silicon junction devices.   The work is thus an extension of the original results reported by McCaldin and Widmer [2] and of the device studies of Waldner and McQuaid. [3]

Sodium ion-injection doping of silicon as employed in these studies is characterized by the following general properties:

1. Sodium appears to function as an electrically active donor in silicon from the interstitial positions which the ions acquire upon injection into the crystal lattice. [2, 4]

*This work was carried out with the cooperation of the Rocketdyne Division of North American Aviation, Inc., Canoga Park, California, where the ion bombardment experiments were performed under the direction of J. F. Hon.

**A preliminary report on these studies was given at the Spring Meeting of the Electrochemical Society, San Francisco, May 1965. See Reference 1.

2. Silicon host crystals in a wide range of initial acceptor doping concentrations can be converted to n-type by sodium ion injection; crystals in a six-decade resistivity range have been so doped in this work.

3. Only moderate ion energies are required for most device purposes; ion beam energies of 20 keV and below were used here.

4. Moderately elevated sample temperatures provide sufficient annealing of ion-induced radiation damage to permit the injected chemical doping to predominate. Sample temperatures from 300 to 600°C during ion injection have been employed; most experiments were carried out with the sample at 500°C. As a rule, no post-injection annealing steps were used.

5. Injected impurity concentrations much greater than the equilibrium (substitutional) solid-solubility limit for sodium in silicon [4] can be achieved.

6. The injected ion penetration depends strongly upon the crystallographic direction of the ion path because of the channeling phenomenon. [5, 6] Ion injection in the < 110>, <111>, and <100> crystallographic directions has been investigated in these experiments.

APPARATUS

The ion injection experiments were carried out in a large (2-ft. dia. x 6-ft. long) metal vacuum system with a ten-inch oil diffusion pump, elastomer seals, and appropriate liquid nitrogen trapping surfaces. In most experiments, the system pressure was approximately 10^{-6} Torr during ion injection.

The ion beam apparatus is shown schematically in Fig. 1. A surface-contact ionizer, with a porous ionizer button of sintered tungsten powder maintained at approximately 1100°C, was used as the ion source. The sodium reservoir was inside the vacuum chamber in this apparatus, although a later model involves a reservoir external to the vacuum system.

An accel-decel type of electrode system was employed, but the equipment was usually operated in the accel-only mode. An einzel lens was available for focusing the beam; however, a nominally unfocused beam was generally used,

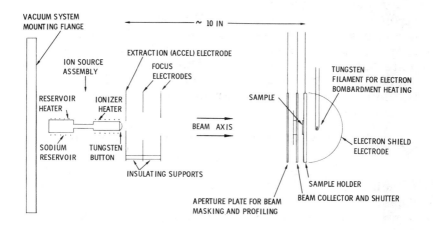

Figure 1. Ion beam apparatus (schematic).

to provide a beam diameter at the sample in excess of one inch. Ion energies ranged from 1 to 20 keV, with ion beam current densities up to 150 $\mu a/cm^2$ in the sample plane. Most injection experiments involved current densities in the range from 5 to 40 $\mu a/cm^2$.

The target crystal was mounted on a stainless-steel plate and held in place by small stainless-steel spring tabs. The sample temperature was controlled by electron bombardment heating of the sample plate, as indicated in the figure. Sample temperatures were monitored by means of a thermocouple in contact with the front face of a dummy crystal, mounted immediately adjacent to the target crystal and exposed to part of the ion beam.

A movable beam collector and shutter plate could be interposed in the beam in front of the sample for measure-

ment of beam currents. A flat-plate type of collector was
used, with a wire grid provided for secondary electron
suppression.

A movable aperture plate was also provided, to restrict or select that portion of the ion beam to strike the
target crystal. Cross-section profiles of the ion beam
current density could be obtained by use of this aperture
plate. Relative motion of both the sample holder and the
aperture plate permitted considerable flexibility in expos-
ing selected portions of a target crystal to chosen parts of
the ion beam.

INJECTED IMPURITY CONCENTRATION PROFILE

These studies have led to a much improved understanding of the injected impurity profile for sodium ion
doping of silicon. The general profile shape originally
suggested by McCaldin and Widmer [2] has been verified.
The profile consists of a thin region of high impurity concentration at the surface of the crystal with an abrupt
transition to a region of much lower concentration and
small concentration gradient farther into the crystal interior.

Figure 2 illustrates, in somewhat idealized fashion,
typical profiles obtained for sodium ion injection in the
<110> crystallographic direction in a silicon host crystal
having good structure and a relatively undamaged surface.
Figure 2(a) illustrates the dependence of the profile upon
the energy of the incident ions for a fixed total ion dose,
and Fig. 2(b) shows the dependence upon total ion dose for
a fixed ion energy. The horizontal dashed lines in both
figures represent typical acceptor concentrations in the
host crystal; metallurgical junctions occur at the inter-
sections of the acceptor impurity concentration lines and
the injected donor concentration profiles.

Data for experimental profiles of this type, specific
examples of which are to be published elsewhere, [7] have
been obtained for total ion doses ranging approximately
from 10^{15} to 10^{18} ions/cm^2 and for ion energies from 1

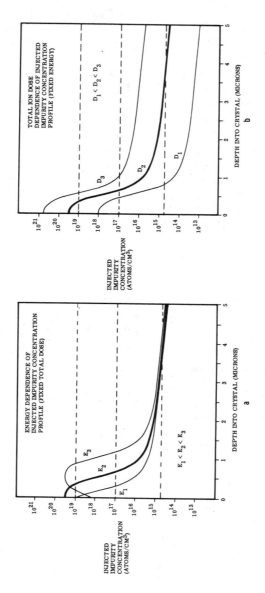

Figure 2. Idealized impurity concentration profiles for sodium ions injected in <110> direction in silicon, showing (a) energy dependence for fixed dose, and (b) dose dependence for fixed energy. Typical host crystal acceptor concentrations shown by dashed lines.

to 20 keV.* These data have resulted principally from experiments in which several crystals of different acceptor doping were simultaneously exposed to the sodium ion beam and the location of the resulting metallurgical junction then determined by appropriate beveling and staining techniques. Additional confirmatory data have also been obtained from four-point-probe measurement of sheet resistivity as a function of depth, and by electron microprobe examination of the surface of small-angle bevels on ion-doped host crystals.

Surface concentrations of injected impurity in excess of $10^{20}/cm^3$ have been obtained both in heavily doped p-type host crystals and in heavily doped boron-diffused p-type layers on the surface of n-type host crystals. A range of eight decades in injected donor impurity concentration has thus been detected in silicon host crystals as a result of sodium ion injection employing the above experimental parameters.

It is clear that both very shallow and very deep junctions can be obtained in silicon by sodium ion injection at low energies. Junctions less than $0.1\,\mu$ deep have been obtained in silicon crystals in a variety of initial resistivities, and junctions at depths in excess of $50\,\mu$ have been observed in high resistivity host crystals. **

*The use of heated host crystals (usually 500°C) probably precludes the occurrence of saturation effects at total ion doses as low as those reported by Davies et al;[6] in that work, an amorphous layer apparently formed on the silicon surface during xenon ion bombardment of the unheated crystal, significantly reducing ion penetration for doses larger than about 10^{13} ions/cm^2. No specific evidence of such saturation has yet been found, although it would be expected toward the upper end of the dose range employed here.

**It is important to distinguish between junction depth, which corresponds in some instances to injected donor concentrations of $10^{14}/cm^3$ or less, and median range R_m or most probable range R_p (occurring at the peak of the impurity profile) parameters which are usually employed in discussions of energy-range relationships. Clearly, these parameters are significantly less than most of the junction depths measured here, except for those in very low resistivity host crystals.

Figure 3(a) shows the surface of a 5° bevel-section on a 60 ohm-cm p-type (110) silicon crystal exposed to a 15 keV sodium ion beam to produce a total ion dose of 8×10^{16} ions/cm^2 at 500°C. Conventional staining has delineated the ion-doped n-type region, which extends to a depth of about 40 μ. The ion-doped region terminates in the left-hand portion of the figure in that part of the crystal shielded by one of the stainless-steel spring tabs used to mount the specimen. Figure 3(b) shows the same bevel photographed with monochromatic yellow light (5890Å), with a glass flat placed over the specimen; the resulting interference fringes, although not well resolved in the figure, provide an accurate measure of the junction depth.

Figure 4 shows photomicrographs of part of a similar 60 ohm-cm crystal, exposed to a 10 keV sodium ion beam for a total dose of 9×10^{16} ions/cm^2. The specimen has been encapsulated and sectioned normal to the surface upon which the ions were incident. Undoped regions, shielded from the ion beam by a mounting tab, are visible in all four views. Reduced penetration of the ions due to surface or internal imperfections is evidenced by regions of shallower junction depth in Figs. 4(a) and (b).

For sufficiently high energy (greater than about 15 keV in these experiments) the peak of the injected impurity concentration profile occurs below the surface of the host crystal, as shown by curve E_3 in Fig. 2(a). This is predicted by classical considerations of range-energy relationships for charged particles injected into solids, [8] and the same phenomenon would be expected for ion injection into single-crystal materials when channeling phenomena are also present.

These studies have verified the existence of so-called "submerged profiles" in the more heavily doped host crystals employed. Figure 5 illustrates the formation of two p-n junctions when the total dose employed is sufficiently low for the initial level of host crystal acceptor doping. Whereas a total dose D_2 will result in a single junction, as shown in the upper curve, reduction of the total dose for the same ion energy produces the double junction shown, resulting in a p-n-p structure. This type

Figure 3. Junction formed 40 μ deep in 60 ohm-cm p-type (110) silicon by injection of 15 keV sodium ions at 500°C. Total dose 8 x 10^{15} ions/cm^2. (a) Sodium-doped n-type region (light color) delineated by staining on 5° bevel. (b) Junction depth indicated by interference fringes (λ = 5890Å).

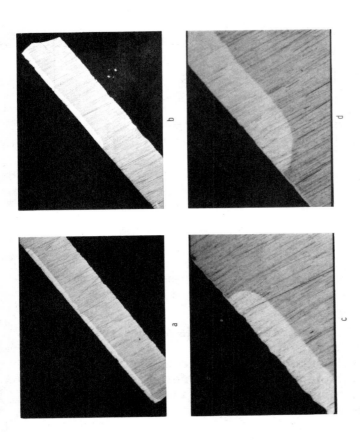

Figure 4. Normal cross-section views of 60 ohm-cm sample with 45 μ junction depth formed by 10 keV sodium ions and dose of 9×10^{16} ions/cm^2 . (a) and (b) show undoped central part of sample shielded by stainless-steel tab during injection. (c) and (d) show corresponding edges of doped regions at high (unequal) magnifications.

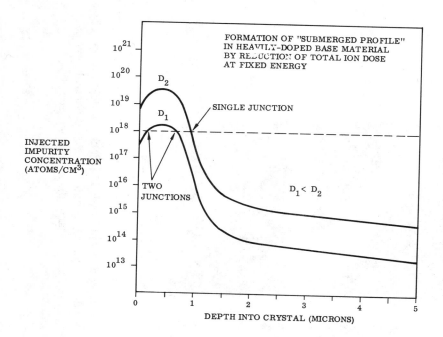

Figure 5. Formation of double-junction p-n-p structure due to "submerged profile" in appropriately doped host crystal.

of ion-doped impurity configuration is of special importance for multilayer device structures.

Figure 6 illustrates such submerged profiles obtained in host crystals of several different resistivities, both by full-area exposures and by injection through apertures in surface oxide masks. Host crystal resistivity represented in the figure ranges from 0.005 to 1 ohm-cm. It has not been possible to observe submerged profiles in higher resistivity material for the ion beam energies and ion doses employed.

The acceptor centers responsible for the p-type layer nearest the surface are believed not to be associated primarily with radiation damage. Evidence from experi-

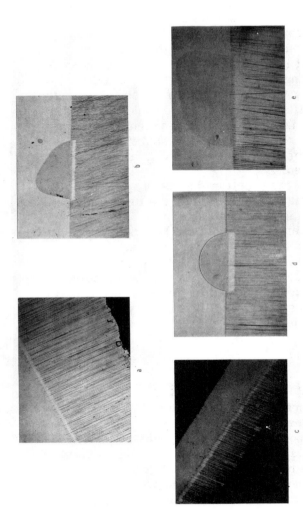

Figure 6. Submerged profiles by sodium ion injection in p-type silicon host crystals, shown by staining on beveled surfaces. (a) Junctions 0.07 and 0.29 μ deep in 0.005 ohm-cm silicon; 20 kev, 8×10^{16} ions/cm^2. (b) Diode structure in 0.02 ohm-cm silicon; 15 kev, 3.6×10^{17} ions/cm^2, junctions 0.15 and 0.44 μ deep. (c) Junctions 0.10 and 0.25 μ deep in 0.1 ohm-cm silicon; 18 kev, 8×10^{16} ions/cm^2. (d) Diode structure in 0.1 ohm-cm silicon; 15 kev, 3.6×10^{17} ions/cm^2, junctions 0.14 and 0.73 μ deep. (e) Diode structure in 1 ohm-cm silicon; 15 kev 8×10^{16} ions/cm^2, junctions 0.10 and 0.44 μ deep.

ments in which the total injected dose for a given energy has been varied for a particular host-crystal acceptor-doping level in the manner shown in Fig. 5 indicates that the initial acceptor impurities are responsible for the p-type conductivity observed in the surface layer.

The deep penetrating "tail" of the injected impurity profile for sodium ions in silicon is significantly influenced by diffusion of the sodium at the sample temperatures employed during injection. Doping a sample to identical ion doses in several separate zones in sequence clearly shows the effects of the diffusion taking place at injection temperatures in the vacuum system immediately following exposure. Similar diffusion doubtless also occurs during the injection process itself, although this is not easily observed.

Measurement of the junction depths in such samples permits an approximate calculation of the diffusion co-efficient of interstitial sodium in silicon at injection temperatures. * Where a thin surface layer of an impurity of initial concentration several orders of magnitude larger than the host-crystal doping level serves as a finite (limited) source of diffusion, the diffusion coefficient D of the impurity is related to the effective time of diffusion t and the resulting junction depth x_j by the approximate expression [9]

$$D \approx \frac{x_j^2}{30t} ,$$

with D in cm^2/sec, x_j in cm, and t in seconds.

*The presence of an excess of both sodium and silicon interstitials and lattice vacancies during and following the ion injection process assures the existence of a complex set of diffusion and recombination processes at the temperatures used here. Some interstitial sodium will become substitutional during this time, but experimental evidence indicates that interstitial sodium retains its identity for long periods at and above these temperatures, [2,4] and that the diffusion coefficient of substitutional sodium in silicon at these temperatures must be extremely small. [4] Thus, the diffusion characteristic observed here is essentially that of interstitial sodium in silicon.

When this expression is applied to the data obtained in the above experiments, approximate values of $1\text{-}5 \times 10^{-12}$ cm^2/sec and $5\text{-}10 \times 10^{-11}$ cm^2/sec are obtained for the diffusion coefficient at 400 and 500°C, respectively. This represents rapid diffusion compared with that of the more conventional impurities in silicon at these temperatures. Rapid diffusion is generally characteristic of interstitial impurities; however, these results for sodium in silicon are still three to four orders of magnitude smaller than the corresponding diffusion coefficients for lithium in silicon at these temperatures. [10]

Measurement of the shift in junction depth resulting from a separate annealing step subsequent to the initial ion injection process provides confirmation of these results. This approach has been employed by McCaldin, who has recently reported values in substantial agreement with the above. [11]

Figure 7 illustrates possible consequences of post-injection diffusion upon the impurity profile and the resulting junction location in the host crystal. A shift from the impurity profile shown as resulting from the injection process to that representing the diffusion-modified profile could cause complete disappearance or reduction of the depth of the junction for heavily-doped host crystals, essentially no change in junction depth for crystals of some intermediate doping level, and an increase in junction depth in lightly-doped host crystals. All three types of result have been observed in appropriately-doped silicon target crystals in these investigations, tending to corroborate the process suggested in Fig. 7.

The exposure times generally employed in these studies have been relatively short; some junction structures have been fabricated with total exposure to the incident beam of only a few seconds. As a result, the diffusion of interstitial sodium in silicon represented by the above values for the diffusion coefficient is such that although measureable and significant, it does not preclude the controlled formation of useful junction structures for specific device purposes.

The strong dependence of ion penetration upon the crystallographic direction of the ion path, originally studied in silicon with xenon ions by Davies et al. [6] has been verified for sodium ions in silicon. [1] The results

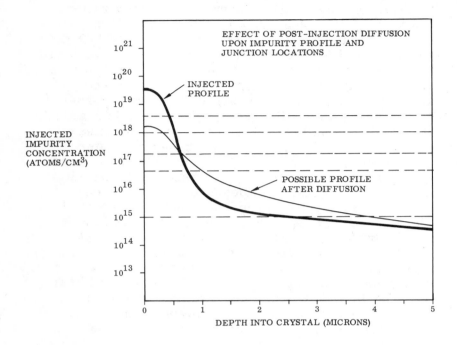

Figure 7. Possible effect of sodium diffusion in silicon upon impurity profile shape and junction location.

of numerous experiments in which crystals of different orientations from the same parent ingot were simultaneously exposed to the same sodium ion beam indicate progressively decreasing ion penetration in the <110>, <111>, and <100> crystallographic directions, for a given set of experimental parameters. Because of channeling, the deeply penetrating portion of the injected impurity profile is much more prominent for injection in the <110> direction than in the other two directions. Thus, a given injected impurity concentration is found at widely differing depths in the crystal for injection in the three crystallographic directions, the magnitude of the difference depending upon the part of the injected profile involved. An impurity concentration occurring in the steep gradient region of the profile has been found at depths in the approximate ratio 10:4:3 for the < 110>, < 111>, and < 100> directions, respectively, for a typical set of experimental parameters. Additional data appear in the reference cited earlier. [7]

EFFECTS OF SURFACE LAYERS

Ion penetration is strongly influenced by the presence of mechanically damaged surface layers, structural imperfections in the crystal interior, surface contaminants, and amorphous or polycrystalline layers (such as oxides) deliberately applied to the host crystal surface. Such effects are especially pronounced with respect to the channeling tail of the injected impurity profile. [6]

The effect of surface damage resulting from mechanical polishing used in preparation of silicon crystals for ion injection experiments is illustrated by an experiment in which 60 ohm-cm p-type silicon was exposed to a 10 keV sodium ion beam with a current density of 22 μa/cm^2, with a total dose of 8 x 10^{16} ions/cm^2. Prior to injection, a wafer with a standard 12.5 μ lapped finish was cut into four pieces, three of which were polished to a 6 μ diamond finish. Two of these were then polished to a 1 μ diamond finish, and one was then optically polished to a 0.05 μ alumina finish. The resulting junction depths (corresponding to injected impurity concentrations the order of 10^{14} /cm^3) were in the ratio 1.0:1.1:6 for the second, third, and fourth finishes, respectively.

The drastic improvement in ion penetration obtained with a fine optical polish, with its correspondingly thinner damaged layer, is still further enhanced by removal of most of this damaged layer by thermal oxidation followed by subsequent chemical removal of the oxidized region. This has been the principal method used in preparing samples for ion injection in the work described here, although other preparation techniques (such as chemical polishing and vacuum sputtering) have also been employed.

Silicon oxide surface layers have been used extensively to restrict the region of the host crystal exposed to the incident ion beam. Although aperture masking has been the primary use of oxide layers, it is also possible to employ oxides of varying thickness for the purpose of "tailoring" the doping level in the host crystal by virtue of partial absorption of the incident ion beam in the oxide layers.

Figure 8 shows a wafer of 60 ohm-cm silicon with a thermally grown oxide layer of thickness graded along the diameter indicated by the diagonal bare stripe. The oxide thickness ranged from 1200 to 300Å. A ring-dot aperture pattern photoetched in the oxide allowed the ion beam access to the host crystal; a 15keV sodium ion beam was used to inject a total ion dose of 10^{17} ions/cm² at a temperature of 500°C.

Figure 8(b) shows the surface of a 3° bevel polished in a direction perpendicular to the bare stripe at the thick (1200Å) end of the oxide. The junction depth in this region was found to be about 20 μ. The doped regions below both the bare stripe and the adjacent ring-dot device pattern are seen to be wider than the nominal width of the corresponding apertures in the oxide layer (indicated by the darkening of the original silicon surface at the top of the figure). This discrepancy in width is due to penetration of a significant fraction of the incident ions through the tapered edge of the oxide surrounding the aperture. Figure 8(c) further illustrates the effective doping achieved by penetration of ions through the tapering edges of the oxide apertures; this ring-dot device pattern was in an oxide region of approximately 1000Å thickness.

The staining procedure was terminated prematurely on the specimen of Fig. 8(b) to show the lower net acceptor concentration in regions nearest the crystal surface (that is, at the top of the bevel) but under the oxide masking layer, as evidenced by the absence of the characteristic (dark) p-type stain. This was caused by penetration of sodium ions through the full thickness of the oxide layer in the regions between the apertures. Figure 8(d) shows a ring-dot pattern in a region where the oxide layer was only about 500Å thick, and in this case the

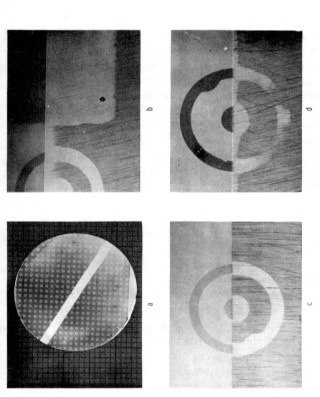

Figure 8. 60 ohm-cm silicon doped by 15 keV sodium ions through ring-dot aperture mask in oxide at 500°C. Total dose 10^{17} ions/cm^2. (a) Wafer with oxide thickness graded from 1200Å (upper left) to 300Å (lower right), shown in millimeter-grid background. (b) Stained 3° bevel at 1200Å oxide end; junction depth ~ 20 μ. (c) Stained 1° bevel through device in 1000Å oxide region. (d) Stained device (1° bevel) in 500Å oxide region. (Magnifications unequal in b, c, d.)

completed staining procedure clearly indicates extensive
impurity doping through the oxide layer surrounding the
device pattern.   Complete conductivity-type conversion
of a thin region of silicon near the surface has occurred.
Prolonged contact of the stain with the beveled surface of
this specimen to explore the extent of this n-type region
has begun to obliterate the previously well-defined ion-
doped region in the crystal interior (that is, at the bottom
of the photograph).

A group of device patterns near the center of the same
sample, where the oxide thickness was approximately
550Å, is shown in Fig. 9.   Continuing the staining process
for three different time intervals on the 1° beveled surface
is seen to move the apparent junction progressively
toward the top of the bevel, that is, closer to the initial
oxide-covered silicon surface.   The staining behavior illustrated in these photomicrographs indicates a degree
of sodium counterdoping (through the oxide) in the silicon
near the surface that is comparable with that obtained
deeper in the crystal through the device apertures.   The
gradual change in depth of the apparent junction under the
oxide with prolonged staining also is consistent with a
very gradual transition from the host crystal acceptor
level to the net donor doping level which exists in the
region just below the surface.

In a typical experiment, p-type silicon of 0.1 ohm-cm
resistivity exposed to a sodium ion beam of 20 keV energy
and 20 μa/cm^2 current density to produce a total dose of
8 x 10^{16} ions/cm^2 at 500°C will experience conductivity-
type conversion in a surface layer of 0.2 μ deep when
covered by an oxide layer of 500Å thickness, but an oxide
layer 900Å thick prevents such conversion.   It is clear,
however, that sufficient ions do penetrate 900Å of oxide
to produce significant doping of the underlying host
crystal near the surface.   The effects of such penetration
are seen in the electrical properties of devices formed
by injection through apertures in oxide layers.   (See next
section.)

Sodium ion beams of the characteristics used in these
studies produce some sputtering of the silicon oxide
layers.   Oxides of thickness greater than 1 μ have

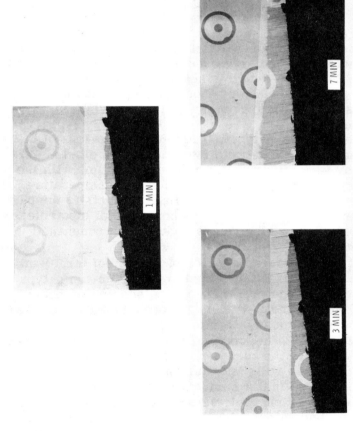

Figure 9. Effect of prolonged staining on apparent location of p- and n-type regions on 1° bevel through devices in 550Å oxide portion of sample of Fig. 8.

generally been used in preparing device structures. A sodium ion beam of 15 keV energy and 20 μa/cm^2 current density produces negligible loss in oxide thickness due to sputtering in a 10 to 12 minute exposure (total dose about 7 x 10^{16} ions/cm^2). A total dose an order of magnitude larger has been found to produce a sputtering loss in oxide thickness the order of 100Å.

DEVICE FABRICATION

Large numbers of mesa and planar-type diodes have been made in silicon crystals of resistivity throughout the range studied by injection of sodium ions of energies from 1 to 20 keV. Temperatures during injection have ranged from 300 to 500°C. Diodes with junction depths from less than 0.1 μ to greater than 30 μ have been fabricated.

Contacts to the n-type (sodium-doped) regions of these devices have been made both by vacuum-deposited aluminum and by vacuum-deposited gold-on-titanium, with the silicon crystal held at moderately elevated temperature during deposition in both cases. Back contacts to the p-type material have in most cases consisted of electroless gold deposited over electroless nickel, on a roughened silicon surface.

The reverse characteristics of a group of ten 10 mil diameter mesa diodes fabricated in 0.08 ohm-cm p-type (110) silicon are shown in Fig. 10. A sodium ion beam of 10 keV energy and 27 μa/cm^2 current density was used to produce a total dose of 5 x 10^{16} ions/cm^2 with the sample at 500°C. The junction formed in this crystal was about 0.5 μ below the surface. The reverse breakdown voltage of 11 to 15 volts is about what would be expected for diodes formed in 0.1 ohm-cm base material. The distribution of I-V characteristics shown is typical of that observed in diodes formed in material of this resistivity.

Figure 11 illustrates the high degree of uniformity sometimes encountered in groups of these diodes. The 14 reverse characteristics shown superimposed in this composite photograph represent about half of the diodes on this sample of 8 ohm-cm p-type (110) silicon. The remaining diodes exhibited reverse characteristics only

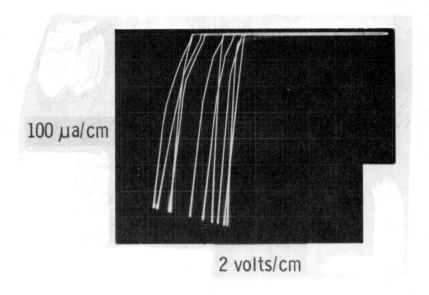

Figure 10. Reverse characteristics of 10 typical mesa diodes in 0.08 ohm-cm p-type silicon doped by 10 keV sodium ions at 500°C. Total dose 5×10^{16} ions/cm^2, junction depth 0.5 μ.

slightly different from the group shown in the photograph. This degree of uniformity exceeds that often found in production runs of diffused diodes. The breakdown voltage observed is about that expected for base material of this resistivity.

In general, reverse breakdown voltages in diodes formed by this technique have varied from a few volts for those in low resistivity p-type material to greater than 1000 volts for diodes formed in p-type material of initial resistivity of 60 to 100 ohm-cm. The devices fabricated in high resistivity material, usually with deep junctions, have generally had very good electrical properties, with abrupt or hard breakdown characteristics and low reverse leakage current. Diodes formed in low resistivity material, resulting in shallow junctions, have exhibited much softer breakdown characteristics.

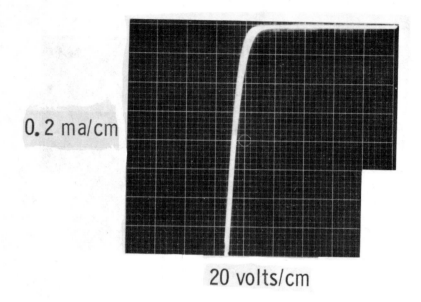

0.2 ma/cm

20 volts/cm

Figure 11. Reverse characteristics of 14 mesa diodes in 8 ohm-cm p-type (110) silicon doped by 10 keV sodium ions at 500°C. Total dose 3.8 x 10^{16} ions/cm^2 , junction depth 1.2 μ.

This difference is attributed either to unannealed radiation damage centers remaining near the crystal surface in the junction depletion region or to inadequate over-doping in the surface n-type region because of insufficient total ion dose. Recent experiments in which junctions a few tenths of a micron below the surface of 0.02 ohm-cm p-type material have been formed by injection of very high total ion doses have resulted in improved diode properties. It thus appears that the poorer electrical properties which have been observed in devices formed in low resistivity material are probably not to be associated primarily with radiation damage effects. This question is receiving further attention at the present time.

Planar-type diodes formed by ion injection through apertures in oxide masks have, to a degree, the structural

advantage of an oxide-protected intersection of junction
and crystal surface, as with their diffused planar-diode
counterparts. This is illustrated in Fig. 12, which shows
details of the type of structure obtained when 0.1 ohm-cm
silicon is doped by a 15 keV sodium ion beam through
holes in a thermally grown oxide layer about 1 μ thick.
The upper part of the figure shows a 1° bevel-section
through a 10 mil diameter device aperture in the oxide.
The sloping edge of the aperture is readily visible, as
defined by the white-light interference fringes in the
oxide. The lower part of the figure shows the same device after staining, which has delineated the junction and
completely removed the oxide layer, leaving the characteristic discolored silicon surface in the exposed region. Injection of a total dose of 8 x 10^{16} ions/cm^2 at a
temperature of 500°C resulted in a junction 0.3 μ deep
in this specimen.

Examination of the figure reveals the slightly greater
width of the doped region with respect to that of the exposed surface area, caused by ion penetration of the thin
oxide at the bottom of the tapered aperture wall. As a
result, the junction as formed intersects the crystal surface in a region covered by oxide.

The nature of the discoloration on the surface of the
silicon following sodium ion injection is not yet understood. The degree of discoloration is a function of the
total ion dose and the beam energy; studies are in
progress to determine if there is quantitative correlation
between the concentration of injected impurity at the
surface and the optical properties of the doped silicon
surface.

The formation of planar-type diodes by ion injection
through apertures in oxide masks is accompanied by the
problem of surface leakage due to ion penetration of the
main part of the oxide, as discussed previously. Figure
13 shows the reverse characteristics of five different
planar-type diodes from the sample shown in Figs. 8 and
9. Five different oxide layer thicknesses are represented,
ranging from 1200 to 300Å. The effect of the ion injection
doping through the oxide layer, shown metallographically
in Figs. 8 and 9, is also clearly demonstrated by the

Figure 12. Detail of planar-type diode structure formed in 0.1 ohm-cm p-type (110) silicon by 15 keV sodium ions injected through aperture in 1 μ oxide layer. Total dose 8 x 10^{16} ions/ cm^2 at 500°C. Top: 1° bevel through device aperture in oxide. Bottom: Same device after staining to delineate junction.

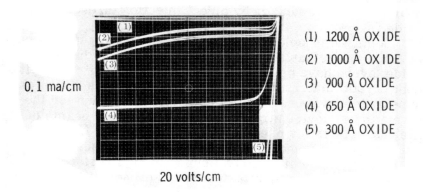

0. 1 ma/cm

20 volts/cm

(1) 1200 Å OXIDE

(2) 1000 Å OXIDE

(3) 900 Å OXIDE

(4) 650 Å OXIDE

(5) 300 Å OXIDE

Figure 13.   Reverse characteristics (origin at upper right) of 5 planar-type diode structures on sample of Figs. 8 and 9, formed in regions covered by oxide thicknesses shown.

electrical properties of Fig. 13.   Only the diode formed in the region protected by 1200Å of oxide exhibits tolerable electrical characteristics.

Sodium ions absorbed in the oxide layer during the injection process could subsequently diffuse to the oxide-silicon interface and enter the silicon lattice by diffusion at elevated temperatures.   However, the diffusion coefficient for sodium introduced substitutionally into silicon by an equilibrium process has been estimated [4] to be only about 6×10^{-12} cm^2/sec at 800°C.   Thus, the amount of substitutional diffusion expected at injection temperatures for the times involved could not account for the effects observed in this work and exemplified by Figs. 8, 9, and 13.   The presence of sodium atoms or ions residing in the oxide layer during electrical evaluation of the planar-type diodes could, of course, produce deleterious electrical effects.   However, results such as those in Fig. 13 were found to persist after complete removal of the oxide layer by chemical means. It is thus concluded that such effects are due to sodium ion doping of the silicon near the crystal surface by direct injection through the oxide.

Some evidence of diode leakage due to ion penetration of oxide masks has also been found when much thicker oxide layers have been used, especially on high resistivity host crystal material. Thermally grown oxides 2 μ thick appear to provide essentially complete protection for the formation of device structures with sodium ion beams of the characteristics used in this work, and 1 to 1.5 μ of oxide has been found sufficient for most purposes. *

Planar diode structures formed in high resistivity (8 ohm-cm) silicon by injection of 15 keV sodium ions (current density 21 $\mu a/cm^2$, total dose 4 x 10^{16} ions/ cm^2) at 500°C are shown in Fig. 14(a). The oxide layer in this case was pyrolytically-deposited (TEOS) silicon oxide of thickness approximately 1.1 μ. Figure 14(b) shows a bevel-section through one of the diodes with the oxide still in place; a ring-dot photomask was employed in forming the contact to the ion-doped layer, accounting for the granular deposit seen in the figure. The same device is shown in Fig. 14(c) after staining to delineate the junction.

Some of the electrical characteristics of the planar-type diodes formed in this sample are illustrated in Fig. 15. It should be emphasized that the highest temperature

---

*There is evidence that sodium ion penetration of thermally grown oxides considerably greater than that expected for the ion energies involved and for established range-energy relationships for amorphous or polycrystalline materials has occurred. Since diffusion, although undoubtedly present, does not appear to account for the experimental observations (see text), other possibilities, such as enhanced ion penetration of the grown oxide due to partial orientation of regions of the oxide layer, must be considered. Further investigation of this question is in progress.

Figure 14. Planar diode structures in 8 ohm-cm silicon formed through apertures in 1.1 μ pyrolytic oxide layer by 15 keV sodium ions at 500°C; total dose 4×10^{16} ions/cm^2. (a) Three diodes shown on 3° bevel. (b) Device aperture with oxide layer and ring-dot deposited-metal contact. (c) Same device, stained to delineate n-type doped region and uniform junction 1.7 μ deep.

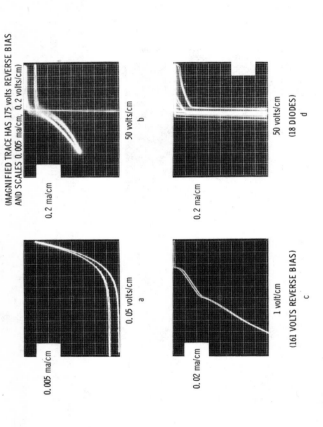

Figure 15. Electrical characteristics of diodes in sample of Fig. 14.   (a) Representative forward characteristic; parameter A about 2.4 in diode equation $J = J_S$ (e $qV/AkT-1$). (b) Reverse characteristic, showing 200-volt breakdown on normal and magnified scales. (c) Breakdown region of reverse characteristic of another diode in array, with evidence of microplasmas.   (d) Reverse characteristics of 18 diodes of array.

experienced by the silicon wafer used in fabricating these diodes was 650°C, the pyrolytic oxide deposition temperature. The possibility of completely fabricating devices in silicon at moderate temperatures is one of the more important aspects of the alkali-metal ion-injection doping process. *

The forward characteristic of one of the diodes is shown in Fig. 15(a); the resulting value for this parameter A in the diode equation $J = J_S (e^{qV/AkT} - 1)$ for moderate forward bias is found to be almost 2.4 for the particular device. The reverse characteristic is shown in Fig. 15(b); reverse breakdown occurs at about 200 volts. The breakdown characteristic is shown on a magnified scale in the same figure, and evidence of localized microplasma breakdown can be seen there and in Fig. 15(c), which is the reverse characteristic for another diode of the same array. Isolated microplasma are not always found in the breakdown characteristic of diodes formed by the ion injection technique, however, and a uniform breakdown may be more typical of the better diodes. Figure 15(d) is a composite photograph of the reverse characteristics of eighteen different diodes of this array. A high degree of uniformity is again found, with the exception of two or three high-leakage devices presumably resulting from defects in the oxide or non-uniform doping due to imperfections or contaminants on the surface of the exposed silicon.

Measurement of junction capacitance C versus reverse bias voltage V for the devices studied has indicated a value sometimes appreciably less than 1/3 for the exponent n in the equation

$$C = KV^{-n},$$

for those junctions formed in heavily doped (0.1 ohm-cm or less) host crystals. This capacitance-voltage behavior

*Recent experiments with metal aperture masks, in place of surface oxide masks, have resulted in the complete fabrication of silicon planar-type diodes at processing temperatures not exceeding 500°C.

is similar to that often observed for junctions containing a high density of trapping centers in the depletion region, and in this case may be attributable to unannealed radiation damage centers. Junctions formed in lightly doped (greater than 1 ohm-cm) host-crystal material have exhibited exponents ranging from 1/3 to 1/2, depending upon the location of the junction on the injected impurity profile. A step junction (n = 1/2) would be expected to occur on the steep part of the injected impurity profile near the knee, while a graded junction (n = 1/3) would be expected to result at depths corresponding to the low-gradient penetration tail of the profile. Such results have been obtained on these devices.

Several more complex types of device structures have also been fabricated; an example is the micropower test circuit shown in Fig. 16. This circuit consists of three transistors and six integrated circuit resistors of the double-junction type. Normally the circuit is fabricated by two separate diffusion processes in n-type silicon of resistivity the order of a few ohm-cm. In this instance, however, the second diffusion step has been replaced by sodium ion injection. By means of an appropriate oxide mask, apertures were provided to permit formation of the emitters and collector contacts of the transistors and the upper junctions of the resistors by ion injection.

Figure 16(a) shows one of an array of about 90 such circuits on a silicon wafer, after forming the lower junctions of the resistors and the base regions of the transistors by boron diffusion and after opening the apertures in the oxide layer for injection of the sodium ions. Figure 16(b) shows the same individual circuit after exposure to an 18 kev sodium ion beam to produce a total dose of 3×10^{17} ions/cm^2 at 500°C. Although changes in oxide layer thickness have occurred in this experiment due to the large total dose employed (as evidenced in the figure by changes in the color tone of various regions of the specimen) there has been no drastic damage to the oxide layer.

Figure 17(a) shows a bevel-section through two transistors of another example of the same micropower circuit exposed in a different experiment. The difference

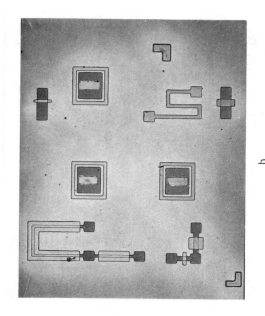

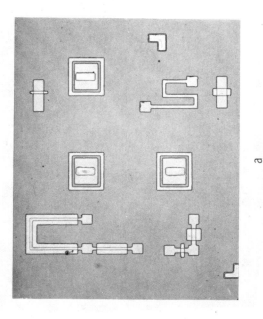

Figure 16. Micropower test circuit (without interconnections and contacts) with apertures in oxide mask for sodium ion injection. (a) Before ion injection. (b) After doping with 18 keV sodium ion beam at 500°C; total dose 3×10^{17} ions/cm^2.

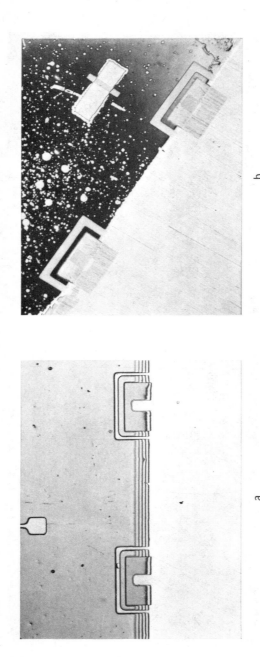

Figure 17. (a) Bevel section (1°) through two transistors of circuit like that of Fig. 16, after ion injection, with oxide. (b) Another pair of transistors, after staining. Diffused base–collector junction ~ 1.3 μ deep; ion–doped emitter ~ 0.2 μ deep.

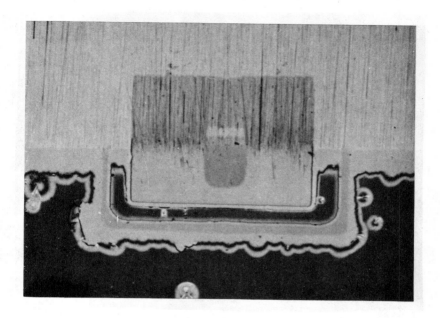

Figure 18. Transistor structure from specimen represented in Fig. 17(a). High magnification shows p-n-p-n structure resulting from submerged ion-doped emitter. Base-collector junction ~ 1.3 μ deep.

in the oxide layer thickness in the transistor base region and over the remainder of the specimen is shown by the white-light interference fringes; the oxide over the base is that grown during the boron base diffusion. Figure 17(b) shows a different pair of transistors, after staining to delineate the junctions. The boron-diffused base-collector junction in this case is approximately 1.3 μ deep; the ion-doped emitter junction is less than 0.2 μ deep, too shallow to produce satisfactory electrical characteristics.

Figure 18 illustrates, at high magnification, a transistor structure from the specimen represented in Fig. 17(a); this is an example of a completely submerged n-type region produced by sodium ion injection, resulting in a p-n-p-n structure.

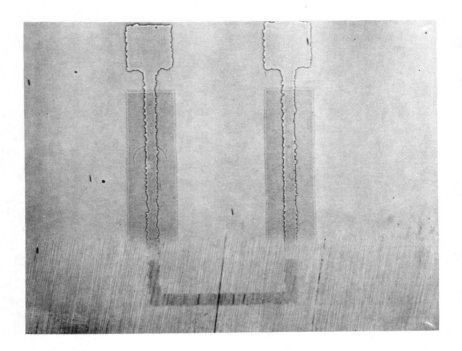

Figure 19. 1° bevel-section through U-shaped double-junction resistor of micropower circuit of Fig. 16. Deep junction formed first by boron diffusion through narrow stripe; shallow junction formed by subsequent sodium ion injection through wide-strip aperture (darkened).

Although the above photomicrographs illustrate ion-doped emitters which are too shallow, emitter-base junctions have been formed by this technique at depths up to the point where emitter-collector shorts have been obtained. Structures with intermediate emitter-base junction depths are now undergoing electrical evaluation.

Figure 19 is a photomicrograph of a bevel-section through one of the resistors of the micropower circuit. The boron-diffused p-type channel has been delineated by staining. The sodium-doped n-type region at the crystal surface appears as the break in the two legs of the U-shaped trace of the boron-doped channel, at the top of the bevel.

CONCLUSION

The fundamental characteristics of the alkali-metal ion injection doping process as applied to silicon have been studied by means of sodium ion beams. Knowledge of the nature of the injected impurity concentration profile, the diffusion properties of the injected impurity, and other characteristics of the technique have permitted the fabrication of device structures ranging from simple diodes to parts of microcircuits.

The results obtained with these device structures to date have demonstrated the value of the ion-injection doping technique to several specific device problems. Further development of these and other practical applications is indicated, and is now in progress.

ACKNOWLEDGMENT

The ion injection experiments were carried out by Richard L. Steele and W. A. Kennedy of the Rocketdyne Division of North American Aviation, Inc., under the direction of John F. Hon; their contribution to this work is gratefully acknowledged.

Several Autonetics personnel have participated in the investigations described here. In particular, special gratitude is due Frank L. Chiaretta and Jerrold Cohen, who were responsible for fabricating and evaluating the device structures, and Julia L. Healy, who prepared the many metallographic specimens required in this work.

REFERENCES

1. J. Cohen, R. P. Ruth, J. F. Hon, and R. L. Steele, The Electrochemical Society, Spring Meeting, San Francisco, May 1965. (Late news paper.)
2. J. O. McCaldin and A. E. Widmer, J. Phys. Chem. Solids 24, 1073 (1963); Proc. IEEE, 52 301 (1964).
3. M. Waldner and P. E. McQuaid, Solid-State Electronics 7, 925 (1964).
4. J. O. McCaldin, M. J. Little, and A. E. Widmer, J. Phys. Chem. Solids 26, 1119 (1965).

5. (a) G. R. Piercy, F. Brown, J. A. Davies, and M.
McCargo, Phys. Rev. Letters 10, 399 (1963);
H. Lutz and R. Sizmann, Phys Letters 5, 113 (1963);
G. R. Piercy, M. McCargo, F. Brown, and J. A.
Davies, Can. J. Phys. 42, 1116 (1964); B. Domeij,
F. Brown, J. A. Davies, G. R. Piercy, and E. V.
Kornelsen, Phys. Rev. Letters 12, 363 (1964);
E. V. Kornelsen, F. Brown, J. A. Davies, B.
Domeij, and G. R. Piercy, Phys. Rev. 136, A849
(1964).
(b) M. T. Robinson and O. S. Oen, Appl. Phys.
Letters 2, 30 (1963); Phys. Rev. 132, 2385 (1963);
C. Lehmann and G. Leibfried, J. Appl. Phys. 34,
2821 (1963); J. R. Beeler and D. G. Besco, J. Appl.
Phys. 34, 2873 (1963).
6. J. A. Davies, G. C. Ball, and F. Brown, Bull. Am.
Phys. Soc. 9, 109 (1964); J. A. Davies, G. C. Ball,
F. Brown, and B. Domeij, Can. J. Phys. 42, 1070
(1964).
7. R. P. Ruth, J. F. Hon, and R. L. Steele, to be
published.
8. J. Lindhard, M. Scharff, and H. E. Schitt, Kgl.
Danske Videnskab. Selskab. Mat. -Fys. Medd. 33,
No. 14 (1963); J. Lindhard and M. Scharff, Phys.
Rev. 124, 128 (1961). See also M. McCargo, F.
Brown, and J. A. Davies, Can. J. Chem. 41, 2309
(1963); J. A. Davies, F. Brown, and M. McCargo,
Can. J. Phys. 41, 829 (1963).
9. H. Reiss and C. S. Fuller, in Semiconductors, ed. by
N. B. Hannay (Reinhold Publishing Corporation, New
York, 1959), p. 232.
10. C. S. Fuller and J. C. Severiens, Phys. Rev. 96, 21
(1954).
11. J. O. McCaldin, Nuclear Instr. and Methods (1966),
to be published.

Variation of Physical and Electrical Concentrations of Donnors During Thermal Annealing

P. Glotin* and J. Grapa**

Center of Nuclear Studies
Grenoble, France

INTRODUCTION

For the last five years, the Research Nuclear Center of Grenoble has been interested in solid state circuits with emphasis on advanced integrated circuits technology. That is to say, conventional ways of semiconductor selective doping are now well known in our laboratories.

However, it is well known that circuit performances are limited by the ability one has to vary the surface concentrations and the concentration profiles when impurities are diffused by high temperature processes. These limitations have led us to try several other possibilities of doping - epitaxy, for example, is now currently used by most of semiconductor manufacturers.

The technology we are concerned with here is doping with energetic ions which we have been interested in for several years.

In this field of research which is quite new to us, it seems natural to begin with some solid state physics studies. In this paper we will try to determine the shape of the concentration profiles that one can get and also the optimal annealing temperature necessary to eliminate the lattice defects created by the incoming ions.

*Center of Nuclear Studies, Grenoble, France
**National Institute for Scientific Investigation

AIM OF THE EXPERIMENTS

It is well known that, when a heavy ion strikes a crystal surface of a substrate with an ordered lattice, the penetration and behavior of this ion are different depending on the crystal orientation in relation to the ion beam direction. In particular, Davies' studies have shown, in the case of a diamond type lattice (which is common to both silicon and germanium), that the 110 direction, called easy channeling direction, let the ions of a given initial energy arriving perpendicular to the surface to penetrate much deeper into the crystal than for any other lattice direction.

This is the reason why all the work we have carried out until now is concerned with slices cut in the preferential <110> direction. Once the ion has entered the crystal, it is slowed down either by energy losses during electronic ionization, or by knocking an atom out of the lattice. The problem we have tried to solve in this paper is the nature of the injected ion profile and also the annealing temperature which will reorder the lattice.

Indeed one knows that impurity atoms may remain on two different sites, interstitial or substitutional, and that it is only in the last case that they are electrically active. Generally one tries to get as high a percentage as possible on the sutstitutional sites, and this may necessitate a high temperature annealing step.

To answer the question we had to know for a given initial energy of the ion beam:

a) The physical concentration profiles that is to say the distribution of all the impurity atoms implanted in the cyrstal. This measurement was done with radioactive tracers. The incident beam contained a given proportion of P^{32} ions which will disintegrate by the reaction:

$$P^{32} \rightarrow S^{32} + \beta^-$$

Measurement of beta activity gives a number proportional to the sum of phosphorus atoms actually present in the slice.

b) The electrical concentration profile which was obtained from four point probe measurements. Note that this measurement is related not only to electrically active impurity ions, but also to the effects of lattice defects acting as recombination centers or traps.

In this paper, variation in both profiles were examined for different annealing temperatures and also for several dose levels of impurity ion.   These measurements have been made in the case of thermal diffusion and with the same experimental process by E. TANNENBAUM.

EXPERIMENTAL DETAILS

Sample Preparation

The samples were of P-type silicon 2 Ωcm resistivity cut in the preferential <110> direction.   Before bombardment, samples were cleaned in four successive ultrasonic baths: Trichloroethylene, alcohol, hydrofluoric acid (HF) in deionized water.

Each sample was a quarter of a 27mm diameter round slice.   After cleaning it was placed in the target chamber of the accelerator and covered by a 6mm diameter metallic mask.

Irradiation Apparatus

Fig. 1 shows the general view of the experimental apparatus.   The phosphorus ions are obtained from a radio-frequency source with a phosphorus pentachloride vapor feed.   The delivery rate of this vapor to the source is regulated by controlling the temperature of the PCl_5 container.   To get the optimum 10^{-2} to 10^{-3} torr pressure in the source, the container temperature was maintained at about $25°C$.

Then, ions with a maximum of 30 keV energy having been focused and accelerated in a classical optic system, are deflected and selected by an electromagnet to give a maximum resolution of the order of 50.   This deflection eliminates partially ionized molecules and a particularly chlorine atoms.   The ionic pattern one gets after this electromagnet is a line 1mm wide.

Figure 1 - General view of the bombardment apparatus

The beam is then deflected with a quadrupolar lens to get a convenient pattern on the target and give a uniform impurity concentration on a large area.

The target temperature is kept constant at 25°C. The use of phosphorus pentachloride has been found convenient for two main reasons: The apparatus is able to operate for several days without cleaning (which is not true when one uses pure phosphorus vapor), and it is reasonably easy to make this compound with radioactive P^{32}.

Typically the current density of phosphorus ions on the target was of the order of $3x10^{-8}$ Amperes/cm^2. The total dose was measured by a charge integrator.

Depth Measurements

To measure both physical and electrically active concentrations profiles, it was necessary to make measurements at different depths in the crystal. In our experiments, the procedure used to etch very thin uniform layers of silicon from the slice was to anodically oxidize the sample and then to selectively etch the oxide by hydrofluoric acid HF. In our experiments, layers of 800 Å oxide were formed during each step, (which are equivalent to 350 Å of silicon) were removed between two successive measurements. The anodizing solution used as N-Methylacetamide in an 0.04N solution of potassium nitrate.

The main advantage of this procedure is to keep the sample temperature reasonably low (40°C) during the experiment, which avoids any undesired post irradiation diffusion.

Ten successive etches were made on each sample.

Resistivity and Radiotracer Measurements

After each etching operation, two measurements were made on the sample (Fig. 2 shows the different parts described in this paragraph) they were:

Four point probes measurement was done with a classical system, the probes having $5/\pi$ mm spacing. 1mA current was usually obtained between extreme probes. The voltage difference measured between the two central probes could be related to the sheet resistance of the remaining doped layer. From the difference of the reciprocals of the two successive measurements, one can get the resistance of the layer 350 Å thick that has been etched.

Radiotracer activity was measured in each case. Precautions were taken to avoid excessive atmosphere noise; however, this noise was very disturbing for low activity samples. The number of counts was directly proportional to the number of impurity atoms remaining under the surface, and thus, one could get the number of phosphorus radioactive atoms present in a layer by difference between two successive measurements.

Figure 2 – General View of the Measurement of Items
- at left: four point probes
- at right: radioactivity counter

Measurement Precision

To make measurements as reproducible as possible, after the sample was doped and annealed at the desired temperature, it was held in a box against a 6 mm diameter hole with a spring. All of the following operations (oxidation, HF etch, four point probe and radiotracer measurements) were made without removing the sample from the box to insure that the measurements were always made at the same place on the slice.

ANALYSIS OF DATA

Calculation of the Total Concentrations of Atoms

The total concentration in a given layer is directly proportional to the number of counts due to the layer. To get the relation between the actual concentration and the activity, we used the total ionic charge measured in the target chamber.

On the first activity measurement A, before any etching, the activity was proportional to the total impurity atoms present in the beam. As we know the total charge q, the relation is:

$$\theta = \frac{\text{activity}}{\text{dose per cm}^2} = \frac{A \times S}{q} \times 1.6 \times 10^{-19}$$

where S is the sample surface area.

This relation was used for the succeeding measurements on the same slice, correcting for activity loss of phosphorus. The half life is 14. 3 days. In each case the background count was subtracted.

Calculation of Electrically Active Atom Concentrations

The experimental data deduced from four point probe measurements were plotted in the form of ρ_s^{-1} as a function of depth x where ρ_s is the sheet resistance. The slope of this curve at any point is a measure of the conductance in the layer corresponding to the depth. The conductance is related to the electrically active atoms concentration by the expression:

$$\frac{d(\rho_s^{-1})}{dx} = \mu'_x \, e(N_x - N_o)$$

where e is the electron charge, N_x the desired concentration and μ'_x the effective mobility for electrons.   This mobility was obtained from the data compiled by Prince [1] and Backenstoss [2]

EXPERIMENTAL RESULTS

List of Experiments

The following table gives the list of the experiments we have completed for this paper:

Dose Ions/cm²	Annealing Temperature	Number of Samples
6.6×10^{13}	150°C	1
3.3×10^{14}	150°C	1
3.3×10^{15}	150°C	1
6.6×10^{13}	400°C	1
3.3×10^{14}	400°C	1
3.3×10^{15}	400°C	2
6.6×10^{13}	550°C	1
3.3×10^{14}	550°C	1
3.3×10^{15}	550°C	2
6.6×10^{13}	700°C	1
3.3×10^{14}	700°C	1
3.3×10^{15}	700°C	2

Results

During our experiments we had trouble with the furnace and the 550°C thermal annealing experiments were not successful.   These measurements will not appear on the following diagrams.

Examples of both electrical and physical concentration profiles are shown in Figs. 3, 4, 5 and 6.

at/cm³

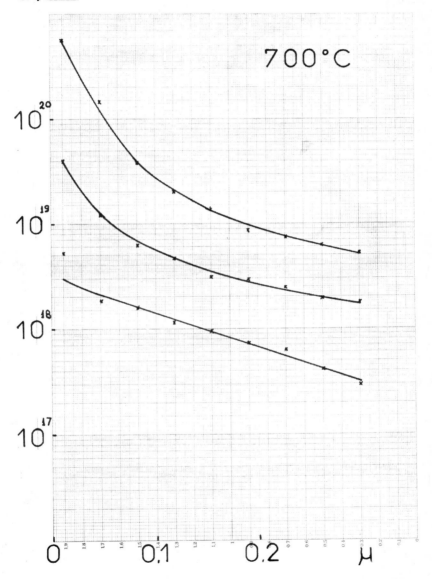

Figure 3 – Physical Concentrations Profiles After 1 Hour
Annealing at 700°C

1: 3.3×10^{15} ions/cm^2
2: 3.3×10^{14} ions/cm^2
3: 6.6×10^{13} ions/cm^2

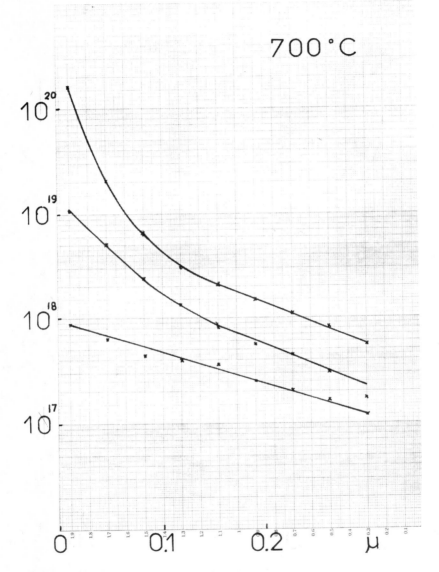

Figure 4 – Electrically Active Atoms Concentration Profiles in the Same Condition as Figure 3.

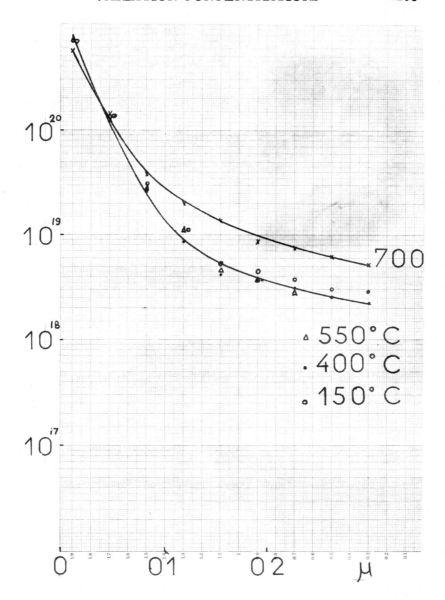

Figure 5. Physical Concentrations Profiles at Different Annealing Temperatures and for the same Total Dose: 3.3×10^{15} ions/ cm^2.

at/cm³

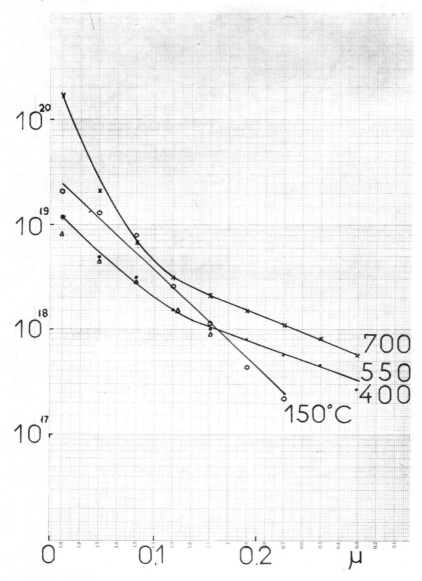

Figure 6.   Same as Above for Electrically Active Profiles.

Figure 3 shows physical or total profiles at constant annealing temperature and dose varying from 6, 6. 10^{13} to 3.3x10^{15} ions/cm^2.

Figure 4 shows electrically active profiles for the same conditions.

Figures 5 and 6 indicate the influence of annealing temperature on both profiles for a given total dose.

It is very interesting to compare the two profiles when the slice receives the same dose and is annealed at the same temperature.

We call η the relation between physical or total concentration and electrically active concentration.

Figures 7 and 8 show variation of η for one dose as a function of temperature of anneal and for a given temperature as a function of doses.

General Remarks

This study needs complementary experiments to provide more evidence before we are able to give a physical interpretation to correlate the two profiles. However, the first results we have presented here allow conclusions to be drawn and to propose some hypothesis from the observed curves.

TENTATIVE INTERPRETATION

Influence of Total Dose

Physical Profiles

One sees that the physical or total profiles have almost the same shape for any dose implanted in the semiconductor. However the surface concentration increases much more strongly with the increasing dose than the concentration at a certain depth (~2000 Å). This evidence shows that the first atoms entering the crystal are able to reach a large depth because the crystal is still ordered. These ions have created defects in the structure during their penetration, thus the following ions are stopped much closer to the surface.

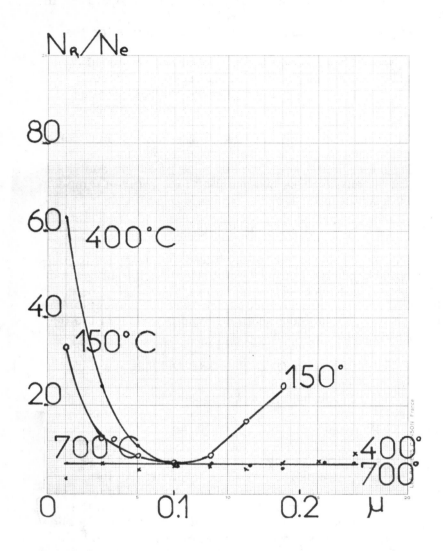

Figure 7 – Ratio η as a Function of Depth for Various Annealing
Temperatures.   Total dose is Constant: $3.\text{x}10^{15}$ ions/cm^2

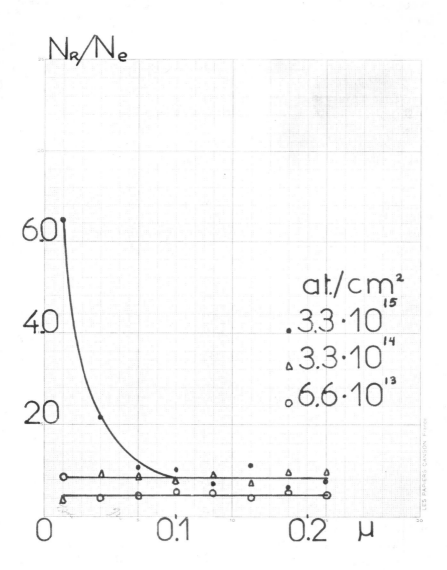

Figure 8. Ratio η as a Function of Depth for Various Total Doses
Annealing Temperature is 400°C

With large total doses, the surface concentration may become very high and the slope of the profile near the surface increases very rapidly with dose. This phenomenon is observed at any annealing temperature.

Evolution of the Relation η

This relation is characteristic of the site occupied by the phosphorus ions when they have been stopped in the crystal.

One observes that this relation is strongly dependent on the total dose. At low doses, the relation is nearly constant as a function of depth. This shows that the same proportion of impurity atoms occupies substitutional sites.

As the dose increases, the temperature being not too high, the relation remains at a comparable level in the bulk, but increases tremendously near the surface. This could be explained by the very high concentration in this region: the phosphorus atoms are then too numerous, so that each one has a very little probability of finding an empty site in the lattice and most of them remain in interstitial sites with no effects on the electrical characteristics.

Influence of Annealing Temperature

Three main processes are observed which are related to the annealing temperature:

Lattice Defects Annealing

One observes that the relation η is less than one at low temperature (150°C) and low doses. This is explained by the very high concentration of defects, the effects of which are preponderant compared to the electrical effect of the doping impurities.

Then, as the temperature increases, the relation η decreases because the defects disappear. Only the effects of chemical impurities remain apparent. This phenomenon is already clearly apparent on the 400°C curves.

Changing of Sites

When one looks at the variation of η values as a function of temperature for small doses at 2000 Å depth, one sees that η tends to unity when the annealing temperature increases. It proves that the phosphorus atoms move from interstitial to substitutional sites, the jumps being helped by the thermal agitation due to higher temperatures.

Thermal Diffusion

At high temperature (700°C), the physical profile changes: the surface concentration decreases while the slope of the curve and the concentration at 2000 Å depth increase.

This is typical of a thermal diffusion the parameters of which have not yet been calculated. This diffusion at a temperature where usually thermal diffusion does not occur is most certainly due to the presence of remaining defects.

CONCLUSION

The experiments presented in this paper have made evident some physical phenomena that occur during ion doping bombardment and followed by thermal annealing. These are:

- Disappearance of the channeling for high doses ($10^{15}/cm^2$)

- Decrease of the ratio η at the surface when the dose increases.

- Lattice defects annealing mainly under 400°C.

- Jumps of the phosphorus atoms to substitutional sites between 400°C and 700°C.

- Occurrence of thermal diffusion at high temperatures (~700°C)

The main conclusion we may draw from these results is that to obtain a given profile of electrically active impurity atoms in silicon by ion bombardment, one has to take into account not only the total implanted dose but also the annealing temperature. This latter determines the ratio of atoms effectively active and also the shape of the profile.

It will be interesting, in the future, to observe the influence of these profiles on the electrical characteristics of the diode.

REFERENCES

1. PRINCE, M. B., Drift Mobilities in Semiconductors II Silicon, Phys. Rev. 93 - 1204 (March 1954)
2. BACKENSTESS, G., Conductivity Mobilities of Electrons and Holes in Heavily Doped Silicon, Phys. Rev. 108 - 1416 (December 1957)
3. SCHMIDT, P. F. and MICHEL, W., Anodic Ionization of Oxide Films on Silicon, Jour. Electro Soc. 104 - No. 4 - p. 230 (April 1957)
4. MANCHESTER, K. E. and SIBLEY, C. B., Doping of Silicon by Ion Implantation, Bull. Amer. Phys. Soc. 10 - No. 1 - 123 - (1965)
5. TANNENBAUM, E., Detailed Analysis of Thin Phosphorus Diffused Layers in p-Type Silicon, Solid State Electronics 2 - 123 (1962)

Micro - Machining by Ion Bombardment

R. Castaing and M. Bernheim

Faculty of Sciences
Orsay, France

The modern electronic techniques demand the micro-miniaturization of electronic circuits, which requires great precision in the machining techniques and the study of new processes for localized doping of semi-conductors.

Photo-engraving techniques, which are currently used, permit the formation of masks by optical reduction of a large scale model. Faithful reproduction of the smallest details is essentially limited by the resolving power of the light optics.

The replacement of light by beams of charged particles permits the machining to be performed by the same apparatus utilized for the reduction.

An electron beam may be used for machining the material by thermal evaporation; however, such a process requires a large electronic density. The precision of the machining is related to the possibility of localizing the heating; in other words, large thermal gradients must be obtained. The beam must have a small diameter as well as a high electronic density. These two requirements cannot be met simultaneously.

The same difficulties are met when using lasers, for the phenomenon which is used for the machining is still the thermal evaporation.

An indirect method is used by MOLLENSTEDT, where an electron beam of very weak density deposits an insulating layer of "contamination" on the sample, which then permits the electrodeposition of a metal on the uncontaminated regions; such a process is similar to a micro-photo-engraving.

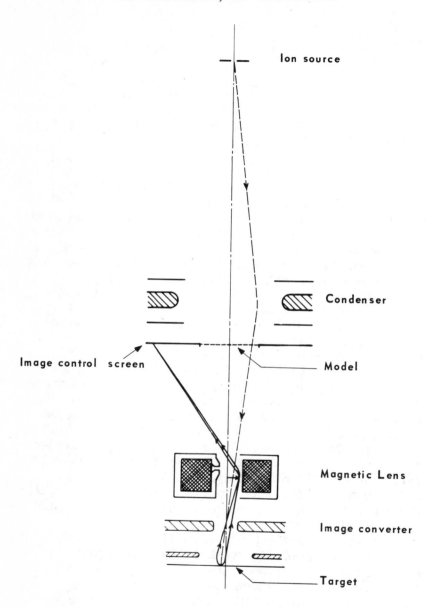

Figure 1. Schematic Diagram of the Apparatus.

We have developed a new technique using the cathodic sputtering produced by an ion bombardment. The essential difference between our technique and the thermal methods lies in the fact that essentially each ion sputters a given quantity of material, independently of the other ions of the beam. The sputtering of a region thus depends only on the number, the nature and the energy of the bombarding ions, but it does not depend upon the ionic density on the sample; the density of the ion beam falling onto the sample may be reduced at will, if one increases the time of bombardment.

As a consequence, there is no longer any limitation on the precision of the machining; it is sufficient to utilize good particle optics, using beams of small aperture and consequently of small density.

PRINCIPLE AND CHARACTERISTICS OF THE APPARATUS

By forming the reduced image of a model on a thin foil by means of an ion optical system, one will machine on the foil openings corresponding to the transparent regions of the model; thus a positive replica of the model will be fashioned in miniature on the thin foil.

One of the difficult points is connected with the fine control of the focussing of the ion image of the model on the surface of the thin foil to be machined. In order to check the focussing, we use an ion-electron image converter. The ion bombardment ejects secondary electrons from the bombarded surface. These electrons are accelerated and focussed by the electrostatic field of the converter, permitting the observation on a fluorescent of an electron image which is an enlargement of the ion image formed on the sample (Fig. 1); on the other hand the post-acceleration of the positive ions by the field produces the focussing and the reduction of the ion image.

In order to obtain an electron image larger than the model, we have added a magnetic lens to the image converter; this magnetic lens has a very small focussing action on the ions, since the focal length is proportional to the mass of the particles.

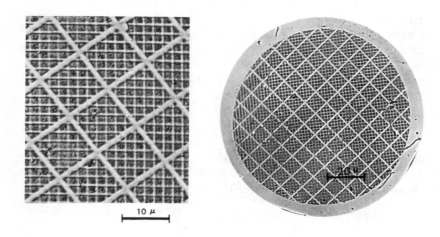

Figure 2(a) (b). Light Optical Micrograph of a 2 μ Steps Grid
Engraved on a Solid Support from a Model Having 100 μ Steps.

It would be desirable that the aberrations of the
electron image - producing optics be smaller than those
of the ion image itself, in order that the focussing can be
checked accurately. Unfortunately the secondary electrons are emitted with initial energies of the order of 10
electron-volts, corresponding to a resolution of one
micron for an extracting field of 15 kV/cm; such a resolution is much worse than may be obtained on the ion image.

The resolution of the image converter may be increased if one reduces the aberration of the electron
image by means of an aperture placed at the cross-over
of the exit beam of the converter.

A condenser focusses an image of the cross-over of
the ion gun, through the model, onto this aperture. The
only effect of the presence of this aperture, whose diameter is 0. 1 mm, is to reduce slightly the brightness of
the ion image.

Figure 3. An Electron Transmission Micrograph of a 2μ Steps, 80% Transparency Copper Grid, Obtained by Micro-Machining a Thin Foil of Copper.

The ions are argon positive ions produced by a conventional arc discharge gun; obviously, other ions and any type of gun could be used for the machining.

OPERATIONAL CHARACTERISTICS AND PRELIMINARY RESULTS

The focussing of the ion image depends essentially upon the degree of post-acceleration of the ions and the polarization of the wehnelt of the converter; it depends a little upon the excitation of the condenser, whose electrostatic fringing field extends over the region where the model is located.

As a consequence the number of adjustable parameters is sufficient for:

a. eliminating the distortion of the ion image by a proper choice of the ratio between the post-acceleration voltage and the initial accelerating voltage of the ions.

b. focussing the ion image by adjusting the polarization of the wehnelt of the converter and the excitation of the condenser lens.

c. focussing the electron image by adjusting the polarization of the wehnelt of the converter and the excitation of the magnetic lens.

By post-accelerating to 53 keV ions whose initial accelerating voltage is 7 kV, one produces, for the geometry utilized in our converter, an ion image which represents a reduction of the model by a factor 50.

The magnification of the electron image is 200, which represents an enlargement by a factor of 4 in relation to the model.   A further enlargement of 10 is obtained with an optical viewer.

A model consisting of a grid with 100 microns steps has permitted us to engrave a grid with 2 microns steps in a polished block of stainless steel.   A large grid, 400 microns steps, was superimposed on the model in order to aid in the preliminary adjustments.   Micrographs of the engraved sample, taken with a light metallographic microscope, are shown in Figs. 2(a) and 2(b).   The resolving power of this microscope was not sufficient for determining the precision of the machining.

We have also used the same model to produce a grid of 2 microns steps in a thin copper foil about one micron thick.   An electron micrograph of this grid is shown in Fig. 3.   The transparency is better than 80%; the radii of the corners are of the order of 0. 2 microns.   Thus this apparatus may be used to fabricate grids and special apertures, for example Fresnel zone plates.   An obviously application would be found in the field of electronic circuits, where the technique could be used for machining high resistances and coils in thin films, but difficulties will arise from the fact that the specimen is subject to a strong electrostatic field.   The field is distorted by the presence of the holes in the foil, and the distortion is particularly high if the specimen is not deposited onto a conducting substrate; undesirable deflections of the ions will occur in the last part of their path, as a result, the resolving power of the machining will be limited. The same difficulty is encountered if one tries to drill deep holes of a very small diameter in a thick sample.

MICRO-DOPING

For this application, it would be sufficient to replace the Ar^+ ion source by a source of doping ions, for example aluminum or phosphorus. This technique, associated with the channeling of ions in well-defined directions of the lattice would permit, on the one hand, the doping of zones with dimensions less than one micron on a semiconductor; this has not been possible till now by using thermal diffusion techniques.

No protecting layer is necessary and successive P and N dopings on various regions might be performed consecutively without any intermediate manipulation of the specimen.

The positioning for doping is controlled solely by the positioning of the model; for example, a 0.2 micron positioning of the doping could be obtained by a 10 microns positioning of the masks; this would permit much more accurate reproduction of circuits.

However, the application of this technique will require an increase of the post-accelerating voltage of the ions and of the useful size of the ion images.

ACKNOWLEDGMENT

This work has been supported by the Délégation Générale à la Recherche Scientifique et Technique.

REFERENCES

K. H. v Grote, G. Möllenstedt and R. Speidel, Herstellung von Kurzbrennweitigen Zonenlinsen für Röntgen und UV-Strahlen und von Korrekturplatten für Elektronenmikroskope, Optik, 22, Heft 4, pp. 252-269 (1965).

R. Speidel, Elektronenoptischer Mikroschreiber mit magnetischer Strahlablenkung unter Elektronenmikroskopischer Arbeitskontrolle, Optik 23, Heft 2, pp. 124-144 (1966).

Metallic Ion Deposition

A. R. Wolter

The Boeing Space Center
Kent, Washington

INTRODUCTION

When a beam of metal ions impinges on a substrate, a metal film will form on the substrate surface if the energy of the ions is sufficiently low to prevent excessive sputtering or evaporation.

This phenomena can be used to advantage for depositing thin film circuits. The beam can be scanned over the substrate in a precisely controlled manner so that conductive patterns can be formed without masks, and the important film properties (thickness, rate of formation, and purity) can be directly controlled by controlling the properties of the beam itself. Because the energy of the ions which form the deposit is well above thermal energies, surface contaminants such as adsorbed residual gas and thin oxide layers can be removed during the deposition process by sputtering resulting in good adhesion and an intimate electrical contact to the substrate.

This report describes experimental studies of metal ion deposition on glass and is a continuation of previous reports. [1, 2] Since the practical utility of the technique depends critically on the equipment necessary to make these deposits, the apparatus and its operating characteristics are discussed in detail. Some electrical properties of chromium deposits on glass and an ion-beam-deposited functional circuit are described.

APPARATUS

The ion gun, shown in Fig. 1, was developed for this study and operated in a vacuum of 5 x 10^{-6} Torr.

The ion source, which has been previously described [2] , produces ions by low-energy electron bombardment of metal vapor. Briefly, an arc discharge is maintained between an incandescent tungsten filament (cathode) and an externally heated crucible containing the desired metal (anode). The arc is sustained by the metal vapor produced as the anode disintegrates. Many ions diffuse away from the dense plasma region and are drawn out of the ion source by electrostatic fields. A recent improvement is a discharge current controller which automatically adjusts the temperature of the ionization filament so that a constant discharge current is maintained even though the arc length constantly increases. Some features of this ion source are similar to other designs [3] , but this device has the advantage of producing a beam with a very high ratio of ions to neutral atoms (as much as 500 to 1 at the substrate for chromium) and is ultra-simple in construction and operation.

Ions are accelerated from the ion source by the negative potential on electrode B and an ion current of a few microamperes passes through the aperture in this electrode. Although the aperture in electrode B removes an unnecessarily large portion of the beam, exclusion of some outer portions of the beam is necessary to remove low-energy particles (see the next section).

Electrode C decelerates the ions to an energy sufficiently low for deposition (the exact value depends on the type of metal), and strongly focuses the beam so that it reaches its minimum diameter a few centimeters from the aperture in this electrode. The beam current density of the substrate will be higher if the focal spot is close to the aperture in electrode C, because of space charge effects in the beam. [2, 4] Since conventional electrostatic deflection plates placed between electrode C and the substrate unnecessarily limit diminution of this focal length, Electrode C was designed to deflect as well as focus the beam. As shown in Fig. 2, electrode C is composed of

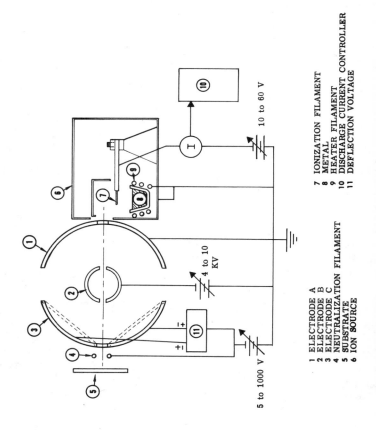

1 ELECTRODE A
2 ELECTRODE B
3 ELECTRODE C
4 NEUTRALIZATION FILAMENT
5 SUBSTRATE
6 ION SOURCE

7 IONIZATION FILAMENT
8 METAL
9 HEATER FILAMENT
10 DISCHARGE CURRENT CONTROLLER
11 DEFLECTION VOLTAGE

Figure 1. Schematic of the Ion Beam Deposition Device.

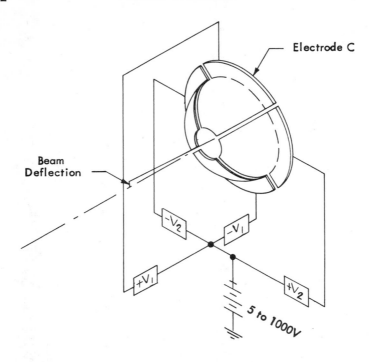

Figure 2.   Schematic of Electrode "C" Which Focuses, Decelerates, and Deflects the Beam.

four electrically isolated quadrants, to which voltages are applied in a "push-pull" arrangement.   A precise analysis of the electric fields between electrodes B and C (Fig. 1) would be most complex and has not been carried out. However, it has been determined experimentally that the deflection is linear with voltage for deflection 0.05 inches from center and the position of minimum beam diameter was not altered detectably by sectioning electrode C.   In addition, in many experiments, electrode C was approximated in shape by four planar sections arranged to form a truncated pyramid (dotted lines in Fig. 1) and the operation was still satisfactory.

The neutralization filament continually supplies electrons to the Substrate to prevent excessive charge

build-up on the insulating surface. This incandescent
tungsten loop also heats the substrate to an average temperature of about 200°C as measured with a conventional
thermocouple, but the local surface temperature is probably higher.

The Substrate is at the position of minimum beam diameter and is mounted on a mechanically operated x-y
movement for use in conjunction with, or in place of,
electrostatic deflection.

Chromium deposits as small in diameter as 0.002
inches and current densities of 0.1 A/in² have been
achieved. It is believed that minor modification in the
deposition system - primarily in design of the electrodes -
will allow 0.001 inch spots to be made at current densities
of 0.2 A/in², although those values should not be interpreted as limits for the technique. (The speed of film
formation with these current densities can be understood

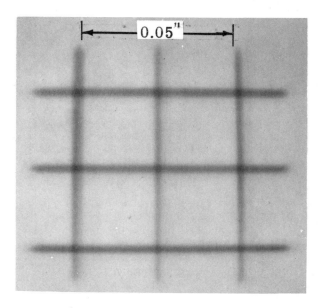

Figure 3. Grid Pattern of Chromium Deposits on Glass. Beam
was Electrostatically Deflected.

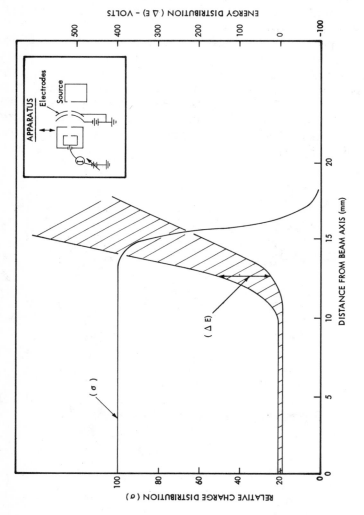

Figure 4. Charge and Energy Distributions of a Copper Ion Beam Near the Source.

by reference to the last section of this report where the resistors were formed at current densities of 0. 1 A/in^2).

A network of chromium lines on glass, made by electrostatic deflection of the beam, is shown in Fig. 3 which is a typical pattern used to check operation of the deposition device.

BEAM CHARACTERISTICS

To permit predictable deflection and focusing, the beam should be monoenergetic. The energy distribution of the beam was studied both at the substrate and at a position close to the source where the total current was high.

For measurements near the source, the equipment was modified as shown in the inset of Fig. 4. By varying the potential on the inner collector cup of a Faraday cage arrangement, ion-current versus repeller-voltage curves were plotted for adjacent positions along the beam diameter. Relative charge distributions were determined from current saturation values at negative repeller voltages and energy distributions from the positive and negative voltage values of current saturation.

Figure 4 shows the relative charge and energy distributions within a copper beam as a function of distance from the beam axis. Very similar curves were obtained for operation with chromium, silver, and aluminum. The charge distribution was uniform for a large portion of the beam and was as expected since the total distance of beam travel was short. The energy distribution curve shows a central core where 99% of the beam was within ±10 ev of its average energy (±3 ev at half maximum intensity), but a large portion of the outer edge of the beam contained ions whose energy was appreciably below that of the central core and whose extreme energy value was more than ±100 ev from the average.

Total current measurements of this central core exceeded 100μA for all the metals studied with chromium typically yielding twice this value. By collecting the central core ions on glass substrates inside the collector cup and measuring the film thickness interferometrically, it was shown that the beam was composed of singly-charged ions within the accuracy of the measurement (about 10%).

The beam at the substrate in the normal gun configuration was of small diameter and low current (a few microamps), so the energy distribution there was estimated from the effect of electrostatic deflection on the shape of deposits made on glass. Figure 5 shows the superimposed cross sections of two deposits on glass when one was electrostatically deflected to a position 0.6 mm from the normal beam axis. The distribution of metal was measured by the extent of X-ray fluorescence in an ARL electron microprobe.

It is evident from these distributions that an appreciable portion of the beam at the substrate was not composed of ions whose energy was ±100 ev from its mean value since the deflected deposit would then have been greatly distorted. Thus the aperture in electrode B (Fig. 1) had permanently removed the low energy ions found in the beam near the source. If one assumes the energy of the ions in the tails of the deposit distributions to be less by an amount ΔE than that of the ions which formed the peak, a "tail shift" $\Delta x \approx \Delta E \cdot x/E$ would be expected, where x is the linear separation of the two peaks and E is the mean beam energy. For these deposits x = 0.6 mm, E = 200 ev, and from Fig. 5, the maximum "tail shift" is roughly 0.025 mm. Thus $\Delta E \approx 10$ ev, which is in good agreement with the energy spread measured near the source. Therefore the beam retained the energy characteristics it possessed near the source and was not grossly effected by collisions with residual gas atoms or electrons during its flight to the substrate.

ELECTRICAL PROPERTIES OF CHROMIUM FILMS

The electrical properties of chromium films as a function of deposition rate were studied. Figure 6 shows the dependence of temperature coefficient of resistance

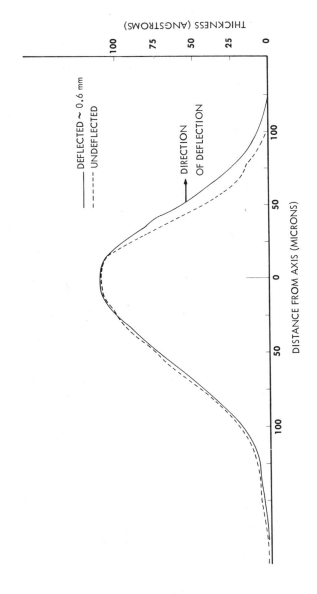

Figure 5.   Cross Sections of Two Chromium Deposits on Glass.   The Deflected Distribution is Superimposed on the Undeflected Distribution for Comparison.

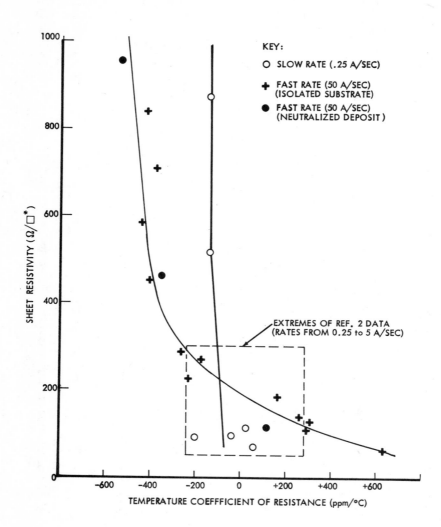

Figure 6. Plot of Sheet Resistivity Versus Temperature
Coefficient of Resistance of Chromium Deposits for a High
and Low Deposition Rate.

(TCR) on the sheet resistivity* for high and low deposition rates. Resistors were deposited on glass using electrostatic deflection of the beam and had cross sections similar to those shown in Fig. 5. To produce a high deposition rate (about 50 Å/sec for the peak), the resistors were drawn in a single trace, while for the low-deposition-rate deposits (an average rate of 1/4 Å/sec for the peak) the beam was continually scanned over the entire length of the resistor at a frequency of 130 cps.

The curve for the high-deposition-rate resistors is very similar in shape to those obtained for vacuum evaporated chromium in our laboratory and elsewhere [5], although a comparison in the absolute sense is not reliable due to the different physical structure of the deposits. These films had a typical metallic behavior in that films of low sheet resistivity had positive TCR, while the high sheet resistivity films had negative TCR presumably due to their extreme thinness.

The curve for low-deposition-rate resistors shows behavior which is more typical of metal-metal oxide films since only a weak dependence of TCR on sheet resistivity is observed. It is reasonable to assume that these films contained appreciable oxide since the ratio of oxygen atom to metal ion impacts at the surface was probably as high as 10 to 1 for these temperature and pressure conditions. In these resistors the TCR of the film material itself more strongly governed the TCR of the resistor than the thinness of the layer and high positive TCR was not expected even for very thick films.

The conclusion that these differences were due to varying degrees of oxidation was supported by resistivity estimates of 5×10^{-3} and 1×10^{-4} ohm-cm for low- and high-deposition-rate resistors, respectively, for a peak thickness of 100 Å.

---

*The term sheet resistivity does not retain its usual meaning because of the nonuniform distribution of metal (see Fig. 5). The sheet resistivity was defined equal to $R \cdot w'/L$ where R is the resistance of the deposit, L is the length of the deposit, and w' is the width of the electrically conducting portion of the deposit. Typically, w' included all the film thicker than 25A.

It is well known that a beam of ions incident on glass surfaces can produce a surface charge sufficient to slow the beam to a very low velocity, and in these experiments this could effect the electrical properties of the films. While deposits were usually made on electrically isolated portions of a glass substrate, a few deposits of Fig. 6 were begun on a large aluminum pad maintained at a potential of 200 v (beam potential) by a battery externally connected to ground. Deposition then proceeded onto the glass surface and a charge buildup could not take place. Because the electrical properties of these grounded deposits did not deviate appreciably from resistors formed on isolated glass substrates, the credibility of the data is enhanced.

Figure 6 also explains an apparent contradiction contained in Ref. 2 for similar experiments. It was reported there that no definite dependence of sheet resistivity and TCR on deposition rate had been found and that all films had near-zero TCR. It is clear that within the deposition rates of these early experiments (1/4 to 5 Å/sec) the dependence of sheet resistivity on TCR was very weak and easily obscured by experimental error.

Some chromium resistors on glass (deposition rate 5 Å/sec and sheet resistivities of 200 ohms/sq.) were life tested under high DC loading. A monotonic increase in resistance with time was observed, corresponding to an average drift of 0.4%/1000 hours.

ION BEAM DEPOSITED CIRCUITRY

The passive circuitry for an inverter amplifier-emitter follower circuit was formed by ion beam deposition. Figure 7 shows the chromium resistor network and the schematic.

This network, made by mechanical movement of the substrate relative to a fixed beam, contained five resistors ranging in value from 6 to 18 K ohms. The length of each resistor was the same; the sheet resistivity of each resistor was varied to obtain the desired resistance value. A discrete transistor was attached to the substrate and the circuit bonded in a flat pack. Connections to the circuit were made by ultrasonically bonding 0.002-inch aluminum wire directly to the thick, ion-beam-deposited chromium terminations.

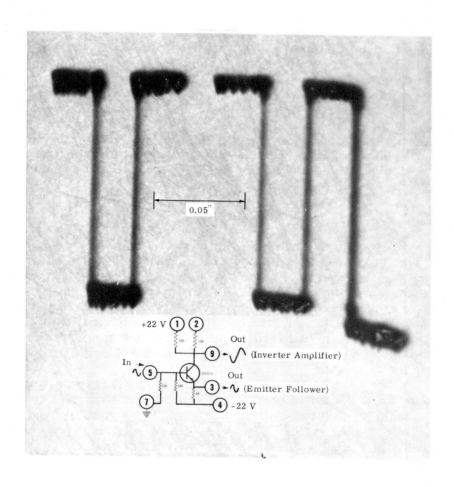

Figure 7. Circuit Schematic and Chromium Resistor Network for an Inverter Amplifier–Emitter Follower Circuit.

The total time to form the resistors was 2. 5 minutes per circuit and, because the total ion current was low, an additional 15 minutes was necessary to deposit the terminations. No attempt was made to minimize the deposition time or the circuit size but it is estimated that a miniaturized version of this circuit could be made in one to two minutes if minor modifications were made in the deposition device (0. 001 inch spot size, 0. 2 A/in² current density, and increased total current).

Considering the simple techniques used to make the circuits, the results were considered very satisfactory. Excluding circuits which were incomplete due to operator error, about 50% were functional. Many of these circuits had resistors all of which were within 10% of the design resistance value and so met the gain, phase, and linearity requirements of the circuit design.

SUMMARY

A simple ion beam deposition device has been designed to make metallic deposits on glass. The ion source produces currents of more than 100 μ A of single-charged ions of any of several metals. An unusual deflection system is used because it allowed higher current densities to be attained at the substrate. The energy distribution of the ions is not great ($\pm$10 ev) as long as low energy fractions found on the outer edge of the beam are removed by apertures.

The general dependence of TCR on sheet resistivity of ion-beam-deposited chromium is similar to that of vacuum evaporated chromium films. The resistivity and TCR of the chromium films are a function of deposition rate, presumably due to varying degrees of oxidation.

A functional circuit using ion-beam-deposited chromium resistors has been fabricated.

ACKNOWLEDGMENT

REFERENCES

1. A. R. Wolter, Microelectronics and Reliability, $\underline{4}$, 101, 1965.
2. A. R. Wolter, Proc. of Fourth Microelectronics Sym. (St. Louis section of IEEE) 2A-1, 1965.
3. G. Magnuson, C. Carlston, P. Mahadevan, and A. Comeaux, Rev. of Scient. Instr., 36, 136, 1965.
4. J. Thompson and L. B. Headrick, Proc. IRE, 28, 38, 1940.
5. D. Hoffman and J. Riseman, 1959 Vac. Sym. Trans. (Pergamon Press) 218.

Microanalysis of Surface by Ion Beam Scattering

M. Peisach[1] and D. O. Poole[2]

[1]Southern Universities Nuclear Institute, Faure, C. P.,
South Africa
[2]South African Atomic Energy Board, Isotope Unit

INTRODUCTION

The limited penetration of charged particles with energies of a few MeV makes them suitable for the analysis of surface layers. By measuring the energy spectrum of the particles scattered from an incident beam of monoenergetic ions, the chemical composition of surfaces may be determined. Such measurements have been carried out with ions of hydrogen, helium and nitrogen using semi-conductor detectors to determine the energy of the scattered particle.

Earlier work had been carried out with ions of $^1H^+$ and $^2H^+$ using magnetic spectrometers to analyze the energy spectra of scattered beams [1-4]. Nevertheless, despite the lower resolution obtainable with semi-conductor detectors, they have already been used to measure thin layers of gold by scattering of accelerated hydrogen ions $^1H^+$ [5], thin surfaces by the scattering of accelerated helium ions, $^4He^+$ [6], and geological samples by the scattering of alpha particles, $^4He^{++}$, emitted by a radioactive source [7].

In this paper the use of ion beams for the microanalysis of surfaces is discussed.

THEORY

The Rutherford differential cross section P, per unit solid angle, at a mean scattering angle, θ, measured in centre-of-mass coordinates, for non-relativistic

1195

bombarding ions is given by

$$P = \frac{(Z_1 Z_2 e^2)^2}{16 E^2 Sin^4(\frac{\theta}{2})} \tag{1}$$

where Z_1 and Z_2 are respectively the atomic number of bombarding ion and scattering atom, e is the electronic charge and E the energy of the bombarding ion.

The energy of the scattered ion, E' is given by

$$\frac{E'}{E} = 1 - 2(1 - Cos\theta) \frac{M_1 M_2}{(M_1 + M_2)^2} \tag{2}$$

where M_1 and M_2 are respectively the masses of the incident ion and the scattering atom. To convert the centre-of-mass angle θ to the laboratory angle θ_L, the value of θ may be expressed as

$$\theta = \theta_L + arc\ Sin(\frac{M_1}{M_2} Sin\theta_L) \tag{3}$$

When a monoenergetic beam of ions is scattered by a target consisting of a monolayer of isotopic nuclei, the energy spectrum of the scattered particles measured at a selected angle is expected to consist of a single line. Due to the non-ideal behavior of the measuring apparatus, the line will appear as a narrow normal distribution, of which the width at half its maximum height, is a measure of the resolution of the system.

As the target thickness increases, more scattering nuclei are presented to the incident beam, so increasing the number of particles measured. However, the energies of the bombarding and scattered particles are degraded in traversing the target material, so that the energy spectrum will spread to lower energies. With thick targets where the energy lost along the path length of the particle may be sufficient to stop the particle, the energy spectrum will appear as a plateau ending with a maximum energy E'.

When attempting to differentiate between targets with different masses M_2 and M_2^1 it is desirable to have the energy difference between their corresponding values of

E' as large as possible, in order to overcome the inherent
resolution limitations of the measuring system. It follows
from equation (2) that the use of high energy ion beams is
indicated. However, because the scattering cross section
decreases with energy the increase in resolution has to be
weighed against the decrease in count rate. Also, because
the method is based entirely on elastic scattering, an upper limit is imposed on the energy of the bombarding ion;
it should not reach that level where inelastic scattering becomes significant.

Selection of Experimental Conditions

Selection of Bombarding Particle

The nature of the ion beam used for surface analysis
determines the depth to which the ion of a fixed energy
will penetrate, as well as the extent to which peaks from
M_2 and M_2^1 will be resolvable. It is clear that a fixed
energy E, penetration will decrease with increasing mass
of the particle. Accordingly if information of composition,
or composition changes, is sought at depths below the surface, lighter elements would prove more useful. Con-
versely for the investigation of surfaces, heavy ions would
a priori be expected to produce better results.
The bombarding particle most suitable to distinguish
between M_2 and M_2^1 may be selected by comparing the variation of E' with the mass of the scatterer M_2 for different
particles. If the "mass sensitivity", $S(M_1)$ for the particle
M_1, is defined as the variation of E'/E with unit mass increase, at constant angle θ or θ_L we have

$$S(M_1)_\theta \equiv \frac{\partial}{\partial M_2} \left(\frac{E'}{E}\right)_\theta = \frac{2M_1(1-Cos\theta)(M_2-M_1)}{(M_1+M_2)^3} \tag{4a}$$

$$S(M_1)_{\theta_L} \equiv \frac{\partial}{\partial M_2} \left(\frac{E'}{E}\right)_{\theta_L} = \frac{2M_1(1-Cos\theta)(M_2-M_1)}{(M_1+M_2)^3}$$

$$+ \frac{2M_1}{(M_1+M_2)^2} Sin\theta \ Tan (\theta-\theta_L) \tag{4b}$$

from which the particle giving the greatest mass sensitivity for the mass number of the scatterer under investigation, may be selected. A comparison between the mass sensitivities of singly charged hydrogen, helium and nitrogen ions scattered at a laboratory angle of 135° is shown in Fig. 1 as a function of the mass number of scatter. At this angle, the use of hydrogen ions is inddicated for mass numbers less than 7, helium ions in the range 7 to 25 and nitrogen ions for mass numbers greater than 25 as determined by the points of intersection of the corresponding curves.

The mass number corresponding to the intersection points, vary with the angle of scatter; at 90° for example, the curves of $S(^4He^+)$ and $S(^{14}N^+)$ intersection at about 16, whilst for angles approaching 180° (laboratory angles) the intersection is at about 30. In general in c. m. coordinates the maximum mass sensitivity is obtained for

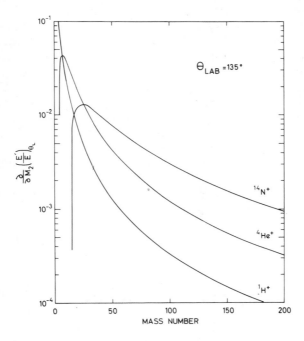

Figure 1. Mass sensitivity of different ion beams calculated at $\theta_L = 135°$.

$M_2 = 2M_1$, but at a fixed laboratory angle θ_L the relationship is angle dependent.

Selection of Angle and Energy

Once the bombarding beam has been selected, the parameters that determine the experimental conditions are the scattering angle and the bombarding energy, which in turn have to be chosen so that the E' values obtained from M_2 and M_2' are separated by an amount compatible with the resolution of the detecting system. The selection of suitable experimental conditions would thus require repeatedly solving equation (2). For this purpose, the nomogram shown in Fig. 2 has been constructed.

The lines in the nomogram are labelled θ, E, B, $\Delta E/E$ and A. The angle θ is the scattering angle in centre-of-mass coordinates, but for most practical purposes and especially so for heavy elements with light-ion beams, the value is sufficiently close to the laboratory angle. Where light elements or heavy-ion beams are used, adjustments may be made by using equation (3). E refers to the energy of the incident ion and $\Delta E = E - E'$. B is the difference in energy between the scattered particles from two target nuclei M_2 and M_2' as obtained from equation (2) thus,

$$B = \left| (\Delta E)_{M_2} - (\Delta E)_{M_2'} \right| \tag{5}$$

and represents the separation of two peaks in the energy spectrum. The mass factor, A, is defined by

$$A = \frac{M_1 M_2}{(M_1 + M_2)^2} \tag{6}$$

For ease of operation extra scales have been included to convert M_2 to A for M_1 values of 1, 2, 3 or 4, but more scales may be added to suit.

The following two examples show how the nomogram may be used to select experimental conditions and to obtain qualitative data from experimental results, rapidly.

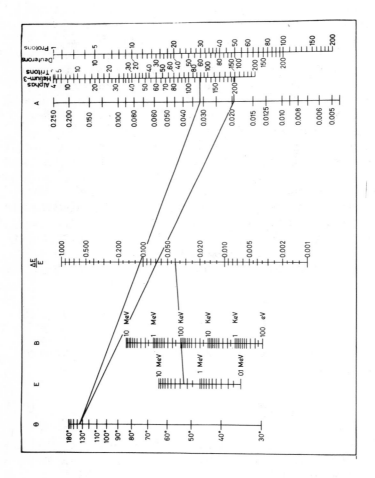

Figure 2. Nomogram for Selecting Experimental Conditions and for Rapid Evaluation of Experimental Data. The Lines Drawn Refer to Example 1 (see text).

Example 1

Thin sandwiches of tin on gold on aluminum were to be measured with a beam of helium ions. The resolution of the detecting system was about 50 keV so that it was desirable to have $B \geq 100$ keV, $M_1 = 4$, $M_2 = 197$ (for gold), $M_2^1 = 119$ (for tin). θ was arbitrarily chosen as 135°, being a convenient angle for measurement. To obtain the irradiation energy, the line joining $\theta = 135°$ to the A value for each metal was drawn to obtain $\Delta E/E$. The difference between them was plotted on the same scale and connected with the point $B = 100$ keV. This line cut the E scale at 2.5 MeV (see lines in Fig. 2).

Example 2

A geological sample was analyzed with 2.5 MeV helium ions scattered through 135°. The energy spectrum consisted of a series of plateaux with steps at ΔE values of 154, 497 and 920 keV. To identify the element associated with each step the energy of the scattered beam is compared with the incident beam energy, (or equivalent to an infinite mass for which $(\Delta E)_{M_2^1}$ in equation (5) is zero). Under these conditions $B = \Delta E$, so that by aligning the B value with $E = 2.5$ MeV a value of $\Delta E/E$ is obtained. A second line joining this value to $\theta = 135°$ gives the corresponding value of A and hence M_2. In this example it was found M_2 had values of 204, 64.5 and 32, being respectively Pb, Cu or Zn and S.

EXPERIMENTAL

Ion beams were obtained from the 5.5 MeV Van de Graaf accelerator at the Southern Universities Nuclear Institute, from which beams of $^1H^+$ ions up to 2.5 MeV, $^4He^+$ ions up to 3 MeV and $^{14}N^+$ ions up to 1.771 MeV were used for surface analysis. The upper energy for nitrogen ions was limited by the frequency measuring equipment which determined the magnetic field of the analyzing magnet of the accelerator.

A collimated beam with a cross sectional area of
5×10^{-3} cm² was used for surface analysis.

Scattering was measured in an evacuated scattering
chamber in which the relative directions of incident and
scattered beam could be externally adjusted, and in which
the angle between the incident beam and the target surface could be pre-set. The scattered particles were
measured with semi-conductor detectors which transmitted
pulses to the counting apparatus.

2000 ohm-cm n-type silicon, as obtained from Messrs.
Wacker-Chemie G.M.B.H., Munich, was used to con-
struct surface barrier type semi-conductor detectors [8]
with an active area of about 0.2 cm². With 5.48-MeV
alpha particles from americium-241 these detectors gave
resolutions of about 30 to 60 keV. The window thickness
was about 0.05μ which gave rise to an energy loss not exceeding 50 keV for hydrogen and helium ions and about
160 keV for nitrogen ions, but this energy loss varied
with the energy of the particle falling on the detector in
such a way that no deviation from linearity could be observed in the calibration line relating pulse height to
particle energy for the three types of ions studied. However, with increased detector bias, the pulse height increased as is shown for example in Fig. 3 for the 1166
keV nitrogen ion scattered from cadmium at 120° (lab)
from a beam of 1700 keV incident nitrogen ions. For
most measurements the detector bias was 50 volts.

MEASUREMENT OF METAL FILMS

From equation (2) the maximum energy, obtainable
from scattering at a selected angle, per unit energy of
incident particle, E'/E, is a function of the mass of the
scattering nucleus. This function is shown in Fig. 4
calculated for helium ions for a laboratory angle of 135°,
about the largest angle of scatter that could conveniently
be measured in the experimental scattering chamber.
The resolution attainable with a detector of 50 keV resolution and an incident beam of 2.5 MeV is shown for some
elements.

Calibrated gold films ranging from about 0.2 to 40
μg/cm² in thickness, were deposited on various backing

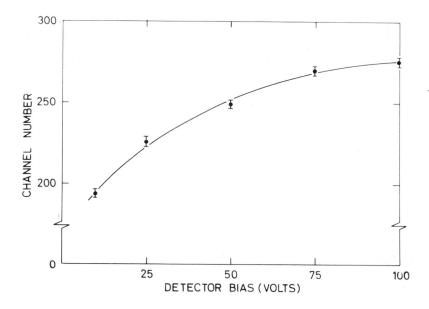

Figure 3.   The variation of pulse height with detector bias.
Measured with 1.70 MeV nitrogen-ions scattered through 120°
(lab) off cadmium.

materials and measured with hydrogen [5] or helium
ion [9] beams. The counts obtained from scattering off
the gold, as obtained by integrating the counts under the
peak due to gold in the energy spectrum, was used as a
measure of the gold thickness. The results showed that
the precision of the thickness measurement by scattering
was better than ±3%, the precision with which the films
could be calibrated by other means. The advantages of
helium ion beams for such analyses have already been
discussed [9].
    Similar results were obtained with thin tin deposits,
but for the analysis of tin plate, relatively thick tin deposits on an iron backing, the same procedure could not
be used. Instead, inspection of the measured energy
spectra showed that the broad peak due to tin was separated from a plateau due to the underlying iron (see Fig. 5),

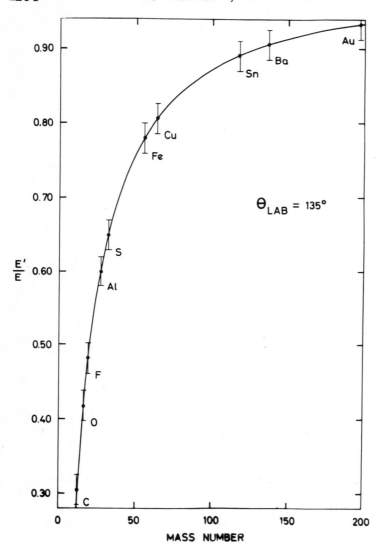

Figure 4. The variation of the energy of scattered helium ions
with the mass number of the scattering nucleus; expressed as a
ratio relative to the energy of the incident-ion and measured
at 135° (lab). The error flags indicate resolution limits when
a 2.5 MeV beam is used with a detector of 50 keV resolution.

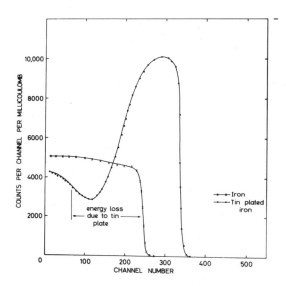

Figure 5. Energy spectrum of helium ions scattered from a thick tin coating on iron. The thickness of the tin may be obtained from the relative shift of the position for iron.

and that the maximum energy of the ion beam scattered from the iron had been degraded by energy loss of both the incident and scattered beams passing through the tin. This energy loss served as a means of measuring thick surface deposits. In the case of nitrogen ion beams, the beams were not sufficiently penetrating to show the underlying iron.

When a film of an element has to be measured on a backing consisting of an element with larger atomic number, the expected peak in the energy spectrum would appear superimposed on the continuum corresponding to the backing (see Fig. 8 of reference 9). In such cases the precision with which the film thickness can be measured is marred by the statistical errors inherent in the subtraction of large counts. Similarly the sensitivity of the analysis is expected to be somewhat less.

MEASUREMENT OF OXIDE FILMS ON ALUMINIUM [10]

The anodization of aluminium results in the formation of a uniform film of aluminium oxide over the metal, and the thickness of this film is a function of the anodizing conditions.

Standard thicknesses of aluminium oxide on aluminium were obtained by anodization of the metal, followed by a determination of the oxygen content by activation analysis using helium-3 beams. These standard films were analyzed by ion beam scattering. A typical spectrum obtained with helium-4 ions is shown in Fig. 6.

The spectrum clearly showed three plateaus, corresponding to relatively thick layers of three entities. The energies corresponding to the edges of two of these plateaus agreed with the energies calculated for surface atoms of oxygen and aluminium whilst the middle plateau, the energy corresponding to the edge of which varied with oxide film thickness, was identified as due to the ions scattered from the unanodized aluminium. As before, the energy difference between helium ions scattered from surface aluminium atoms in the aluminium oxide and aluminium atoms in the unanodized metal could be used as a measure of oxide film thickness.

Some results are shown in Fig. 6 where the maximum energy of helium ions scattered from the aluminium metal are shown plotted as a function of oxide film thickness. From this figure it is clear that the thickness of oxide films from 10 to 100 $\mu g/cm^2$ thick could readily be measured with a precision of about $\pm 3\%$. This procedure could generally be applied to oxide films on metals, provided the film is thick enough to cause a moderate change in the energy spectrum of the ions scattered from the backing material.

When similar films were analyzed by nitrogen-ion scattering it was found that the low penetration of the beam made it impossible for ions scattered from the metal to be observed. It was also observed that the approximate experimental data as obtained from the nomogram (Fig. 2) was grossly in error for the case of oxygen, owing to the fact that the mass numbers of

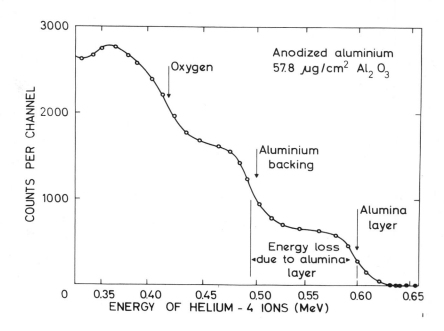

Figure 6. Energy spectrum obtained with 1000 keV helium ions scattered from anodized aluminium.

nitrogen and oxygen were so close that the assumption that the centre-of-mass angle was approximately the same as the laboratory angle, no longer applied.

Calculated values of E'/E for nitrogen-ion scatter from oxygen and aluminium are shown plotted in Fig. 8 as a function of laboratory angle. From these two curves the corresponding variation of B(Al-O) with scattering angle was obtained. This showed a maximum at about 75° after which the value decreased to 180°. However, even at 75°, the energy of nitrogen-ions scattered from surface oxygen would only be some 165 keV per MeV incident energy. To obtain somewhat higher energies, it was found

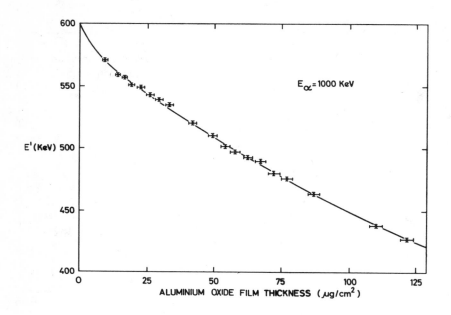

Figure 7. The variation of the energy of helium ions scattered from aluminium metal, as a function of the thickness of aluminium oxide on the surface.

to be more convenient to measure nitrogen ions scattered through 60° (lab). The separation B(Al-0) is still sufficiently large at 60° to enable the elements to be resolved.

Anodized aluminium with oxide films of about 30 $\mu g/cm^2$ when measured at a laboratory scattering angle of 60° with an incident beam of 1.70 MeV nitrogen-ions, appeared as an infinite layer of aluminium oxide.

ANALYSIS OF SELF-SUPPORTING ALUMINA FILMS [10]

Self-supporting alumina films ranging from 50 to 150 $\mu g/cm^2$ in thickness were analyzed by helium-ion scatter. A typical energy spectrum is shown in Fig. 9. As was

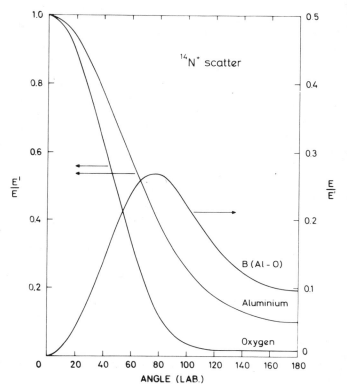

Figure 8. The variation of energy of nitrogen–ions scattered from aluminium and oxygen with angle of scatter (lab).

the case with metal films, the integrated count under the respective peaks could be used as a measure of the content of the respective element. Results showed that the precision of the analyses were about ±3%.

In Fig. 9 the shape of the peak for each element clearly shows it to be a double peak. As the number or particles scattered from a target of fixed mass at a fixed angle from a monoenergetic beam of fixed energy can only depend on the number of target nuclei per unit volume, the protruding peak indicates a region of higher density within the film. The profile of the peak could thus serve to obtain density variations within a thin target, which could not be similarly analyzed by other methods.

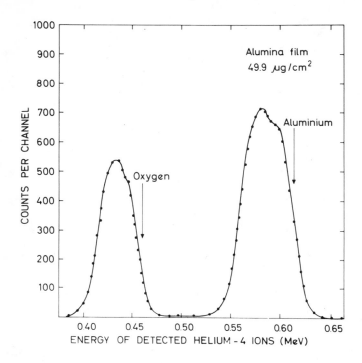

Figure 9. Energy spectrum obtained from helium ion scatter off a self-supporting film of aluminium oxide.

The same samples, analyzed by nitrogen-ion scatter appeared to be infinitely thick.

ANALYSIS OF FILMS OF COMPOUNDS

Where the thickness of a thin film of a compound has to be measured on a backing material with atomic number less than that of the constituent elements of the film, the spectra that are obtained resemble those obtained from self-supporting films. An example of one such spectrum is shown in Fig. 10; the spectrum was obtained from a thin layer of cadmium sulphide evaporated onto aluminium and measured with an incident nitrogen-ion beam of 1.70 MeV at a scattering angle of 75° (lab). The peak due to cadmium is higher than that due to sulphur because the scattering cross section increases with increasing atomic

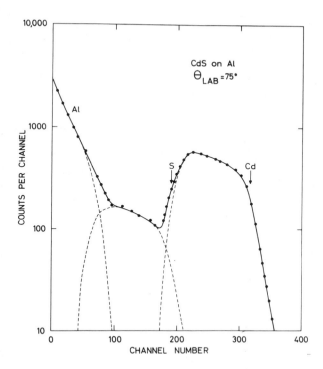

Figure 10. Energy spectrum obtained from nitrogen-ion scatter off a thin deposit of cadmium sulphide on aluminium.

number (see equation (1)). Although the elements are clearly resolved, the thickness of the deposit causes the "peak" to appear squat and to merge into that due to sulphur, which in turn merges with the continuum from the aluminium backing. It will be noted that the maximum energy of the nitrogen-ions scattered from aluminum is less than that calculated for surface aluminum. The difference between the measured and calculated energy can again serve as a measure of the film thickness of CdS, which can be obtained either from calibration or from a knowledge of the rate of energy loss of nitrogen-ions in CdS, $(dE/dx)_{N^+}$.

ANALYSIS OF GEOLOGICAL SAMPLES

Slices of geological samples when analyzed by ion-scattering appear as infinitely thick compounds and produce spectra consisting of a series of plateaus each ending at an energy characteristic of the element under the conditions of the measurement. Such spectra have been obtained for helium-ion scatter (see Fig. 11) and for alpha particle scatter [7]. With nitrogen-ions, the penetration is much less, so that local variations in the ore composition could have a marked effect on the analysis.

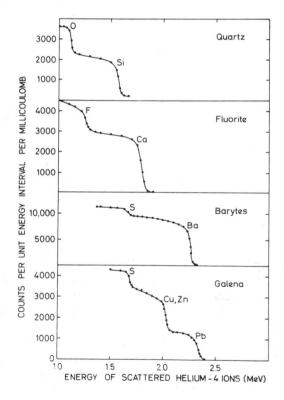

Figure 11. Spectra obtained from some geological samples analyzed by helium ion scatter.

ACKNOWLEDGMENTS

The authors acknowledge with thanks the willing assistance of Messrs. René Pretorius, Albert Bottega and Herman Rohm and the cooperation of the staff of the Southern Universities Nuclear Institute. Geological samples were kindly loaned by the Geology Department of the University of Stellenbosch.

One of us (D. O. P) thanks the South African A. E. B. for permission to include his work in this report.

REFERENCES

1. Rubin, S., Passell, T.O., Bailey, L.E., Anal. Chem. 29, 736 (1957)
2. Sippel, R. F., Phys. Rev. 115, 1441 (1959)
3. Buechner, W.W., Robertshaw, J. E. Trans. Amer. Nuc. Soc. 5, 197 (1962)
4. Green, F. L., Cooper, M. D., Robertshaw, J. E., Trans. Amer. Nuc. Soc. 5, 197 (1962)
5. Peisach, M., Poole, D.O., J.S. Afr. Chem. Inst. 18, 61 (1965)
6. Peisach, M., Poole, D.O. To be published.
7. Patterson, J.H., Turkevich, A.L., Franzgrote, E., J. Geophys. Res. 70, 1311 (1965)
8. Dearnaley, G.,Whitehead, A. B., U.K. At. Energ. Res. Estab. rept R-3437 (1960)
9. Peisach, M., Poole, D.O., Proc. Intern. Conf. Modern Trends in Activation Analysis ICAA-II/37, (1965)
10. Peisach, M., Poole, D.O., Rohm, H.F., To be published.